# GUIDE
# TO
# ACTIVATION
# ANALYSIS

# GUIDE TO
# ACTIVATION ANALYSIS

*Edited by* William S. Lyon, Jr.

Leader, Nuclear-Radiochemical Group,
Analytical Chemistry Division
Oak Ridge National Laboratory

PREPARED UNDER AUSPICES OF THE DIVISION OF
ISOTOPES DEVELOPMENT UNITED STATES ATOMIC
ENERGY COMMISSION

PUBLISHED UNDER AUSPICES OF THE
DIVISION OF TECHNICAL INFORMATION
UNITED STATES ATOMIC ENERGY COMMISSION

D. VAN NOSTRAND COMPANY, INC.

PRINCETON, NEW JERSEY

TORONTO        NEW YORK        LONDON

D. VAN NOSTRAND COMPANY, INC.
120 Alexander St., Princeton, New Jersey (*Principal office*)
24 West 40 Street, New York 18, New York

D. VAN NOSTRAND COMPANY, LTD.
358, Kensington High Street, London, W.14, England

D. VAN NOSTRAND COMPANY (CANADA), LTD.
25 Hollinger Road, Toronto 16, Canada

Library of Congress Catalog Card No. 64-23964

# FOREWORD

ACTIVATION ANALYSIS has become an extremely important peaceful use of atomic energy. It has taken its place in the laboratory as a versatile and sensitive tool. It has opened new horizons in analysis of elements throughout all branches of science and technology. The technique is being continually improved, and its application is being demonstrated in important areas of public interest, such as crime detection, biology, nutritional studies, etc. In addition, industry is increasingly applying the technique to help solve numerous research and routine quality control problems.

The idea for a Guide to Activation Analysis was first proposed by the AEC's Advisory Committee on Isotope and Radiation Development. The book is recommended to help the uninitiated get started with limited personal assistance from those knowledgeable in the technique and to provide the newcomer with most of the knowledge he needs to plan and undertake operation.

A major objective of the AEC's Isotopes Development Program is to achieve rapid development of the full spectrum of isotope and radiation applications. Their use will increase as rapidly as scientists and engineers become aware of specific possible applications and conceive of ways to apply techniques to meet their particular problems.

To determine the content needed for an activation analysis guide, discussions were held with a number of groups, particularly university people who have access to research reactors. From those discussions a broad outline evolved that emphasizes the technical fundamentals upon which the technique is based. Another objective was to describe some of the modern instrumental contributions to the technique, such as machine generation of neutrons and gamma-ray spectra analysis. Lastly, the Guide sets forth a few typical examples that the beginner may utilize for trial runs. Emphasis is placed more on fundamentals, however, because of the availability of *Radioactivation Analysis* by H. T. M. Bowen and D. Gibbons, Oxford University Press, 1963. Since that book devotes much attention to examples, the two books should complement each other very well.

Many persons have helped in the preparation and editing especially by reading the manuscript and making suggestions for improvements. Particular thanks are due Richard Wainerdi, Texas A & M University; Russell Heath, National Reactor Testing Station; Derek Gibbons, United Kingdom Atomic Energy

v

Authority; Vincent P. Guinn, General Atomics Corporation; and Leland Thatcher, U. S. Atomic Energy Commission.

OSCAR M. BIZZELL, Chief
Isotopes Technology Development
and
PAUL C. AEBERSOLD, Director
Division of Isotopes Development

# PREFACE

Activation analysis is a technique based upon the disciplines of nuclear physics and inorganic chemistry. The remarkable success of the method, and its general acceptance by analytical chemists, is a product of the careful research in these two fields which has resulted in a vast literature of nuclear data and chemical knowledge. This success is also the result of a careful translation of this information into practical analytical use. Much of the applied technology of activation analysis was developed at Oak Ridge National Laboratory, and the purpose of this book is to put some of this information in a usable form for others.

It may come as a surprise to some to learn that the first neutron activation analysis was reported in 1936 by G. Hevesy and H. Levi; one tends to think of nuclear techniques as of very recent origin. The first published U. S. work in activation analysis was that of G. T. Seaborg and J. J. Livingood in 1938. But it was the Manhattan District Project, of course, which gave the real impetus to all radiochemical and nuclear techniques. The work at Oak Ridge owes much of its success to the interest and encouragement of G. E. Boyd and D. N. Hume, who published their war-time researches in 1946, and to the early Atomic Energy Commission program begun by R. T. Overman and H. Clark in 1947. In 1949, G. E. Boyd, through publications and talks, and by his personal enthusiasm, did much to stimulate interest in activation analysis nationally; locally, these efforts resulted in the establishment of an exploratory service group at Oak Ridge. Beginning in 1950 and continuing until 1962, G. W. Leddicotte headed the Activation Analysis Group of the Analytical Chemistry Division, at Oak Ridge National Laboratory, and to him must go a great share of the credit for the success of the Oak Ridge program. In this task he was ably assisted by a number of scientists, not only in the activation group, but in other groups and divisions at the Laboratory. Prominent among those who contributed to the program are M. T. Kelley, who, as Director of the Analytical Chemistry Division, was responsible for over-all direction, and S. A. Reynolds with whom G. W. Leddicotte often coauthored papers and whom he continuously consulted.

During the years 1950 to 1962, there were a number of scientists directly associated with the activation program. In addition, a continually changing group of visitors served apprenticeships in the Laboratory,

In this book an effort has been made to present the information that the authors and editor feel to be important or helpful in formulating an activation analysis program. The material is presented in a logical and chronological fashion; thus the basic concepts of nuclear physics necessary to a minimum background for activation analysis are presented in Chap. 1, "Basic Nuclear Properties and Activation Analysis." This chapter, as all the chapters, contains references to permit the student or researcher to pursue a more detailed study.

To prevent the size of the Guide from reaching encyclopedic proportions, we have restricted the more detailed discussions to those subjects that have been incompletely treated in other compilations or have been discussed primarily in scientific journals or Government reports. Chapter 2, "Reactor Neutron Flux: Characteristics and Uses," and Chap. 3, "Nonreactor Neutron Sources," are both of this nature. In Chap. 2, the subjects of resonance integrals and flux monitoring are discussed in greater detail than perhaps the average activation analyst might feel necessary. It has been our experience that the analytical radiochemist is usually called upon by the physicist, engineer, and reactor operator to make measurements relating to these parameters. No real understanding of either the potential or the pitfalls of nuclear analysis techniques is possible without a reasonable knowledge of neutron-flux distribution and measurement.

The portable 14-Mev neutron generator has been highly advertised as an important advancement in analytical techniques. In Chap. 3, "Nonreactor Neutron Sources," an attempt is made to give an honest evaluation of this and other machines that have been used in activation analysis. The discussion covers a number of very practical areas, such as neutron output, shielding, sensitivities, and operating assemblies. The subject of desk-top neutron sources is given a similar *hard-look* treatment.

The first three chapters provide the background information necessary for an understanding of the principles and methods of activation analysis. The next four chapters discuss various techniques, equipment and its use, and the applied technology of nuclear methods of analysis.

Chapter 4, "Radiochemical Separations," outlines the methods and general philosophy of radiochemical separations. No specific examples of *tried and true methods* are given; the National Research Council has published some 70 monographs, each of which contains a number of tried and true methods. From this the reader might conclude that each analysis must be treated on an almost individual basis. This is often true and explains why our treatment is general, rather than specific.

The Geiger counter is the traditional radiation-detection device in radiochemistry. It, and other gas counters, are discussed in Chap. 5, "Radiation Detectors and Counting Statistics." In addition, information regarding the recently developed solid-state detector is given, not because of its present usefulness, but rather because of its potential for the future. The often dull but always important subject of statistics is presented in a somewhat unusual manner, and it is hoped that the material will be used in applied activation analysis.

The sodium iodide gamma-ray scintillation spectrometer has, of course, brought activation analysis to its present highly-respected position. Chapter 6, "Scintillation Counting Techniques," discusses the theory and application of scintillation spectrometry, the associated electronics, and particularly multichannel analyzers and the techniques of interpretation of gamma-ray spectra. The two great advantages of activation analysis, high sensitivity and nondestructiveness, are closely correlated with gamma-ray spectrometry. This chapter is fundamental to any modern analytical application of nuclear analysis and, although complete in itself, offers a number of references to each important facet of the subject.

In Chap. 7, "Present Byways and Future Trends in Activation Analysis," the editor asserts his prerogative to justify certain omissions from the preceding chapters and attempts to predict the course of some future developments.

Finally, in Chap. 8, "Practical Examples of Activation Analysis," four detailed problems are given in which information previously presented is utilized. The calculations are shown in arithmetical detail, and every parameter is included in every calculation and is appropriately labelled. This may appear to be an oversimplification, but a number of years experience with beginners in the laboratory assure us that it is not.

Appendix A, which was compiled by members of the Nuclear Radiochemical Group over a period of years, is a veritable treasure-house of information for the practical chemist. It lists for each element not only the theoretical calculated sensitivity, which is often unattainable in the matrix under analysis, but also actual concentrations of the element found in a variety of matrices. Reference is also made to the original work. It is recommended that reference to Appendix A be made a part of the planning for each activation problem. Appendix B presents general information on safe-handling techniques for radioisotopes and on licensing requirements. In activation analysis these requirements usually can be met without undue difficulty.

A goodly number of nuclear-data charts are available. However, the editor recommends that the beginner considers the Sullivan Trilinear Chart of Nuclides, available from the Superintendent of Documents, U. S. Government Printing Office, Washington 25, D. C., price $2.00. It contains a great deal of useful nuclear data, such as cross sections, half-lives, types of nuclear reactions, and gamma branching; one may quickly and easily trace out a variety of reactions. This information is vital to an understanding of limitations and interferences in activation analysis.

Our hope is that the Guide meets the objectives stated in the Foreword. We all owe a large debt of gratitude to the scientists, past and present, who have gathered the data upon which activation analysis has been built.

In addition to those persons mentioned earlier, the editor has benefited from the wise counsel and loyal support of J. C. White, Assistant Director of the Analytical Chemistry Division. Finally, to Doris L. Willson, the editor's assistant, must go a large share of the credit for the successful preparation and completion of the manuscript. Her efforts to assure freedom from errors, consistency of style, and clarity of presentation have made each author's assignment less arduous.

This, then, is our *Guide to Activation Analysis.* May it guide the reader to a better understanding of the theory and techniques of activation analysis and to more successful applications of the method.


WILLIAM S. LYON, JR.

*January 1964*

# TABLE OF CONTENTS

## LIST OF SYMBOLS

| | | |
|---|---|---|
| $A$ | = | disintegration rate of the induced radionuclide present at the end of an irradiation |
| $A_{Abs.}$ | = | correction factor for absorption of gamma ray in any absorbing material present between the source and detector |
| $a_d$ | = | measured activity of a source with absorber of thickness $d$ |
| $a_o$ | = | measured activity of a source without absorber |
| $A_o$ | = | initial disintegration rate or disintegration rate at time 0 |
| $A_r$ | = | disintegration rate of the induced radionuclide (cadmium shielded sample) present at the end of irradiation |
| $A_s$ | = | disintegration rate of standard |
| $A_t$ | = | disintegration rate at time $t$ |
| $At. Wt.$ | = | atomic weight |
| $A_x$ | = | disintegration rate of unknown |
| $b$ | = | constant |
| $c$ | = | speed of light |
| $CR$ | = | cadmium ratio $= \dfrac{A}{NS} \Big/ \dfrac{A_r}{N_c S_c}$ |
| $C_s$ | = | total observed number of counts from a radionuclide in a standard |
| $C_x$ | = | total observed number of counts from a radionuclide in a sample |
| $d$ | = | thickness of absorber material, cm |
| $d_i$ | = | deviation of the i-*th* member from $\overline{m}$ |
| $\Delta t$ | = | time interval |
| $E_b$ | = | energy of a backscatter peak, Mev |
| $E_c$ | = | energy of a Compton edge, Mev |
| $e_i$ | = | error of i-*th* measurement |
| $E_\gamma$ | = | energy of an incident photon, Mev |
| $E_T$ | = | threshold energy in Mev |
| $\epsilon$ | = | counting efficiency of a detector |
| $\epsilon_p(\gamma)$ | = | intrinsic peak efficiency for a given gamma-ray energy |
| $\epsilon_t(\gamma)$ | = | calculated value of total detection efficiency for gamma ray |
| $f$ | = | parameter associated with $t_i$ |
| $F$ | = | fraction of nuclei which have decayed |
| $f_x, f_y$ | = | explicit dependence of $f$ on $x$ and on $y$ |
| $f(x,y)$ | = | quantity obtained by combination of $x$ and $y$ |
| $\gamma/d$ | = | gamma rays emitted per disintegration for a particular nuclide. This is sometimes referred to as the branching ratio for the given gamma ray |
| $h$ | = | Planck's constant |
| $I_o$ | = | activation cross section for resonance neutrons (resonance integral) |
| $k$ | = | isotopic abundance |
| $l$ | − | normalization factor for neutron irradiation of sample and standard |
| $\lambda$ | = | radioactive decay constant |

| | | |
|---|---|---|
| $M$ | $=$ | the number of members of a set of quantities, $m$ |
| $\overline{m}$ | $=$ | average value of a set of $m$ |
| $M_e$ | $=$ | mass of the electron |
| $m_i$ | $=$ | the i-*th* member of a set of $m$ |
| $\mu$ | $=$ | linear absorption coefficient of absorbing material, cm$^{-1}$ |
| $N$ | $=$ | number of atoms |
| $\overline{n}$ | $=$ | average number of atoms |
| $N_{Av}$ | $=$ | Avogadro's number |
| $N_c$ | $=$ | number of atoms of a cadmium shielded specimen |
| $N_o$ | $=$ | number of atoms at zero time |
| $N_\gamma$ | $=$ | absolute number of gamma rays of a given energy emitted from a source in a given time interval |
| $\nu$ | $=$ | incident photon frequency |
| $\nu'$ | $=$ | scattered photon frequency |
| $1/E$ flux | $=$ | resonance neutron flux |
| $\Omega$ | $=$ | solid angle subtended by the source at the detector |
| $P$ | $=$ | probability that $e_i > b\sigma$ |
| $P_{(\gamma)}$ | $=$ | total integrated area within the photopeak from a given gamma-ray energy |
| $P_t(\gamma)$ | $=$ | experimental peak to total ratio for a gamma ray |
| $\phi$ | $=$ | neutron flux |
| $\phi_f$ | $=$ | integrated fast neutron flux |
| $\phi_r$ | $=$ | resonance neutron flux |
| $\phi_{th}$ | $=$ | thermal neutron flux |
| $R$ | $=$ | observed counting rate in a given detector |
| $R_B$ | $=$ | background counting rate |
| $R_N$ | $=$ | net counting rate |
| $R_o$ | $=$ | true counting rate |
| $R_s$ | $=$ | net counting rate of standard sample |
| $R_t$ | $=$ | counting rate at time $t$ |
| $R_T$ | $=$ | total counting rate |
| $R_x$ | $=$ | net counting rate of unknown sample |
| $S$ | $=$ | saturation factor for an irradiation $(1-e^{-\lambda t_i})$ |
| $\sigma$ | $=$ | cross section |
| $\overline{\sigma}$ | $=$ | average cross section for reactor fast neutrons |
| $\sigma_{14\,\text{Mev}}$ | $=$ | 14 Mev neutron cross section |
| $\sigma_m$ | $=$ | standard deviation of a set of $m$ |
| $\sigma_m^2$ | $=$ | variance of a set of $m$ |
| $\sigma_o$ | $=$ | 2200 m/sec cross section |
| $\sigma_{th}$ | $=$ | thermal neutron activation cross section |
| $t$ | $=$ | elapsed time |
| $t_i$ | $=$ | instant of time during $\Delta t$ which should be associated with $R$ |
| $t_i$ | $=$ | irradiation time |
| $t_o$ | $=$ | beginning of counting interval |

$T_{1/2}$ $\quad$ = half-life
$\theta$ $\quad\quad$ = angle between incident and scattered photons
$\tau$ $\quad\quad$ = resolving time
$w$ $\quad\quad$ = weight
$W_s$ $\quad\quad$ = weight of element in standard
$W_x$ $\quad\quad$ = weight of element in unknown
$x, y$ $\quad\quad$ = experimentally measured quantities
$Z$ $\quad\quad$ = atomic number

# Chapter 1

## BASIC NUCLEAR PROPERTIES AND ACTIVATION ANALYSIS

### Harley H. Ross

The scientist has always searched for a method of elemental analysis which is accurate, precise, specific, nondestructive, fast, economical, and universally applicable. Activation analysis is an analytical technique that comes close to satisfying these criteria. The technique is particularly suited for the sensitive and accurate determination of a wide variety of elements which are not conveniently determined by standard methods of trace analysis. In contrast to conventional chemical analysis, the principal limitations of the technique arise from the nuclear properties of an element and not its chemistry.

The basic principle of activation analysis is that a stable isotope, when irradiated by neutrons (or charged particles), can undergo a nuclear transformation to produce a radioactive nuclide. After the radionuclide is formed and its emanations have been characterized by radiation detection equipment, qualitative and quantitative inferences can be made of the elemental composition of the original sample before irradiation.

## 1-1 REACTIONS

Stable isotopes can undergo a variety of nuclear transformations. A reaction used extensively in activation analysis is the neutron–gamma $(n,\gamma)$, which is illustrated in Eq. 1.1 and 1.2.

$$_{33}\text{As}^{75} + {}_0n^1 \rightarrow {}_{33}\text{As}^{76} + {}_0\gamma^0 \tag{1.1}$$

$$_{55}\text{Cs}^{133} + {}_0n^1 \rightarrow {}_{55}\text{Cs}^{134} + {}_0\gamma^0 \tag{1.2}$$

The above reactions are usually expressed simply as

$$\text{As}^{75}(n,\gamma)\text{As}^{76} \tag{1.3}$$

$$\text{Cs}^{133}(n,\gamma)\text{Cs}^{134} \tag{1.4}$$

1

The $(n,\gamma)$ reaction is primarily a thermal-neutron ($\sim$0.025 ev) reaction, although it can occur with neutrons of other energies. The neutron is captured by a target atom, and one or more gamma rays are emitted immediately (a prompt $\gamma$). Since no change of the atomic number (charge of the nucleus) occurs, the radioelement retains the chemical identity of the target material.

Although the $(n,\gamma)$ reaction is the most widely applied nuclear reaction for activation analysis, a number of other reactions are important.

In the $(n,p)$ reaction, which requires higher-than-thermal energies, a neutron enters a target nucleus with sufficient energy to cause a proton to be released. The atomic number is reduced by 1, thereby converting the target atom into a different element as

$$_{16}S^{32}(n,p)_{15}P^{32} \tag{1.5}$$

The $(n,\alpha)$ reaction, like the $(n,p)$ reaction, usually requires high-energy neutrons. In the $(n,\alpha)$ process, a neutron enters a target atom and causes an $\alpha$ particle to be emitted. The atomic number of the target atom is reduced by 2 as

$$_{13}Al^{27}(n,\alpha)_{11}Na^{24} \tag{1.6}$$

Other reactions which have found some use include $(n,2n)$, $(p,n)$, $(p,\gamma)$, $(d,p)$, $(d,n)$, $(d,\alpha)$, $(d,n)$, $(\alpha,n)$, $(\alpha,p)$, and $(n,$ fission$)$. Table 1.1 gives properties of particles of interest in activation analysis.

Table 1.1—PARTICLES AND THEIR PROPERTIES OF INTEREST

| Name | Symbol | Mass* | Charge |
|---|---|---|---|
| Electron | $e^-$, $\beta^-$ | $5.4388 \times 10^{-4}$ | $-1$ |
| Positron | $e^+$, $\beta^+$ | $5.4388 \times 10^{-4}$ | $+1$ |
| Neutron | $n$ | 1 | 0 |
| Proton | $p$ | 0.99862 | $+1$ |
| Deuteron | $d$ | 1.9980 | $+1$ |
| Triton | $t$ | 2.9969 | $+1$ |
| Alpha | $\alpha$ | 3.9948 | $+2$ |
| Photon | $\gamma$ | 0 | 0 |

* Units of $1.6747 \times 10^{-27}$ kg.

## 1-2 DECAY

As with any radioactive source, the induced activity in an irradiated sample decreases as time passes. The rate of decrease is exponential and varies with the individual isotope. The period of time taken for the activity to decrease by one half is known as the half-life $(T_{1/2})$. The manner of decay of radioactivity may be expressed mathematically by the equation

$$A_t = A_o\left(e^{-\frac{0.693t}{T_{1/2}}}\right) \tag{1.7a}$$

where $A_o$ = initial activity (dis/unit time: dis/sec, dis/min)
　　　　$A_t$ = activity remaining after time $t$

$T_{1/2}$ = half-life, expressed in convenient units

$t$ = elapsed time, in same units as $T_{1/2}$

$e$ = base of natural logarithims

Equation 1.7a may also be expressed in terms of the count rate $R_t$ and $R_o$ corresponding to the disintegration rates $A_t$ and $A_o$, respectively. Since

$$R = A\epsilon \qquad (1.7b)$$

where $R$ = count rate

$\epsilon$ = counting efficiency of the detector

then $R_t = R_o \left( e^{-\frac{0.693t}{T_{1/2}}} \right) \qquad (1.7c)$

A semilog graph of decay is illustrated in Fig. 1.1. It should be noted that the decay law is statistical in nature and does not hold at very low levels of activity.

The processes by which radionuclides decay from higher to lower energy states are quite varied. The processes of most interest in activation analysis are beta emission $(\beta^-)$, positron emission $(\beta^+)$, photon emission $(\gamma)$, and orbital electron capture (EC).

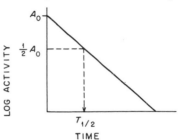

FIG. 1.1—Decay of a radionuclide.

Beta emission occurs with a large majority of radionuclides. The beta particles radiated from a given nuclide are not monoenergetic but exhibit a continuous energy distribution from zero to some maximum-energy that is characteristic of the radionuclide. The maximum energy of most $\beta^-$ emitters is less than 2.5 Mev. A typical differential beta spectrum is shown in Fig. 1.2.

Positron emission from a nucleus is quite similar to beta emission. Again there is a continuous distribution of energies from zero to some maximum energy; however, the shape of a positron spectrum is slightly different from that of a typical beta spectrum. This shape change is due to the different coulombic forces between nucleus–electron and nucleus–positron pairs. Positron emission can occur when the amount of energy available in a nucleus with a low neutron–proton ratio is at least 1.02 Mev, i.e., twice the rest mass of an electron.

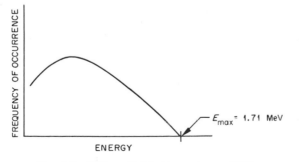

FIG. 1.2—Differential beta spectrum of P[32].

Photon emission from a radionuclide can arise from two different and distinct sources. A photon emission that originates directly from the nucleus of an atom is called a gamma ray. This type of emission is usually preceded by a beta-decay event from the same nucleus. Also it is possible for the nucleus to capture orbital electrons (electron capture). This event in itself does not exhibit a photon emission; however, higher order orbital electrons falling into the vacant $K$ or $L$ positions give rise to X-ray photons or X rays. Then it might be said that photons originating directly from the nucleus are gamma rays, and those originating from the extranuclear structure are X rays. Unlike $\beta^-$ or $\beta^+$ emissions, photon emissions are monoenergetic. Of course, this is true for both gamma-ray photons and X-ray photons. The energies of these photons are characteristic of the radionuclide producing them, and an energy analysis of photons emitted from an unknown source can lead to the identification of the nuclide. The pulse height spectrum of a source emitting both an X ray and a gamma ray is shown in Fig. 1.3. Photon energies of most radionuclides do not exceed 3 Mev.

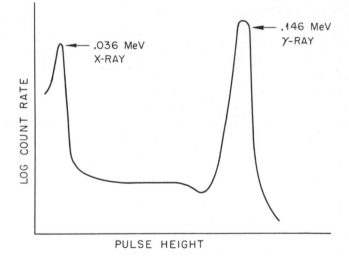

Fig. 1.3—Pulse height spectrum of $Ce^{141}$.

## 1-3 DECAY SCHEMES

A decay (or disintegration) scheme is a convenient method for graphically indicating the modes of decay of a radionuclide. Some examples follow.

1.

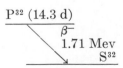

2.

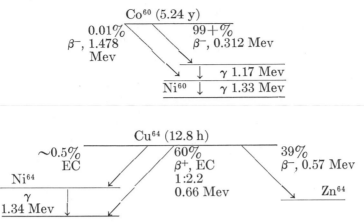

3.

Usually the symbol and mass number of the parent nuclide are written on the top horizontal line. Nuclear transitions are then indicated by arrows right, left, or down, depending on whether there is emission of a negative particle, emission of a positive particle (or capture of an orbital electron), or emission of a gamma ray. These arrows terminate at other horizontal lines to indicate intermediate or ground-state energy levels. If two or more decay modes exist for a given nuclide, the percentage of each is indicated on the appropriate arrow of the decay scheme.

A wide variety of information about the nuclides such as decay modes, half-lives, cross sections, natural isotopic abundances, etc., can be found in the Table of Isotopes by Strominger, Hollander, and Seaborg.[1]

## 1-4 INTERACTIONS

An important property of nuclear radiations is how they interact with matter. An understanding of these phenomena leads directly to the theory of radiation detection.

All charged particulate radiation interacts with matter in essentially the same way. This interaction is primarily between the charged particles themselves and the electrons in the atoms of the absorbing matter. These interactions can raise the electrons in the absorbing material to excited states or completely ionize the absorber atoms thus creating primary ion pairs. Since charged-particle interactions are primarily with orbital electrons in the absorbing medium, the specific ionization (ion pairs/unit path length) of a charged particle is greater in high atomic number materials. Thus lead is a better absorber than aluminum per unit thickness. In many cases of $\beta^-$ absorption, the following equation is valid over a large portion of the absorption curve:

$$a_d = a_o\, e^{-\mu d} \tag{1.8}$$

where $a_o$ = measured activity of source without absorber

      $a_d$ = measured activity of source with absorber

      $\mu$ = absorption coefficient of absorber material, cm$^{-1}$

      $d$ = thickness of absorber material, cm

A typical experimental beta absorption curve is shown in Fig. 1.4.

There is an additional aspect of positron interaction not mentioned previously. As a positron moves through an absorber losing energy in electron interactions, its energy becomes so small that it cannot escape an attracting electron. At this point an electron and positron combine and annihilate each other. Their combined mass is transformed into energy, and momentum is conserved by the emission of two photons in opposite directions, each of which has an energy of 0.511 Mev ($E_\gamma = 1/2m_ec^2$).

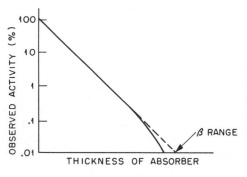

FIG. 1.4—Beta absorption curve.

The primary modes of interaction of photons with matter are quite different from that of particulate radiation; however, the ultimate secondary effects are usually the same. The three main modes of photon interaction are photoelectric interaction, Compton interaction, and pair production.

In the photoelectric effect the photon is considered as interacting with the entire atom with the result that an orbital electron (usually from the $K$ shell) is ejected with an energy equal to that of the photon less the binding energy of the electron. The photoelectric effect is the major mode of interaction by photons of about 0.5 Mev or less in elements of high atomic weight. This is illustrated by the strong absorption of X rays by lead. In elements of low atomic number the photoelectric effect is not significant.

The Compton effect is essentially an elastic collision between a free electron and a gamma photon. Energy and momentum are conserved and the incident photon gives up part of its energy to the electron which recoils at an angle to the direction of the original photon. The degraded photon undergoes further similar interactions and usually ends in a photoelectric event. The energy of the photon after a Compton interaction is determined by the angle between the incident and scattered photons and can be calculated by use of the equation

$$hv' = \frac{hv}{1 + \dfrac{hv}{M_ec^2}\,(1 - \cos\theta)} \tag{1.9}$$

where $hv'$ = energy of the scattered photon

      $hv$ = energy of the incident photon

    $M_ec^2$ = rest energy of the Compton electron

      $\theta$ = angle between incident and scattered photons

Pair production occurs as a result of interaction between an incoming photon and the coulomb field surrounding the nucleus. In this process the photon energy is converted into a $\beta^-$–$\beta^+$ pair and thus requires an incident photon with at least 1.02 Mev of energy ($2\,M_e c^2$). However, more than this minimum amount of energy is usually required for the observation of significant pair production. Energy, momentum, and charge are conserved by the electron–positron pair and the nucleus in the encounter. Once the pair is formed, the electron and positron continue to interact as described under particulate radiation.

The absorption of photon radiation is almost exactly described by the equation

$$a = a_o\, e^{-\mu d} \tag{1.9a}$$

where the terms have the same meaning as those of Eq. 1.8. The numerical values of $\mu$ for many materials can be found in various compilations of nuclear data.

## 1-5 DETECTION

Once a material has been irradiated for activation analysis, it is then necessary to characterize the nature of the resulting radiations by the process of detection. Through the process of detection one can determine: (1) the types of radiation being emitted by the sample, (2) the energies of these radiations, (3) the half-lives of the various nuclides present and (4) the amount of radiation due to each radioactive component.

In some simple cases these characterizations can be made directly from the sample; in other cases a radiochemical separation is required.

There are a number of detection devices available for radiation characterization. These include ion chambers, gas counters, Geiger-Mueller counters, scintillation counters, spectrometers, and semiconductor detectors. The operation and characteristics of these devices are discussed in a later chapter.

## 1-6 QUALITATIVE ANALYSIS

Although activation analysis is usually considered a quantitative method for trace-element analysis, the technique can be used for rapid and sensitive qualitative analysis. The method is based on the fact that most radionuclides exhibit characteristic beta and gamma-ray energies and half-lives. It is only necessary to characterize the radiations from an irradiated sample, using the appropriate detection apparatus, and relate these characteristics to sample composition. It should be noted, however, that for samples of any complexity, radiochemical separations are usually required to reduce the possibility of interferences.

## 1-7 QUANTITATIVE ANALYSIS

One can expand the above technique to do not only qualitative analysis but quantitative analysis. This modification is possible since the induced activity due to a particular element in a sample is proportional to the amount of that element in the sample (under a given set of irradiation conditions). Although this statement is always true, it is important to emphasize that not all of the stable isotopes of a given element will become active during an irradiation. For example, all stable gold is in the form of the $Au^{197}$ isotope and will, therefore, be subject to activation to $Au^{198}$ by the $(n,\gamma)$ reaction. However, naturally occurring iron is found in four stable isotopic forms. These are $Fe^{54}$ (5.82%), $Fe^{56}$ (91.66%), $Fe^{57}$ (2.19%), and $Fe^{58}$ (0.33%). Only $Fe^{54}$ and $Fe^{58}$ will undergo the $(n,\gamma)$ reaction to give active products, and hence activity will arise from only 6.15% of the total iron present in a sample.

A recognition of the isotopic abundance is very important in making sensitivity calculations and neutron flux measurements and for deciding what type of irradiation should be used for a given element.

The activity induced in a sample is not only dependent on the amount of target element present but also on: (a) the cross section of the target nuclide, (2) the irradiation flux, (3) the irradiation time, and (4) the decay characteristics of the radioelement formed.

The cross section $(\sigma)$ of a nuclide is a simple way of expressing the probability that the nuclide will undergo a reaction with the bombarding particles. The value of the cross section is energy dependent; if thermal neutrons are the bombarding particles, then the thermal-neutron cross sections are used in calculations of induced activity. The unit of cross section is the *barn* where 1 barn $= 10^{-24}$ cm$^2$. In some cases the cross section is given for a particular nuclide. In other cases an effective cross section is given which takes into account the normal isotopic abundance of a given element. It is important to distinguish between these alternatives in activity calculations.

The irradiation flux $(\phi)$ expresses the area-time density of the bombarding particles in units such as neutrons per square centimeter per second. The higher the flux, the greater is the induced activity for a given element and irradiation time.

The time $(t_i)$ of an irradiation must be known in order to calculate the magnitude of induced activity. However, the time function is not linear since, during an irradiation, not only is activity being formed but the induced activity is decaying at a rate proportional to the decay constant of the radionuclide product.

At some time $(t_s)$, the rates of formation and decay will be exactly equal, and the sample is said to have reached saturation. The saturation activity is the highest activity that can be produced in a sample with a given irradiation flux. Figure 1.5 illustrates these concepts.

All of the factors influencing the final activity in a sample due to the activation of a given nuclide can be expressed by the following activation equations:

$$A = N\sigma\phi(1 - e^{-\lambda t_i}) \tag{1.10a}$$

and since
$$\lambda = \frac{0.693}{T_{1/2}} \tag{1.10b}$$

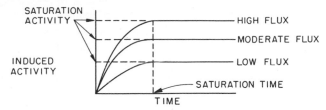

FIG. 1.5—Saturation during irradiation.

$$A = N\sigma\phi \left(1 - e^{-\frac{0.693t_i}{T_{1/2}}}\right) \tag{1.10c}$$

where $A$ = induced activity present at the end of irradiation, dis/sec
$N$ = number of target atoms present
$\sigma$ = cross section, cm²
$\phi$ = irradiation flux, neutrons/cm²/sec
$t_i$ = irradiation time
$T_{1/2}$ = half-life of product nuclide
$\lambda$ = decay constant of product nuclide

The term $(1 - e^{-\lambda t_i})$ is sometimes called the saturation factor, $S$. As the irradiation time $(t_i)$ becomes large compared to the half-life of the product $(T_{1/2})$, the saturation factor approaches unity. Therefore at the saturation time

$$A = N\sigma\phi \tag{1.10d}$$

$N$ can be calculated by means of the following relation.

$$N = \frac{N_{Av}.wk}{At.Wt.} \tag{1.10e}$$

where $N_{Av.}$ = Avogadro's number, $6.02 \times 10^{23}$, atoms/mole
$w$ = weight of element, g.
$k$ = fractional isotopic abundance of given target nuclide
$At.Wt.$ = atomic weight of element

## 1-8 ABSOLUTE DETERMINATIONS

If the activation equation is used, it is possible to make an analysis for a given element. This would require that the values of $\sigma$, $\phi$, $t_i$, and $T_{1/2}$ be known and the value of $A$ be determined experimentally. This type of absolute determination is complicated in many ways, such as: (1) the cross sections of most nuclides are probably known to no better than between 5 and 15%; (2) the flux can vary during the irradiation period, or flux gradients can exist in the sample, or the flux is simply not accurately known; and (3) it is difficult or time consuming to make absolute activity measurements on the sample.

When this technique is used, it is difficult to get accuracy of better than ±20% without extreme care and effort in determinations with most samples.

The majority of activation analyses done today utilize the comparator technique. In this method a pure sample (of known weight) containing the sought element and the unknown sample are irradiated simultaneously for the same time in the same flux. Under ideal conditions, the specific activities (disintegration rate/weight of element) of both standard and unknown are the same. Therefore one can count the unknown and standard under identical conditions (counting efficiencies $\epsilon_s$ and $\epsilon_x$ equal) and use the relation:

$$W_x = \frac{W_s A_x}{A_s} \tag{1.11a}$$

or since by Eq. 1.7b

$$R_x = A_x \epsilon_x \text{ and}$$

$$R_s = A_s \epsilon_s$$

$$W_x = \frac{W_s R_x}{R_s} \tag{1.11b}$$

where $W_x$ = weight of element $x$ in unknown
$\quad\;\; W_s$ = weight of element $x$ in standard
$\quad\;\; A_x$ = disintegration rate of unknown
$\quad\;\; A_s$ = disintegration rate of standard
$\quad\;\; R_x$ = count rate of unknown
$\quad\;\; R_s$ = count rate of standard
$\quad\;\; \epsilon_x$ = counting efficiency of unknown
$\quad\;\; \epsilon_s$ = counting efficiency of standard

This comparison technique eliminates many of the uncertainties in the absolute procedure.

The choice of a standard is a matter of great concern and is influenced by many factors:

1. The standard should be of the highest purity.
2. The standard should have only one activatable species (oxides, nitrates, oxalates, carbonates, and elemental forms are preferable to chlorides, bromides, iodides, etc.).
3. The standard should be easily soluble in conventional solvents.
4. The standard should be nonhygroscopic and easily weighed.
5. The standard should resist radiation and thermal decomposition.

## 1-9 SENSITIVITY CALCULATIONS

When one is considering the use of an analytical technique, it is usually important to have an understanding of the limits of sensitivity for the technique with a given element or chemical species. It is difficult to make absolute sensitivity calculations for an analysis by radioactivation because certain basic assumptions must be made as to required accuracy, detection system efficiency, time of irradiation, etc., before such calculations are meaningful. However, a general treatment can be outlined which is best illustrated by a typical calculation of the sensitivity of activation analysis for chlorine.

*Data*

Stable isotopes:   $Cl^{35}$ 0.754 fractional abundance
$Cl^{37}$ 0.246 fractional abundance

Reactions:   $Cl^{35}$ $(n,\gamma)$ $Cl^{36}$ $\sigma = 44$ barns
$Cl^{37}$ $(n,\gamma)$ $Cl^{38}$ $\sigma = 0.56$ barn

Decay schemes:

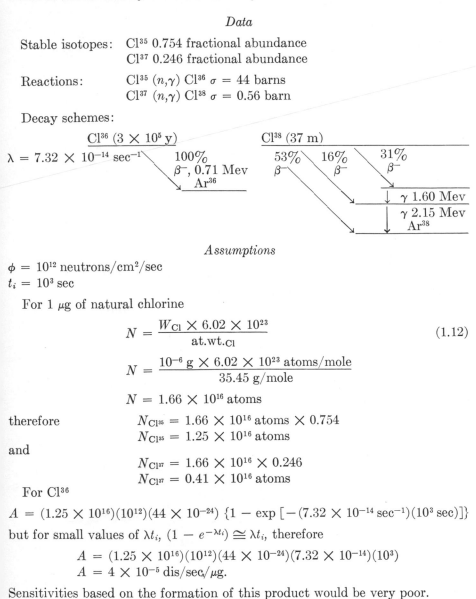

*Assumptions*

$\phi = 10^{12}$ neutrons/cm$^2$/sec
$t_i = 10^3$ sec

For 1 $\mu$g of natural chlorine

$$N = \frac{W_{Cl} \times 6.02 \times 10^{23}}{\text{at.wt.}_{Cl}} \qquad (1.12)$$

$$N = \frac{10^{-6} \text{ g} \times 6.02 \times 10^{23} \text{ atoms/mole}}{35.45 \text{ g/mole}}$$

$$N = 1.66 \times 10^{16} \text{ atoms}$$

therefore $\qquad N_{Cl^{35}} = 1.66 \times 10^{16} \text{ atoms} \times 0.754$
$N_{Cl^{35}} = 1.25 \times 10^{16} \text{ atoms}$

and $\qquad N_{Cl^{37}} = 1.66 \times 10^{16} \times 0.246$
$N_{Cl^{37}} = 0.41 \times 10^{16} \text{ atoms}$

For $Cl^{36}$

$$A = (1.25 \times 10^{16})(10^{12})(44 \times 10^{-24}) \{1 - \exp [-(7.32 \times 10^{-14} \text{ sec}^{-1})(10^3 \text{ sec})]\}$$

but for small values of $\lambda t_i$, $(1 - e^{-\lambda t_i}) \cong \lambda t_i$, therefore

$$A = (1.25 \times 10^{16})(10^{12})(44 \times 10^{-24})(7.32 \times 10^{-14})(10^3)$$
$$A = 4 \times 10^{-5} \text{ dis/sec}/\mu\text{g.}$$

Sensitivities based on the formation of this product would be very poor.
For $Cl^{38}$

$$A = (4.1 \times 10^{15})(10^{12})(5.6 \times 10^{-25}) \left\{ 1 - \exp \left[ - \left( \frac{0.693 \times 10^3 \text{ sec}}{2.22 \times 10^3 \text{ sec}} \right) \right] \right\}$$

$$A = 618 \text{ dis/sec or } 3.7 \times 10^4 \text{ dis/min}/\mu\text{g}$$

If sensitivity calculations are based on beta counting (100% $\beta^-$ as indicated by decay scheme), and total counting efficiency ($\epsilon$) equals 9.5% (typical end window G-M counter), then the count rate equals:

$$3.7 \times 10^4 \text{ dis/min/}\mu g \times 100\% \times 9.5\% = 3.5 \times 10^3 \text{ counts/min/}\mu g$$

For a counting standard deviation of 10% (100 total counts, probably the lowest practical limit) the lower determination limit is

$$\frac{10^2 \text{ counts/min}}{3.5 \times 10^3 \text{ counts/min/}\mu g} = 2.9 \times 10^{-2} \ \mu g$$

When a gross gamma scintillation detector is used (47% $\gamma$ transitions, $\sim$20% counting efficiency), the count rate equals $3.7 \times 10^4$ dis/min/$\mu$g $\times 47\% \times 20\%$ = 3.5 $10^3$ counts/min/$\mu$g and the lower determination limit equals $2.9 \times 10^{-2}$ $\mu$g.

## 1-10 ERRORS

The use of the comparator technique eliminates many of the probable errors associated with activation analysis. In using this technique, it must be recognized that certain differences in the physical characteristics of sample and comparator can lead to significant error. These errors are due to neutron self-shielding by solid materials or high cross-section components of the sample, and *enhancement* of thermal flux by moderation of epithermal neutrons within aqueous samples. Although the effect of neutron self-shielding can be calculated reasonably accurately, techniques to minimize this effect are usually employed. One such technique is to use very small samples for analysis. Another method of correction involves a standard addition of the desired element to a portion of the sample. Both *spiked* and *unspiked* samples are irradiated, and the specific activity of the desired element is calculated by activity differences.

The thermalization effect of aqueous samples will be unimportant if both sample and standard are in the same volume of water. It is not good practice to irradiate the sample in one physical form and standard in another.

Another effect that can lead to errors in activation analysis is that of competing reactions. These reactions can occur either directly (primary interference) or as a second order interference.

A primary interference occurs when reactions take place with nuclides originally in the sample; second order interferences are due to reactions with radioactive decay products. Some examples of primary interference reactions are shown below.

1.   $\begin{matrix} F^{19}(n,p) \\ O^{18}(n,\gamma) \end{matrix} \Big\rangle O^{19}$

2.   $\begin{matrix} Na^{23}(n,\gamma) \\ Mg^{25}(n,p) \end{matrix} \Big\rangle Na^{24}$

REFERENCES

3. $\dfrac{\mathrm{Al}^{27}(n,p)}{\mathrm{Mg}^{26}(n,\gamma)}\Big\rangle \mathrm{Mg}^{27}$

4. $\dfrac{\mathrm{Sb}^{121}(n,2n)}{\mathrm{Te}^{120}(n,p)}\Big\rangle \mathrm{Sb}^{120,120m}$

## 1-11 ACTIVATION ANALYSIS WITH DAUGHTER ACTIVITIES

Occasionally, an activation analysis is desired for a material that has a product with a very short half-life. It may be very inconvenient to base the analysis on measurements of this product due to the need for radiochemical separations or other factors. In this situation it is frequently possible to allow the primary product to decay to a second longer lived radionuclide (a daughter) and base the analysis on measurements of this secondary activity. This can be illustrated by the determination of thorium.

1. $\mathrm{Th}^{232}(n,\gamma)\mathrm{Th}^{233}$

2. $\mathrm{Th}^{233} \xrightarrow[\beta^-,\gamma]{22.1m} \mathrm{Pa}^{233}$

3. $\mathrm{Pa}^{233} \xrightarrow[\beta^-,\gamma]{27.4d} \mathrm{U}^{233}$

The $\mathrm{Th}^{233}$ half-life may be too short for convenient measurement, and, if so, results can be calculated on the basis of $\mathrm{Pa}^{233}$ activity after $\mathrm{Th}^{233}$ has decayed out (allow about 10 half-lives or 221 min).

### REFERENCE

1. D. Strominger, J. M. Hollander, and G. T. Seaborg, *Revs. Modern Phys.* **30**: 585 (1958).

### SUPPLEMENTARY REFERENCES

H. J. M. Bowen and D. Gibbons, *Radioactivation Analysis*, Oxford, Clarendon Press, 1963.

R. D. Evans, *The Atomic Nucleus*, McGraw-Hill Book Company, Inc., New York, 1955.

R. G. Fluharty, Interaction of Isotopic Radiation with Matter I, *Nucleonics* **2**: 5, 28–40 (1948); II, **3**: 1, 46–56 (1948).

H. Semat, Introduction to Atomic Physics, 3d ed., Rinehart & Co., Inc., New York, 1955.

K. Siegbahn, ed., *Beta- and Gamma-Ray Spectroscopy*, Interscience Publishers, Inc., New York, 1955.

D. Taylor, *Neutron Irradiation and Activation Analysis*, George Newnes Ltd., London, 1964.

*Chapter 2*

## REACTOR NEUTRON FLUX: CHARACTERISTICS AND USES

FRANK F. DYER

## 2-1 CHARACTERISTICS OF NUCLEAR REACTORS

### 2-1.1 Nuclear Reactors

Most nuclear reactors consist of a core that contains the reactor fuel as well as neutron moderating and cooling materials. Uranium-235 is the most commonly used fuel, although $U^{233}$ and $Pu^{239}$ may also be used. The major source of neutrons is the fissioning nuclei of $U^{235}$. Each $U^{235}$ nucleus that fissions emits on the average about 2.5 neutrons. A few neutrons, however, arise from the fission of $U^{238}$ and some from the interaction of gamma rays (the $\gamma,n$ reaction) with such materials as deuterium or beryllium that may be present. The maximum neutron flux that has been attained in nuclear reactors is about $10^{15}$ neutrons/cm$^2$/sec.

The neutron moderator is a low atomic-mass material such as water, heavy water, beryllium, or graphite. The energetic neutrons resulting from fission collide with the nuclei of the moderator and slow down (moderate). This results in a more-efficient fission process since the fission cross section of $U^{235}$ is larger for moderated neutrons than for unmoderated neutrons. Additional moderating material is placed around the core to further slow and eventually capture most of the neutrons that escape from the core. Some of the neutrons are reflected to the core by the moderator. Natural uranium can be used as a fuel in graphite- or heavy-water-moderated reactors; the uranium must be enriched in $U^{235}$ if other moderators are used. The reactor core is often enclosed in a reactor vessel. The core in most reactors is surrounded by a heavy thick-walled material or immersed in a deep pool of water which serves as a radiation shield.

### 2-1.2 Neutron Energy Spectrum of Nuclear Reactors

When $U^{235}$ fissions, neutrons are produced that have energies ranging from below 0.1 to about 20 Mev. The energy spectrum of these neutrons is called a

14

fission neutron energy spectrum. The average neutron energy is about 1.5 Mev, and the most probable energy is slightly below 1 Mev. The neutron flux above 0.1 Mev is approximately 99% of the total fission neutron flux; 66% lies between 0.5 and 3 Mev. Above 3 Mev the neutron flux falls off almost exponentially with increasing energy.

Most reactors contain within their cores sizable magnitudes of three fairly distinct neutron-flux components: (1) fast-neutron component, (2) epithermal or resonance neutron component, and (3) thermal-neutron component.

The fast-neutron component is normally thought of as those neutrons above about 0.1 Mev; the epithermal component, as those neutrons with energies between about 0.2 ev to 0.1 Mev; and the thermal component, as those neutrons with energies below about 0.2 ev.

The energy distribution of neutrons in a nuclear reactor has been described by Hughes,[1] Glasstone and Edlund,[2] and Bonilla.[3] The gross features of a neutron energy spectrum that is fairly typical of most nuclear reactors are shown in Fig. 2.1. The curve indicates qualitatively the neutron-flux energy distribution

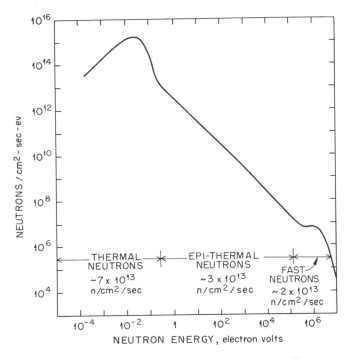

FIG. 2.1—General features of a reactor neutron spectrum.

and not the precise values of neutron flux. In any particular case, the energy distribution of one or more of the flux components may be altered slightly due to effects of moderation, neutron escape, neutron resonance capture, etc. The fast-neutron-flux component in a reactor results from those neutrons that have not suffered enough collisions with the moderator atoms to reduce their energy below 0.1 Mev. Within and near the fuel, the fast neutron flux approximates closely a fission neutron spectrum. As the neutrons travel farther from the uranium, the shape of the fast-neutron energy spectrum changes. The nature and extent of the change depends on the type of moderator and the distance the neutrons travel. A reactor-core neutron spectrum usually agrees closely with a fission spectrum above about 3 Mev.

The manner in which neutrons slow down in a moderator causes the resonance neutron flux to have a characteristic energy spectrum. To a close approximation, the resonance neutron flux per unit energy is proportional to the reciprocal of the neutron energy. The resonance neutron flux is, therefore, frequently referred to as the *1/E flux*. The term, thermal neutrons, refers to the neutrons that have slowed to thermal energies (i.e., $\leq 0.2$ ev). At 20°C, thermal neutrons have a most probable velocity of 2200 m/sec, which corresponds to an energy of 0.025 ev. The energy spectrum of this group of neutrons is similar to the kinetic energy spectrum of the atoms that comprise the reactor moderator. The number of neutrons per unit energy over thermal energies is, therefore, closely approximated by Maxwell's equation, which describes the kinetic energy distribution of gaseous atoms or molecules.

### 2-1.3 Neutron-flux Stability and Variation with Distance

Since neutron activation analyses are in most cases carried out by making irradiations of comparator standards simultaneously with *unknown* samples, the constancy of neutron fluxes is relatively unimportant. Nevertheless, reactor neutron fluxes are usually quite steady, particularly for short periods of time. It has been demonstrated with the Oak Ridge Research Reactor that over a period of a few hours with the reactor operating at constant power the neutron flux varies by not more than a few tenths of one per cent. Such stability makes possible the irradiation of unknowns and comparators at different times provided one has made certain that the neutron flux has not changed between the times of the irradiations. If the unknown and comparator are irradiated simultaneously in the same neutron flux, the reactor power can be changed in any manner without affecting anything but the absolute magnitudes of the induced radionuclides. The relative activation of the unknown and comparators remains the same.

Of more importance than time stability of neutron flux to activation analysis is the variation of neutron flux (spatial gradient) with distance in the reactor. When use is made of the comparator technique, the neutron flux to which the unknown and comparators are exposed should be equal. It is important to know whether or not this condition can be met. A number of studies in typical reactor irradiation facilities has shown how the neutron flux varies with distance in these facilities. Figure 2.2 shows the results of two of these studies—one in the Oak Ridge Research Reactor (ORR) and the other in the Oak Ridge Graphite Reactor (OGR). The relative thermal neutron flux as a function of distance in the two ORNL reactors is plotted. The neutron-flux values shown have been normalized to some flux value obtained in the facility. It can be seen that in certain facilities the neutron flux changes drastically over distances of a few inches, whereas in others there is very little change in the neutron flux over

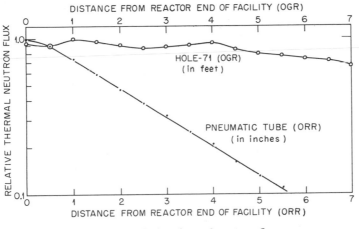

FIG. 2.2—Relative thermal neutron flux.

distances of a few feet. In Hole-71 in the OGR, the thermal neutron flux varies only by about ±5% from the bottom up to 4 ft in the hole. In the pneumatic tube facility in the ORR the neutron flux drops off from the end of the pneumatic tube by about 48%/in. The OGR is a large-core graphite-moderated reactor and the neutron flux varies slowly with distance. The Hole-71 facility, which is in the core is, therefore, subjected to a very uniform neutron flux. The ORR, however, is a relatively small-core water-moderated reactor. The pneumatic tube is on the outside of the ORR core, and here the flux drops off very rapidly with distance from the core. If the end of the pneumatic tube were within the core, less drastic changes in flux would be realized. Neutron-flux gradients would still be present but of lower magnitudes.

The neutron-flux gradients indicated in Fig. 2.2 show that when activation analyses are made it is important to have comparator and unknown samples exposed to the same neutron flux. If it is impractical to subject each sample to the same flux value, calibrations of the flux with distance should be made in order to apply appropriate corrections to the measurements. Such correction factors can be obtained in terms of relative activities induced in samples without actually calculating values of neutron flux.

## 2-1.4 Neutron-flux Monitoring

As has been indicated, it is unnecessary to know exact values of neutron flux to do activation analysis by the comparator technique. However, to estimate the amount of radioactivity formed in a reaction, it is necessary to know approximate values of the neutron flux.

Neutron-flux measurement (often termed flux monitoring) is usually made by the activation of foils. The measurement techniques and conventions for expressing neutron flux have been well explained by Hughes, Stoughton and Halperin, and Westcott.[1,4-5] Neutron flux is defined as the number of neutrons per cubic centimeter multiplied by the neutron velocity. Since reactor neutron velocities vary over wide ranges, there is no single velocity that describes all the neutrons. Neutron flux can, however, be defined and measured to a close approximation for each of the three neutron groups.

Thermal and epithermal neutron fluxes are measured by monitors that become radioactive by $(n,\gamma)$ reactions. If a monitor is placed in a neutron flux composed of both thermal and resonance neutrons, the monitor will be activated by both groups of neutrons. These two activations may be distinguished by so-called *cadmium ratio* or *difference measurements*. When a monitor is placed in an appropriate cadmium container, the monitor will be shielded from the thermal neutrons but not from the resonance neutrons. Cadmium has a very-large absorption cross section for thermal neutrons and thus absorbs them. The absorption cross section is low over resonance energies so that these neutrons are transmitted. The absolute activity, $A_r$, in a thin foil that has been enclosed in cadmium and exposed to a neutron flux is given by

$$A_r = N\phi_r I_o(1 - e^{-\lambda t_i}) \tag{2.1}$$

where     $N$ = number of atoms of the stable monitor nuclide
$\phi_r$ = resonance neutron flux
$I_o$ = activation cross section for resonance neutrons (usually called the resonance integral)
$1 - e^{-\lambda t_i}$ = saturation factor defined in Chap. 1

The activity, $A_r$, in Eq. 2.1 is the measured radioactivity corrected for decay to the time at which the irradiation ends. It can be shown[1] that the resonance flux, $\phi_r$, is the flux integrated over one $e$-fold interval of energy ($e$ equals base of natural logarithms) and not the total integrated $1/E$ flux. The *resonance flux* can thus be obtained by measuring the activity induced in a cadmium-enclosed monitor if values for the other quantities in Eq. 2.1 are known.

The activity $A$ induced in a bare monitor is the sum of the activities due to thermal and resonance neutrons. The equation for this sum can be written as

$$A = N\phi_{th}\sigma_{th}S + N\phi_r I_o S \tag{2.2}$$

where $\phi_{th}$ and $\sigma_{th}$ refer to the thermal neutron flux and the thermal-neutron activation cross section, respectively, and $S$ is the saturation factor. By dividing each of the activities, $A$ and $A_r$, by the appropriate corresponding number of atoms and saturation factors, one obtains the saturation activity per atom for the bare and shielded activations. The difference between these two quantities permits the thermal neutron flux, $\phi_{th}$, to be calculated according to the equation

$$\phi_{th} = \left(\frac{A}{NS} - \frac{A_r}{N_c S_c}\right)\frac{1}{\sigma_{th}} \tag{2.3}$$

where the subscript $c$ refers to the cadmium-shielded monitor, and $S$ denotes the saturation factor. The cadmium ratio, $CR$, can be defined as the ratio of the saturation activity per atom of the bare monitor to the saturation activity per atom of shielded monitor. An equivalent form of Eq. 2.3 for the thermal flux can be shown to be given by

$$\phi_{th} = \frac{A}{NS\sigma_{th}}\left(1 - \frac{1}{CR}\right) \tag{2.4}$$

Occasionally, one of these equations may be more useful than the other. It should be noticed in Eq. 2.4 that, if the shielded activation is small relative to the bare activation, the equation reduces to Eq. 1.10a given in Chap. 1.

The quantity, $\phi_{th}$, is the *conventional* thermal neutron flux based on the standard thermal neutron velocity of 2200 m/sec. If $\phi_{th}$ is divided by $2.2 \times 10^5$ cm/sec, the result is the total number of thermal neutrons per cubic centimeter. Of course, since monitors are irradiated over periods of time, the flux derived from such measurements is an averaged value for the irradiation time. Some investigators prefer to multiply the flux by the irradiation time (in seconds) and express their results in total neutrons per square centimeter for an irradiation. The quantity $\sigma_{th}$ is the thermal-neutron cross section which when multiplied by $\phi_{th}$ gives the activation rate due to the neutrons that are absorbed by cadmium. It is sometimes referred to as the subcadmium cross section. The exact nature of $\sigma_{th}$ has been explained by Stoughton and Halperin.[4] For any nuclide, the value of $\sigma_{th}$ depends slightly on the ratio of $\phi_r$ to $\phi_{th}$ as well as on the thickness of the cadmium shield used. The $(n,\gamma)$ cross sections that are tabulated[6] are in most cases for neutrons with 2200 m/sec velocities usually denoted by $\sigma_o$. For most nuclides $\sigma_o$ approximates $\sigma_{th}$ very closely and can be substituted for $\sigma_{th}$ in neutron-flux equations with only a small amount of error. Stoughton and Halperin[4] have described how $\sigma_{th}$ can be calculated if $\sigma_o$ and some experimental parameters are known.

## 2-1.5 Useful Thermal and Resonance Neutron-flux Monitors

To be most useful, a neutron-flux monitor should: (1) produce by irradiation a radionuclide that has a convenient half-life and emits gamma rays for ease of measurement, (2) contain no impurities that produce activities that interfere with the measurement of the desired activity, (3) be in a convenient form such as a foil, wire, or pellet, (4) be stable over a wide temperature range, and (5) exhibit negligible neutron self-shadowing. Some of the more commonly used monitors for flux measurements include sodium, aluminum, manganese, copper, cobalt, indium, and gold. The cross sections for all these monitors are fairly accurately known, and they can be fabricated to meet most of the requirements listed above. Cobalt, indium, and gold are useful for measuring resonance flux because their resonance integrals are large compared to their thermal cross sections. Table 2.1 gives pertinent activation data for all of these monitors.

Of the above listed monitors, only manganese, cobalt, indium, and gold have

Table 2.1—PROPERTIES OF SOME USEFUL THERMAL AND
RESONANCE NEUTRON FLUX MONITORS*

| | Product | | | | Radiations |
|---|---|---|---|---|---|
| Nuclide | Nuclide | Half-life | $\sigma_o$, barns | $I_o$, barns† | emitted |
| $Na^{23}$ | $Na^{24}$ | 15.0 hr | 0.53 | | $\beta^-, \gamma$ |
| $Al^{27}$ | $Al^{28}$ | 2.30 min | 0.23 | | $\beta^-, \gamma$ |
| $Mn^{55}$ | $Mn^{56}$ | 2.58 hr | 13.3 | | $\beta^-, \gamma$ |
| $Cu^{63}$ | $Cu^{64}$ | 12.82 hr | 4.1 | | $\beta^-, \beta^+, \gamma$ |
| $Co^{59}$ | $Co^{60}$ | 5.27 yr | 37‡ | 75‡ | $\beta^-, \gamma$ |
| $In^{115}$ | $In^{116}$ | 54.2 min | 145 | 2635§ | $\beta^-, \gamma$ |
| $Au^{197}$ | $Au^{198}$ | 2.70 day | 99‡ | 1558‡ | $\beta^-, \gamma$ |

* All data taken from the Sullivan Trilinear Chart of Nuclides, unless otherwise specified (available from Superintendent of Documents, Government Printing Office, Washington 25, D.C., price $2.00).

† $I_o$ values are given only for those monitors for which $I_o$ is significantly larger than $\sigma_o$. The other monitors are useful only for measuring the thermal neutron flux.

‡ Values given by Stoughton and Halperin.[4]

§ Value given by McArthy, Persiani et al.[7]

activation cross sections that are sufficiently large to cause neutron self-shadowing. Both thermal and resonance neutrons are shadowed. Shadowing of resonance neutrons, however, can be much more pronounced than thermal-neutron shadowing. At certain characteristic energies, most nuclides exhibit resonance neutron absorption. Resonance absorption is manifested by large resonance peaks in cross section *versus* neutron-energy curves. Gold, for example, has a resonance peak of 30,000 barns at 4.9 ev.[6] It can be shown that a pure-gold flux monitor would need to be as thin as 600 Å to transmit 99% of the neutrons with an energy of 4.9 ev. Such films would be too thin to prepare and use effectively. If the monitor nuclide is diluted by some material such as aluminum, usable foils can be prepared which show negligible neutron shadowing. It has become common practice to use aluminum alloys containing about 0.1% cobalt or gold.

## 2-1.6 Measurement of Fast Neutron Flux

Fast neutron flux is usually measured by monitors that become radioactive by $(n,p)$, $(n,\alpha)$, $(n,2n)$, and $(n,f)$ reactions. These reactions have a characteristic threshold energy that is determined by the mass and energy changes of the reaction.[1] Neutrons with energies below the threshold energy cannot cause the reaction to take place. Above the threshold energy, the reaction cross section rises fairly rapidly to some value and then tends to level off or decrease with increasing neutron energy. Such monitors are often designated as threshold flux monitors.

Fast neutron flux cannot be measured as precisely as thermal neutron flux. This is because the shape of the fast neutron energy spectrum varies slightly from reactor to reactor and from place to place in any particular reactor. The cross section of a threshold monitor varies considerably over a wide energy range; thus, no single cross section can exactly characterize the fast neutron flux. The fast flux can be approximated by using so-called *average cross sections*. Average cross sections are obtained by measurement in a neutron flux having a fission neutron spectrum or by calculation using cross sections measured as a function of neutron energy and assuming a fission neutron spectrum. Since the shape of a reactor fast neutron spectrum in many instances differs only slightly from a fission neutron spectrum, average cross sections can be used to estimate the quantity of radioactivity produced by a threshold reaction. Using an average cross section, $\bar{\sigma}$, the activity, $A$, induced in a threshold monitor is given by

$$A = N\phi_f\bar{\sigma}S \qquad (2.5)$$

where $N$ = number of atoms of stable monitor
  $\phi_f$ = integrated fast-neutron flux
  $S$ = saturation factor

Thus if values of $\bar{\sigma}$ are known for one or more monitors, the fast flux can be measured. The activity produced by other threshold reactions can then be estimated. Table 2.2 lists information useful in applying Eq. 2.5. The average

Table 2.2—PROPERTIES OF SOME USEFUL
FAST-NEUTRON-FLUX MONITORS

| Element | Reaction | Average cross section ($\bar{\sigma}$), in mb* | Product | |
|---|---|---|---|---|
| | | | Half-life | Radiations emitted |
| Magnesium | $Mg^{24}(n,p)Na^{24}$ | 1.1 | 15.0 hr | $\beta^-, \gamma$ |
| Aluminum | $Al^{27}(n,\alpha)Na^{24}$ | 0.57 | 15.0 hr | $\beta^-, \gamma$ |
| Titanium | $Ti^{46}(n,p)Sc^{46}$ | 9.0 | 85 day | $\beta^-, \gamma$ |
| | $Ti^{47}(n,p)Sc^{47}$ | 15 | 3.43 day | $\beta^-, \gamma$ |
| | $Ti^{48}(n,p)Sc^{48}$ | 0.25 | 1.83 day | $\beta^-, \gamma$ |
| Manganese | $Mn^{55}(n,2n)Mn^{54}$ | 0.18 | 314 day | EC, $\gamma$ |
| Iron | $Fe^{54}(n,p)Mn^{54}$ | 65 | 314 day | EC, $\gamma$ |
| Nickel | $Ni^{58}(n,p)Co^{58}$ | 90 | 72.0 day | EC, $\beta^+, \gamma$ |
| Copper | $Cu^{63}(n,\alpha)Co^{60}$ | 0.42 | 5.27 yr | $\beta^-, \gamma$ |
| Zinc | $Zn^{64}(n,p)Cu^{64}$ | 25 | 12.82 hr | $\beta^-, \beta^+, \gamma$ |
| Molybdenum | $Mo^{92}(n,p)Nb^{92}$ | 6.0 | 10.1 day | EC, $\gamma$ |
| Sulfur | $S^{32}(n,p)P^{32}$ | 65 | 14.3 day | $\beta^-$ |
| Uranium | $U^{238}(n,f)$ Fission products | 310† | Fission products‡ | $\beta^-, \gamma$ |

\* Except where otherwise noted, values of $\bar{\sigma}$ are taken from Hogg and Weber.[8]
† Value given by Durham, Mavalkar, and Ricci.[9]
‡ A fission product, usually $Ba^{140}$–$La^{140}$, is measured.

cross sections in Table 2.2 are largely taken from Hogg and Weber.[8] Slight differences for published values of fast-neutron average cross sections can be found throughout the literature. Such small differences, however, are not of much interest in activation analysis, particularly since the threshold monitor technique is only a method for approximating the fast neutron flux.

## 2-2 APPLICATION, EXPERIMENTAL METHODS, AND TECHNIQUES

### 2-2.1 Sample Preparation for Activation

In general the procedures followed for preparing samples for reactor activations will depend on the irradiation facility chosen. The choice of facility will depend primarily on the sensitivity required and the neutron flux in the facility. Other factors that affect this selection include the chemical, physical, and nuclear properties of the sample matrix and its constituents, the size of sample, and the volume capacity and temperature of available facilities. Encapsulation procedures will normally be specified by personnel operating the reactor. Irradiations of certain types of samples such as liquid mercury and very volatile or explosive solids and liquids may be prohibited.

Activation of solids, liquids, and gases can be made in nuclear reactors. Samples are normally prepared by placing weighed amounts of the unknown and required comparators in containers appropriate for the irradiation facility. Samples should be sealed tightly enough to prevent escape of any portions of the sample or radionuclides formed during the activation. Usually encapsulation requirements for solids will be much less severe than for liquids. Liquids and solids can be sealed in quartz or plastic containers. Some solutions, particularly aqueous ones, may not need to be hermetically sealed if evaporation of the liquid matrix does not affect the activation and measurement of desired nonvolatile constituents. In most cases, however, it is advisable to prepare unknown and comparators in as nearly the same form as possible to minimize the effects of neutron self-shadowing and thermal-neutron flux enhancement. For the same reasons the samples should remain in comparable form during the irradiation. In many instances it may be advisable to evaporate solutions to dryness before the irradiation.

### 2-2.2 Irradiation Facilities in Nuclear Reactors

Irradiation facilities for activation analysis include: (1) hand-loaded, air-cooled, or water-cooled holes, (2) hydraulic tubes, (3) pneumatic tubes, and (4) sample-mounting racks. Each type has its particular advantages and disadvantages depending on the type of reactor, sample to be activated, and other factors. Hand-loaded air-cooled holes normally are large enough so that large volume samples can be irradiated at any one time. If adequate cooling is provided, many samples can be irradiated in conventional plastic bottles.

Pneumatic tubes have many of the desirable features of a hand-loaded, air-cooled facility. However, the primary advantage of a pneumatic tube is the speed with which samples can be removed from the neutron flux and processed. Easily opened sample containers can be made of plastic that does not become radioactive. Radionuclides with half-lives of a few seconds can thus be measured. Usually pneumatic tubes have rather small diameters; therefore the amount of sample that can be activated is limited. If the pneumatic tube is adjacent to a small-core reactor that operates at a fairly high power, the highly intense gamma rays will damage the plastic. This reduces the length of time a sample can be irradiated.

Figure 2.3 is a diagram of the pneumatic tube facility in the Oak Ridge Research Reactor. It is typical of the pneumatic tubes installed in most reactors. The complete arrangement consists of a sample loading station, a control panel, and the pneumatic tube. With the reactor operating at 30 Mw, the maximum thermal, resonance, and fast-neutron fluxes present are about $7 \times 10^{13}$, $2 \times 10^{12}$, and $2 \times 10^{13}$ neutrons/cm$^2$/sec, respectively. Irradiation times from a fraction of 1 sec to 20 min can be preset with the control panel. During an irradiation,

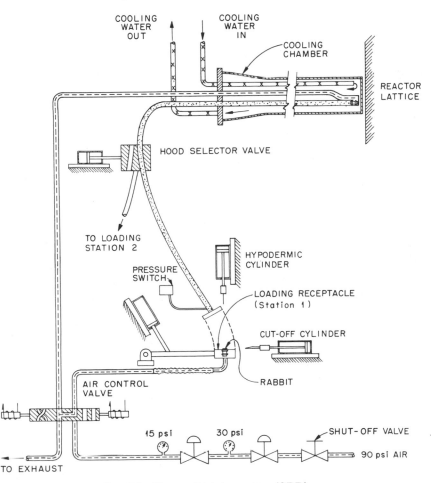

FIG. 2.3—Pneumatic tube system (ORR).

the sample is cooled by a stream of air flowing through the tube. Samples are irradiated in small cylindrical polyethylene containers, which have an internal volume of about 1.2 ml. The containers are made of high density polyethylene to make them dimensionally stable and minimize the deteriorating effects of gamma radiation. Irradiations of one container can be made for about 1 hr before gamma-ray damage makes it unfit for further use. Radionuclides having half-lives of a few seconds to months or years can be measured.

Shelf or rack sample-mounting facilities can hold a large number of samples. Samples irradiated in the water of pool-type reactors must be adequately sealed to prevent water entering the sample container. With small-core reactors the problem of neutron-flux gradient may be difficult to overcome. Rotating sample racks that hold up to 40 samples have been installed in some reactors.[10] Rotation of the rack results in the exposure of each sample to the same average neutron flux.

### 2-2.3 Pulsed Reactors

Certain types of nuclear reactors can be operated at very high power for very short periods of time. This type of operation is called reactor pulsing.[10] The pulse of neutrons is sometimes referred to as a neutron burst. The duration of the pulse of a bare reactor is typically measured in microseconds. A pulse in a moderated reactor may last for 10 to 30 msec. As many as $10^{17}$ fissions of $U^{235}$ nuclei may take place during a pulse; this makes it possible to subject a sample to about $10^{14}$ neutrons/cm$^2$ in a very short time. With such a large integrated neutron dose and short irradiation time, one can make full use of differences in saturation factors for different nuclides and still have large sensitivities for many elements. Although very little has thus far appeared in the literature on the use of such reactors for activation analysis, the method appears to have significant possibilities.

## 2-3 USEFUL NUCLEAR REACTIONS WITH REACTOR NEUTRONS

### 2-3.1 General Considerations

A variety of nuclear reactions useful in activation analysis can be obtained with reactor neutrons. These reactions include $(n,\gamma)$, $(n,p)$, $(n,\alpha)$, $(n,2n)$, and $(n,f)$. The feasibility of using any reaction depends on factors such as the type of sample matrix, cross section, neutron flux, nuclear and chemical properties of the reaction product, and possible interferences. Each factor needs to be considered separately as well as in relation to the others.

### 2-3.2 $(n,\gamma)$ Reactions

Thermal neutron $(n,\gamma)$ reactions are by far the most useful reactions produced in nuclear reactors; this is due to the large thermal-neutron flux in reactors and the large thermal-neutron cross sections exhibited by most stable nuclides.

Several nuclides have very large $(n,\gamma)$ cross sections. Examples are

| Nuclide | Thermal cross section, barns |
|---------|------------------------------|
| $Cd^{113}$ | 27,000 |
| $In^{115}$ | 150 |
| $Sm^{149}$ | 41,500 |
| $Sm^{152}$ | 220 |
| $Eu^{153}$ | 320 |
| $Gd^{157}$ | 240,000 |
| $Dy^{164}$ | 2,000 |
| $Lu^{176}$ | 2,100 |

Some, such as $Cd^{113}$, $Sm^{149}$, and $Gd^{157}$, produce stable nuclides and are not ordinarily useful in activation analysis. The corresponding elements can, however, be determined by $(n,\gamma)$ reactions with other isotopes or by neutron transmission measurements. Some few nuclides have extremely small $(n,\gamma)$ cross sections. Examples are

| Nuclide | Thermal cross section, barns |
|---------|------------------------------|
| $C^{12}$ | 0.0009 |
| $N^{13}$ | 0.00002 |
| $O^{18}$ | 0.0002 |
| $F^{19}$ | 0.009 |
| $Mg^{26}$ | 0.03 |
| $Pb^{208}$ | 0.0005 |

Any $(n,\gamma)$ reaction produces a nuclide which is isotopic with the nuclide that absorbs the neutron. Thus the microscopic quantity of radionuclide formed has the same chemical properties as the bombarded nuclide and, if required, can be chemically separated with it. In many cases the individual radioactivity can be measured without making chemical separations. Whether or not a chemical separation is needed depends on the sample matrix, the minor constituents and their relative concentrations, and the type of induced radionuclides. Table 2.3 gives examples and pertinent information for several $(n,\gamma)$ reactions that are useful in activation analysis. Sensitivities, calculated by Eq. 1.10a, are given for an irradiation of 1 half-life or 1 wk (whichever is less) in a thermal neutron flux of $10^{12}$ neutrons/cm²/sec assuming that 40 dis/sec of radionuclide is formed and can be measured. In practice, sensitivities may be lower than values calculated in this manner because the counting efficiency of each radionuclide will depend on its decay scheme, and counting may not be started immediately after the activation. If two or more radionuclides are formed from the same stable element or nuclide, e.g., $Cu^{64}$ (12.82 hr) and $Cu^{66}$ (5.1 min), it is often advan-

Table 2.3—SOME $(n,\gamma)$ REACTIONS USEFUL IN ACTIVATION ANALYSIS

| Nuclide | Isotopic abundance, % | Thermal cross section, barns | Product | | Sensitivity, $\mu g$* |
|---------|------------------------|------------------------------|---------|---|------------------------|
| | | | Nuclide | Half-life | |
| $Al^{27}$ | 100 | 0.23 | $Al^{28}$ | 2.30 min | 0.02 |
| $Cu^{63}$ | 69.09 | 4.1 | $Cu^{64}$ | 12.82 hr | 0.003 |
| $Cu^{65}$ | 30.91 | 2.0 | $Cu^{66}$ | 5.1 min | 0.01 |
| $Co^{59}$ | 100 | 18 | $Co^{60m}$ | 10.5 min | 0.0005 |
| $Co^{59}$ | 100 | 18 + 19† | $Co^{60}$ | 5.27 yr | 0.04 |
| $Dy^{158}$ | 0.090 | 100 | $Dy^{159}$ | 144 day | 4 |
| $Dy^{164}$ | 28.18 | 2000 | $Dy^{165m}$ | 75 sec | 0.00004 |
| $Dy^{164}$ | 28.18 | 2000 + 800† | $Dy^{165}$ | 2.3 hr | 0.00002 |

* Sensitivity: $\mu g$ necessary to give 40 dis/sec when irradiated 1 half-life or 1 wk (whichever is less) in neutron flux of $10^{12}$ neutrons/$cm^2$/sec.

† Sum of cross sections to produce metastable and ground states of radionuclide.

tageous to measure the shorter-lived one since its activity buildup is more rapid.

The products of some $(n,\gamma)$ reactions decay to other radionuclides that can be chemically separated and measured. Two examples are

$$Sn^{112} \ (n,\gamma) \ Sn^{113} \xrightarrow[T_{1/2} \,=\, 118 \text{ d}]{EC} In^{113m} \tag{2.6}$$

$$\gamma \ \Big| \ T_{1/2} = 1.7 \text{ h}$$

$$In^{113}$$

$$Te^{130} \ (n,\gamma) \ Te^{131} \xrightarrow[T_{1/2} \,=\, 30 \text{ h}]{\beta^-,\gamma} I^{131} \xrightarrow[T_{1/2} \,=\, 8 \text{ d}]{\beta^-,\gamma} Xe^{131} \tag{2.7}$$

Girardi has given other examples in Ref. 11.

In Eq. 2.6, metastable $In^{113m}$ results from the electron-capture decay of $Sn^{113}$. The half-life of $In^{113m}$ is sufficiently long (1.7 hr) to permit it to be separated from the tin and counted. The radiations emitted by $Sn^{113}$ are weak and difficult to detect, whereas the $\gamma$ ray emitted by $In^{113m}$ is easy to measure. In Eq. 2.7, $Te^{131}$ decays by $\beta^-$ emission to $I^{131}$, which has an 8-day half-life. Such reactions can simplify analyses if activity measurements and/or chemical separations can be made more easily for the daughter than for the parent.

### 2-3.3 $(n,\gamma)$ Reactions with Resonance Neutrons

The ease with which an activation analysis can be made depends to a large extent on the types and relative magnitudes of activities induced in a sample. This is particularly true if the measurement of one or more radionuclides is to be done without chemical separations. In certain cases an analysis can be facilitated by activating with resonance neutrons and suppressing the thermal-neutron activation. As previously noted, the $(n,\gamma)$ activation of a nuclide depends on its thermal-neutron cross section and resonance integral as well as the thermal- and resonance-neutron fluxes. The relative activations of two or more nuclides by resonance neutrons depend only on their resonance integrals. Since the resonance integrals of many nuclides differ appreciably, activation with resonance neutrons frequently permits one to make an analysis without chemical separations.

Thermal-neutron activation can be suppressed by irradiating the sample in shields made of cadmium or boron or both elements. Other elements having large thermal-neutron cross sections, such as gadolinium and samarium, can also be used. The irradiations of cadmium-enclosed samples in or near reactor cores can decrease the $(n,\gamma)$ activation rate of certain nuclides by a factor of 30 or more. The activation rate of other nuclides may be changed only by a factor of 2 or less. If the shield is made of both cadmium and boron, the relative activation rates may be changed even more drastically. Borg, Segel, et al.,[12] used this technique to determine manganese and sodium in blood plasma. By irradiating the samples in a boron–cadmium shield, the ratio of manganese to sodium activity was increased by a factor of 6 over that obtained by activations of bare samples. This procedure made the nondestructive measurement of manganese activity in the presence of sodium activity both easier and more precise.

Activation rates in cadmium can be calculated by Eq. 2.1 if the resonance integrals are known for the nuclides in a sample. If Eqs. 2.1 and 2.2 are used, it can be determined whether or not it would be beneficial to irradiate the sample in a thermal-neutron shield. Resonance integrals for a number of nuclides are given in Table 2.4. These values are applicable for activations in cadmium containers. Usually a container having a wall thickness of $\sim 0.040$ in. is used.

## 2-3.4 Fast Neutron Reactions: $(n,p)$, $(n,\alpha)$, $(n,2n)$, and $(n,f)$

Fast neutron reactions in nuclear reactors have been used very little for activation analyses. This is due primarily to the small cross sections found for these reactions. The threshold energies of many nuclides are high (6 Mev or larger), and the neutron flux above these energies is small. Many $(n,p)$ and $(n,\alpha)$ reactions are possible for nuclides of atomic numbers of about 30 or less. The $(n,2n)$ reactions become increasingly favorable for nuclides with atomic numbers above 30.

A few authors have discussed and utilized reactor neutrons for activation analysis with threshold reactions.[9,13,14] Koch[15] has tabulated much of the information regarding threshold reactions for activation analysis. Many of the possible useful reactions are given in Table 2.2. One example of a useful threshold reaction is $Ni^{58}(n,p)Co^{58}$. Nickel is difficult to determine in many matrices by the reaction $Ni^{64}(n,\gamma)Ni^{65}$ since the cross section and abundance of $Ni^{64}$ are low. However, if longer irradiations are made and the short-lived activities are allowed to decay, the $Co^{58}$ formed from $Ni^{58}$ can sometimes be easily measured. The $(n,p)$ reactions of titanium listed in Table 2.2 are other examples of threshold reactions which may be useful. The $(n,\gamma)$ reaction of titanium produces $Ti^{51}$ that has a half-life of 5.80 min. For certain samples it may be impossible to measure the $Ti^{51}$ because of its relatively short half-life. The half-lives of the scandium

Table 2.4—RESONANCE INTEGRALS FOR A NUMBER OF NUCLIDES*

| Nuclide | Resonance integral, barns | Nuclide | Resonance integral, barns |
|---------|---------------------------|---------|---------------------------|
| $Na^{23}$ | 0.30 | $I^{127}$ | 140 |
| $Al^{27}$ | 0.16 | $Cs^{133}$ | 400 |
| $P^{31}$ | 0.10 | $Pr^{141}$ | 15.5 |
| $Cl^{37}$ | 0.35† | $Sm^{152}$ | 2740 |
| $Sc^{45}$ | 10.7 | $Eu^{151}$ | 842† |
| $V^{51}$ | 2.0 | $Dy^{164}$ | 482 |
| $Mn^{55}$ | 14.2 | $Lu^{175}$ | 463 |
| $Co^{59}$ | 75 | $Lu^{176}$ | 887 |
| $Cu^{63}$ | 4.4 | $Hf^{180}$ | 21.8 |
| $Ga^{69}$ | 9.2 | $Ta^{181}$ | 590 |
| $Ga^{71}$ | 15 | $W^{180}$ | 355 |
| $As^{75}$ | 36.8 | $Re^{185}$ | 1160 |
| $Br^{79}$ | 147 | $Re^{187}$ | 305 |
| $Y^{89}$ | 0.91 | $Ir^{191}$ | 3500 |
| $Nb^{93}$ | 8.4 | $Ir^{193}$ | 1370 |
| $Rh^{103}$ | 656 | $Au^{197}$ | 1558 |
| $Ag^{107}$ | 74 | $Tl^{203}$ | 129 |
| $Ag^{109}$ | 1160 | $Tl^{205}$ | 0.5 |
| $In^{113}$ | 913† | $Th^{233}$ | 500 |
| $In^{115}$ | 2640 | $U^{235}$ | 274 |
| $Sb^{121}$ | 162 | $U^{238}$ | 280 |
| $Sb^{123}$ | 138 | | |

* Values apply for cadmium enclosed samples. Unless otherwise indicated values are taken from A. E. McArthy, P. J. Persiani, B. I. Spinrad, and L. J. Templin, News Letter No. 1, Reactor Physics Constants Center, Argonne National Laboratory, June 30, 1961.
† Value taken from Hughes.[1]

isotopes produced by $(n,p)$ reactions range from hours to months. The use of longer-lived nuclides allows ample time for chemical separations. Stable scandium, if enough were present, would interfere with the threshold reaction $Ti^{46}(n,p)Sc^{46}$ by the reaction $Sc^{45}(n,\gamma)Sc^{46}$.

Use of an $(n,2n)$ reaction to determine the $Pb^{204}/Pb^{208}$ ratio in meteorites has been reported.[16] The irradiation was made inside a reactor fuel element. An interesting application of $(n,f)$ threshold reactions has been made by Amiel.[17] Thorium was irradiated with fast neutrons in a reactor, and the delayed neutrons that were emitted by the fission products of thorium were measured. Some of the samples that also contained $U^{235}$ were enclosed in cadmium to reduce the interference caused by the thermal neutron fission of $U^{235}$. Uranium-238 can also be determined by this method in samples in which the $U^{235}$ isotope has been depleted.[18]

## 2-3.5 Secondary and Excitation Reactions

When $Li^6$ and oxygen are placed in a reactor thermal neutron flux, the following reactions take place:

$$\text{Li}^6(n,\alpha)t \tag{2.8}$$

$$\text{O}^{16}(t,n)\text{F}^{18} \xrightarrow[112\text{m}]{\beta^+} \text{O}^{18} \tag{2.9}$$

$$\text{O}^{18}(t,\alpha)\text{N}^{17} \xrightarrow[4.14\text{s}]{\beta^-} \text{O}^{17*} \xrightarrow{n} \text{O}^{16} \tag{2.10}$$

Reactions involving tritons are examples of secondary reactions. Reactions 2.8 and 2.9 have been used by a number of investigators for the determination of oxygen.[19,20] Amiel and Peisach[21] have made use of reactions 2.8 and 2.10 to determine $\text{O}^{18}$. The $\text{O}^{17*}$ in reaction 2.10 is left in an excited state by the $\beta^-$ decay of $\text{N}^{17}$, and the neutron is emitted immediately after the decay of $\text{N}^{17}$. Neutron counting was used to determine $\text{O}^{18}$. This technique is also useful for the determination of $\text{Li}^6$ (Ref. 22). The number of useful secondary reactions in a reactor is very limited. Those listed above appear to be the only ones that have been utilized with nuclear reactors.

Excitation reactions produced by either fast-neutron inelastic scattering or by high-energy gamma rays are also possible in a nuclear reactor. Some examples of neutron-inelastic scattering reactions are

$$\text{Sr}^{87}(n,n')\text{Sr}^{87m} \xrightarrow[2.8\text{h}]{\gamma} \text{Sr}^{87} \tag{2.11}$$

$$\text{Y}^{89}(n,n')\text{Y}^{89m} \xrightarrow[16\text{s}]{\gamma} \text{Y}^{89} \tag{2.12}$$

$$\text{Pb}^{204}(n,n')\text{Pb}^{204m} \xrightarrow[67\text{m}]{\gamma} \text{Pb}^{204} \tag{2.13}$$

$$\text{Pb}^{207}(n,n')\text{Pb}^{207m} \xrightarrow[0.8\text{s}]{\gamma} \text{Pb}^{207} \tag{2.14}$$

For these reactions to occur, an energetic neutron must strike the nucleus of the stable nuclide and recoil leaving part of its kinetic energy with the nucleus. This excites the nucleus to a metastable energy state. The metastable nucleus then decays (with its characteristic half-life) to its ground state by the emission of gamma radiation. In addition, high energy gamma rays may interact with a stable nuclide to produce excitation reactions of the type

$$\text{Y}^{89}(\gamma,\gamma')\text{Y}^{89m} \xrightarrow[16\text{s}]{\gamma} \text{Y}^{89} \tag{2.15}$$

A nuclear reactor is a prolific source of such gamma radiation; hence the production of these excited states is probably the result of $(\gamma,\gamma')$ as well as $(n,n')$ reactions. It has been suggested that reaction 2.13 may be useful for determining lead.[8] Although neutrons and photons produced by accelerators have been used to study these reactions for activation analysis,[23] very little work of this type has been done in reactors.

## 2-3.6 Interferences in Reactor Activations

A number of types of interferences are possible in reactor neutron activations. The extent of interference depends on the sample matrix, its constituents, the reactions that are produced, and the nature of the neutron flux. Such interferences can be loosely categorized as interfering reactions and interferences due to neutron-flux differences. Koch[15] distinguishes between primary and second-order interfering reactions which are important in reactor irradiations. Primary interferences may be obtained when the same radionuclide is formed from two or more different stable nuclides by single neutron reactions. Threshold reactions may interfere with $(n,\gamma)$ reactions if the element to be determined by an $(n,\gamma)$ reaction is in a matrix containing large quantities of a threshold reactant that has an atomic number one or two units higher than the $(n,\gamma)$ reactant. Conversely, the presence of only a small amount of $(n,\gamma)$ reactant may interfere with determinations based on a threshold reaction. Examples of interfering reactions are:

$$\left.\begin{array}{l} \text{Co}^{59}(n,\gamma) \\ \text{Ni}^{60}(n,p) \\ \text{Cu}^{63}(n,\alpha) \end{array}\right\} \quad \text{Co}^{60} \qquad\qquad (2.16)$$

$$\left.\begin{array}{l} \text{P}^{31}(n,\gamma) \\ \text{S}^{32}(n,p) \\ \text{Cl}^{35}(n,\alpha) \end{array}\right\} \quad \text{P}^{32} \qquad\qquad (2.17)$$

$$\text{Ca}^{48}(n,\gamma)\text{Ca}^{49} \xrightarrow{\beta^-,\gamma} \atop \text{Ti}^{49}(n,p)\text{Sc}^{49} \qquad\qquad (2.18)$$

$$\left.\begin{array}{l} \text{Ca}^{46}(n,\gamma) \\ \text{Ti}^{50}(n,\alpha) \end{array}\right\} \quad \text{Ca}^{47} \xrightarrow{\beta^-,\gamma} \atop \text{Ti}^{47}(n,p)\text{Sc}^{47} \qquad\qquad (2.19)$$

Reactions 2.18 and 2.19 show that interferences may arise from decay as well as from the first product of neutron reactions. The use of thermal neutron shields or the choice of well-thermalized neutron facilities can reduce or eliminate many interferences. Preirradiation chemical separations, although normally undesirable, can often be made to eliminate interferences.

A second-order reaction is one in which a product of a neutron capture undergoes an additional neutron capture. Examples of possible interfering reactions are

$$\begin{array}{ll} \text{Matrix reactions:} & \text{Si}^{30}(n,\gamma)\text{Si}^{31} \xrightarrow{\beta^-,\gamma} \left.\text{P}^{31}(n,\gamma)\right\} \\ \text{Impurity reaction:} & \left.\text{P}^{31}(n,\gamma)\right\} \quad \text{P}^{32} \end{array} \qquad (2.20)$$

$$\begin{array}{ll} \text{Matrix reactions:} & \text{Cu}^{63}(n,\gamma)\text{Cu}^{64} \xrightarrow{\beta^-,\gamma} \left.\text{Zn}^{64}(n,\gamma)\right\} \\ \text{Impurity reaction:} & \left.\text{Zn}^{64}(n,\gamma)\right\} \quad \text{Zn}^{65} \end{array} \qquad (2.21)$$

This type of interference depends upon (1) cross sections and abundance of the nuclides that undergo neutron capture, (2) half-lives of the radionuclides formed, (3) neutron flux, and (4) irradiation time. From reaction 2.20 it can be seen that if a trace quantity of phosphorus is to be determined in a matrix of silicon, second-order interference is to be expected. A rather large number of element combinations behave similarly. Many of them have recently been tabulated and the extent of interference calculated[24] so that experimental data may be corrected.

Interferences can result from neutron-flux differences such as neutron-flux gradients, neutron self-shadowing by the sample matrix, and thermal-neutron enhancement in aqueous solutions by moderation of epithermal neutrons in the water. Neutron self-shadowing can be considered as a neutron-flux gradient in which the flux decreases toward the center of the sample. This results in an activation gradient throughout the sample. All of these effects can be minimized or eliminated by making samples thin or by preparing standard samples in a form comparable to the unknown and irradiating all samples in the same neutron flux.

## REFERENCES

1. D. J. Hughes, *Pile Neutron Research*, Addison-Wesley Publishing Company, Inc., 1953.
2. S. Glasstone and M. C. Edlund, *The Elements of Nuclear Reactor Theory*, D. Van Nostrand Co., Inc., Princeton, N. J., 1958.
3. C. F. Bonilla, *Nuclear Engineering*, McGraw-Hill Book Company, Inc., New York, 1957.
4. R. W. Stoughton and J. Halperin, *Nucl. Sci. Eng.* **6**: 100 (1959).
5. C. H. Westcott, *J. Nucl. Energy* **2**: 59 (1955).
6. D. J. Hughes and J. A. Harvey, *Neutron Cross Sections*, USAEC Report BNL-325, Brookhaven National Laboratory, 1958.
7. A. E. McArthy, P. J. Persiani, B. I. Spinrad, and L. J. Templin, News Letter No. 1, Reactor Physics Constants Center, Argonne National Laboratory, June 30, 1961.
8. C. H. Hogg and L. D. Weber, *Fast Neutron Dosimetry at the MTR-ETR Site*, ASTM Special Technical Publication No. 341, p. 134, 1963.
9. R. W. Durham, M. P. Mavalkar, and E. Ricci, in *Proceedings, 1961 International Conference, Modern Trends in Activation Analysis*, p. 67, A & M College of Texas, 1961.
10. J. D. Buchanan, in *Proceedings, International Conference, Modern Trends in Activation Analysis*, p. 72, A & M College of Texas, 1961.
11. F. Girardi, in *Proceedings, International Conference, Modern Trends in Activation Analysis*, p. 119, A & M College of Texas, 1961.
12. D. C. Borg, R. E. Segel, P. Kienle, and L. Cambel, *Intern. J. Appl. Radiation and Isotopes* **11**: 10 (1961).
13. C. E. Miller, USAEC Report No. ORNL-2715, Oak Ridge National Laboratory, 1959.
14. W. A. Brooksbank, Jr., G. W. Leddicotte, and J. A. Dean, *Anal. Chem.* **30**: 1785 (1958).
15. R. C. Koch, *Activation Analysis Handbook*, Academic Press, Inc., 1960, p. 9.
16. G. W. Reed, K. Kigoshi, and A. Turkevitch, in *Proceedings of the Second International Conference on the Peaceful Uses of Atomic Energy, Geneva 1958*, Vol. 28, p. 953, United Nations, New York, 1958.
17. S. Amiel, *Anal. Chem.* **34**: 1683 (1962).
18. F. F. Dyer, J. F. Emery, and G. W. Leddicotte, USAEC Report No. ORNL-3342, Oak Ridge National Laboratory, 1962.
19. H. J. Born and P. Wilkniss, *Intern. J. Appl. Radiation and Isotopes* **10**: 133 (1961).

20. L. C. Bate and J. W. Winchester, USAEC Report CF-57-8-92, Oak Ridge National Laboratory, 1957.
21. S. Amiel and M. Peisach, *Anal. Chem.* **35**: 323 (1963).
22. S. Amiel and Y. Wellwart, *Anal. Chem.* **35**: 566 (1963).
23. J. W. Otvos, V. P. Guinn, H. R. Lukens, Jr., and C. D. Wagner, *Nucl. Instr. and Methods* **11**: 187 (1961).
24. E. Ricci and F. F. Dyer, *Nucleonics* **22** (6): 45 (1964).

# Chapter 3

## NONREACTOR NEUTRON SOURCES

JAMES E. STRAIN

## 3-1 ACCELERATOR NEUTRON SOURCES

There are available, in addition to nuclear reactors, a wide variety of machines that also produce neutrons. In all of these neutron generating machines, a charged particle is accelerated to an appropriate energy and allowed to strike a target which produces neutrons. The energy of a fast neutron so produced is a function of the nuclear reaction in the target, the energy of the incident particle, and the angle at which the neutron is emitted from the target. This is the major difference between nuclear-reactor or fission-produced neutrons and accelerator-produced neutrons; the use of an accelerator allows the selection of a fast neutron of a single energy.

### 3-1.1 Neutron-producing Reactions

The reactions often used in accelerator sources[1] are summarized in Table 3.1. It is emphasized that regardless of the type accelerator used, Van de Graaff, Cockcroft-Walton, cyclotron, or linear accelerator, the nuclear reaction involved is the controlling factor influencing the neutron yield and energy. Another type of reaction that is often used to produce low-energy neutrons ($<100$ kev) with electron accelerators is a secondary photoneutron reaction. A gold target when struck by 2 Mev or greater electrons produces X rays that interact with Be or $D_2O$ to produce neutrons. The advantage of this reaction lies in the fact that any electron accelerator producing $>2$-Mev electrons can be used to produce neutrons for activation analysis.

### 3-1.2 Type of Accelerators

The choice of an accelerator for neutron production is, of course, involved with such factors as cost of equipment, installation, and operation as well as the flexibility of application to problems other than activation. In addition, equipment already available should be considered. All accelerators may be grouped

Table 3.1—CHARGED PARTICLE REACTIONS OFTEN USED
TO PRODUCE NEUTRONS

| Reaction | Threshold,* Mev | Q,† Mev | Neutron energy emitted‡ at threshold bombarding energy |
|---|---|---|---|
| $D(d,n)He^3$ | | +3.266 | 2.448 Mev |
| $T(p,n)He^3$ | 1.019 | −0.764 | 63.9 kev |
| $T(d,n)He^4$ | | +17.586 | 14.046 Mev |
| $Be^9(\alpha,n)C^{12}$ | | +5.708 | 5.266 Mev |
| $C^{12}(d,n)N^{13}$ | 0.328 | −0.281 | 3.4 kev |
| $C^{13}(\alpha,n)O^{16}$ | | +2.201 | 2.07 Mev |
| $Li^7(p,n)Be^7$ | 1.882 | −1.646 | 29.9 kev |

* Threshold: The threshold is the lowest energy of bombarding particle that can initiate a reaction. If the Q of the reaction is positive, there is no threshold energy and only the Coulomb barrier is important.

† Q: This is the energy associated with the nuclear transformation. If negative, the reaction requires energy to be added to force the reaction. If positive, the reaction will proceed, if a zero energy particle enters the nucleus, with the liberation of energy equal to Q.

‡ The energy of the emitted neutron at the threshold bombarding energy. This is the lowest energy neutron that will be emitted by the reaction. The excess bombarding energy above the threshold will be added to the neutron energy listed.

into two classes: positive-ion accelerators and electron accelerators. The positive ion accelerators consist of Van de Graaff machines, which derive their high voltage by means of a moving belt static accumulator, and the Cockcroft-Walton accelerator, which develops its accelerating voltage by transformer action. Both the Van de Graaff and the Cockcroft-Walton machines use an in-line graded electric field to accelerate the ions. The cyclotron differs from the above machines in that the positive ions are accelerated by two electrical *kicks* per revolution while a magnetic field is used to hold them in a circular path. Figure 3.1 is a comparison of the three main components of accelerator systems; i.e., the power supply, the ion source, and the accelerating mechanism. Note that the cyclotron requires three separate power supplies to control the acceleration and the magnetic field and to deflect the accelerated beam onto a target.

The energies of the particles produced by these machines differ markedly. Currently available Cockcroft-Walton accelerators are capable of producing deuterium ions with energies up to 0.7 Mev; the Van de Graaff accelerators will produce up to 10-Mev deuterons, whereas the cyclotrons will produce deuterons upward of 20 Mev.

The electron accelerators are similar to the positive-ion accelerator except that electrons, rather than positive ions, are accelerated. To produce neutrons, the electrons must have an energy greater than 1.67 Mev, the energy that represents the lowest threshold for the production of photoneutrons from Be [$Be^9(\gamma,n)Be^8$].

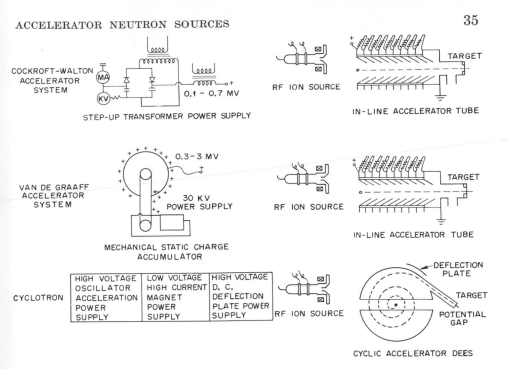

FIG. 3.1—Component comparison of three positive ion accelerators.

### 3-1.3 Neutron Yield and Energy from Accelerators

The magnitude of neutron output in terms of neutrons per second is a function of several interrelated factors. Among these are

1. Neutron reaction used.
2. The energy of the bombarding particle.
3. The beam current, which determines the number of incident particles on the target.
4. The stability of the target to deterioration through exchange reactions or physical damage.
5. Beam characteristics of purity and stability.

The neutron reaction used is interrelated with bombarding particle energy just as neutron-capture reaction cross sections vary with neutron energy. Figure 3.2 relates the production rate with bombarding energy and beam current with some typical reactions.[2] As shown in Fig. 3.2, if one can increase the beam current at a given energy, the total neutron output will be increased. The increased beam current, however, generates heat and increases the target depletion rate so that the neutron production falls more rapidly as a function of time. In the case of the $T(d,n)He^4$ reaction, deuterium exchanges with the

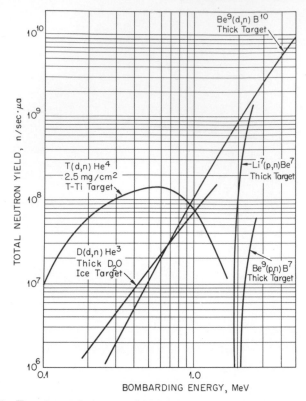

FIG. 3.2—Experimental neutron yields under normal laboratory conditions.[2]

tritium of the target at a rate proportional to the beam current; this reduces the target life and neutron output.*

Another factor influencing both the neutron energy and neutron yield is the quality of the ionized gas used as a source of positive ions. It is obvious that in the case of a deuterium accelerator, if the $D_2$ molecule is ionized and accelerated along with a $D^+$ deuterium ion, the final velocity of the $D_2^+$ ion will be less than that of the lighter ion though its final energy will be the same.[3] This means that if one operates near the neutron-producing-reaction energy threshold that portion of the beam current due to the $D_2^+$ ions will be less efficient for neutron production. If one is operating well above the threshold, it means that the neutron yield will no longer be monoenergetic but will have a component due to the lower-energy incident particle. Therefore the ion source should produce as nearly a pure monoatomic beam as possible for maximum yield and monoenergetic

---

* The yield of a given reaction is expressed in terms of total neutrons per second, while neutron flux (neutrons/cm²/sec) is the pertinent term in nuclear analysis. In general, the maximum useful flux available is approximately a factor of 100 less than the total neutron production rate. This relation is true of both thermal and fast neutrons and is dependent on the sample size and physical arrangement.

neutron application. In general, in neutron activation analysis with thermal or fast neutron activation, this effect is minor and affects only the total neutron flux available.

### 3-1.4 Spatial Distribution and Stability of Neutron Flux

The use of an accelerator neutron source is complicated by the nature of neutron generators. First, they are *point* neutron sources. This means that the neutron flux will decrease exponentially with distance (Figs. 3.3 and 3.4). This makes it

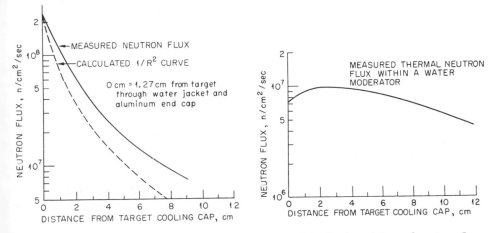

FIG. 3.3—Distribution of 14.7-Mev neutron flux from a water-cooled T–Zr target.

FIG. 3.4—Distribution of thermal-neutron flux from a 14.7-Mev source.

difficult to use large samples without serious nonuniformities in the neutron flux. Also because of this nonuniformity, it is often necessary to use separate sample and comparator irradiations coupled with some type of flux monitor. Second, when one uses a *gaseous* target, such as $T_2$ or $D_2$ absorbed in titanium, zirconium, or yttrium, the neutron flux will decrease as a function of time and beam current, so that fluxes are neither constant nor reproducible except with difficult and careful machine operation.

Figure 3.5 shows the decay of a typical Zr–T target at constant beam current as a function of time. The shape of this curve will vary depending on beam current, target temperature, accelerating voltage, etc. One estimates that the neutron output of a typical Zr–T target will decrease by a factor of at least 2 with each 700-$\mu$a-hr operation.

To monitor the neutron flux during the course of an irradiation, one may use a variety of systems. One method is to place a small activation monitor in each sample irradiated, which can be removed and assayed before or after the sample is counted. The choice of a monitor is dependent on the length of irradiation and the energy of the neutrons generated by the accelerator. Table 3.2 illustrates some of the monitor materials that may be employed for thermal or 14-Mev neutrons.

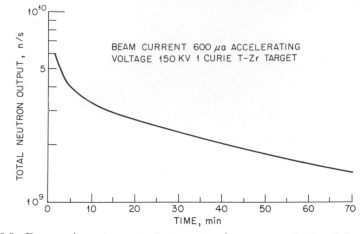

F~IG~. 3.5—Decrease in neutron output at constant beam current from a T–Zr target.

An alternative to flux monitoring is the comparator technique, which is advantageous in that problems of flux variation with time are eliminated entirely. If this technique cannot be used due to time or sample size limitation, then it is necessary to know the flux of each irradiation or at least to monitor an activity

Table 3.2—USEFUL SHORT-LIVED FLUX MONITORS

| Neutron energy | Irradiation time | Monitor reaction | $T_{1/2}$ | $\sigma$ |
|---|---|---|---|---|
| Thermal | 0–5 min | $V^{51}(n,\gamma)V^{52}$ | 3.76 min | $4.5 \pm 0.9$ barns |
| | 5 m–2 hr | $In^{115}(n,\gamma)In^{116}$ | 54.1 min | $145 \pm 15$ barns |
| | >2 hr | $Au^{197}(n,\gamma)Au^{198}$ | 2.7 day | $96 \pm 10$ barns |
| 14.1 Mev | 0–1 min | $Si^{28}(n,p)Al^{28}$ | 2.3 min | $220 \pm 30$ mb |
| | | $P^{31}(n,\alpha)Al^{28}$ | 2.3 min | $150 \pm 30$ mb |
| | 1–10 min | $Cu^{63}(n,2n)Cu^{62}$ | 9.8 min | $550 \pm 100$ mb |
| | >10 min | $Al^{28}(n,\alpha)Na^{24}$ | 15.1 hr | $118 \pm 20$ mb |

produced during the irradiation which is proportional to the flux. There are currently three monitoring systems that accomplish this. The first is the low-geometry neutron counter that monitors the neutron output during an irradiation. A second method in the $T^3(d,n)He^4$ generator is to monitor the $N^{16}$ (7.35-sec half-life) produced by an $(n,p)$ reaction on $O^{16}$ in the target cooling water. The third method, which is presently in the development stage, is to monitor the recoil alpha particles (produced in the generator target via the $T(d,n)He^4$ reaction). The output from all of these devices may be routed to either a scaler for short runs or to a rate meter to record the neutron output as a function of time. This measurement, when related to an accurate flux determination, using a short irradiation time and a standard irradiation position, may be used to correlate separate irradiations at different flux levels.

## 3-1.5 Installation and Shielding

The establishment of the irradiation position and the type of flux monitor system to be used is dependent on the type of neutron generator that is available and the amount of biological shielding necessary to protect the operator. In the case of cyclotron or large Van de Graaff installations, adequate neutron shielding is normally present to eliminate the intense high energy X ray and gamma radiation associated with them. In the smaller Cockcroft-Walton or Van de Graaff machines, it may be necessary to increase the biological shielding to provide for the penetrating 14.1-Mev neutrons. Figure 3.6 shows the attenuation

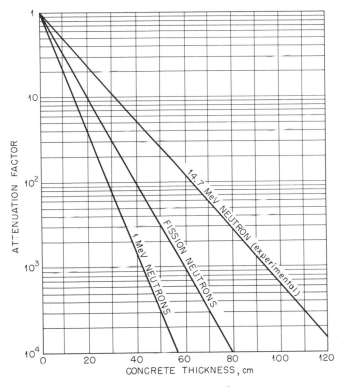

FIG. 3.6—Attenuation of neutrons by concrete.

of 14-Mev neutrons in standard concrete (not high density).[4] Calculations of the effectiveness of water or paraffin relative to concrete indicates that both materials are only about 10% more efficient than concrete,[5] so that the added expense is not justified for 14-Mev neutron attenuation. As the neutron energy decreases, the shielding thickness required decreases.

Some typical small neutron generator installations are shown schematically in Fig. 3.7. Schematics of the larger installations are not shown since the cost of the large cyclotrons and high-voltage Van de Graaff machines will not justify their purchase solely for use in neutron activation analysis. If one, therefore, uses one of these large sources, it will be done in a system already shielded for high-energy charged particle work, and no additional shielding will be required.

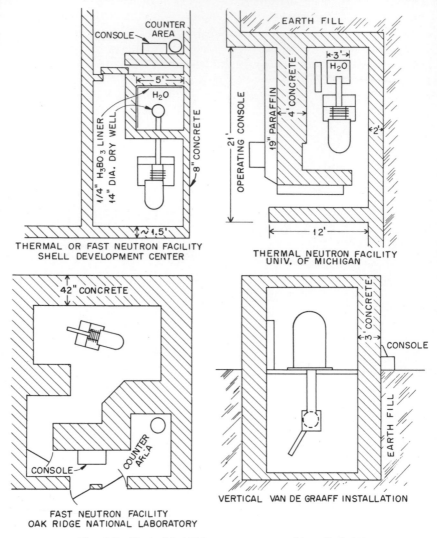

FIG. 3.7—Typical $\geq 100$-kv neutron general installation.

Table 3.3 summarizes the pertinent aspects of neutron health physics[6] and may be used as a guide to the establishment of a satisfactory shield.

In the performance of neutron activation analysis with short half-life radioisotopes, using machine sources, the major problem is the background of the counting device. Since the 3 by 3-in. NaI crystal is very sensitive to fast neutrons, thermal neutrons, and gamma radiation, the amount of shielding necessary

Table 3.3—NEUTRON DOSE EQUIVALENTS

| Neutron energy, Mev | Relative biological efficiency | Flux to deliver 100 mrem in 40 hr,* neutrons/cm²/sec |
|---|---|---|
| 0.0001 | 2 | 500 |
| 0.005 | 2.5 | 570 |
| 0.02 | 5 | 280 |
| 0.1 | 8 | 80 |
| 1.0 | 10.5 | 18 |
| 5.0 | 7 | 18 |
| 10 | 6.5 | 17 |
| 10–30 | 6 | 10 |

* 100 mrem/wk is considered the upper safe limit for continuous exposure.

to permit counting during machine operation will assure adequate biological shielding to the console operation if counter and console are located in the same area.

### 3-1.6 Sample Handling Systems

In routine activation analysis, one would like to position the sample reproducibly in the irradiation position, irradiate it for a predetermined length of time, and then rapidly remove it to a location where it can be processed chemically or counted without chemical separation. The simplest and most economical method is to mount the sample by hand and remove it after irradiation in the same manner. For long-lived ($>1$ min) radioisotope production, this method works well. The major disadvantage is the fact that the generator has to be turned off between irradiations, and the person who attaches and removes the sample is exposed to an undesired amount of radiation from short-lived activities in the T–Zr target and target holder as well as the sample.

Another method is one in which a pneumatic system is used to transfer the sample, which is enclosed in a plastic or metal *rabbit*. Very simple systems have been devised that allow accurate irradiation timing and travel times of less than 1 sec. Two typical systems are outlined in Fig. 3.8. These two systems, the *shuttle* and *one direction*, are the basis of all pneumatic systems. The variation in systems results in different requirements of sample size and travel time. The system choice will depend upon materials available and access through the shielding between the neutron source and counting or processing area.

### 3-1.7 Practical Applications of Neutron Generators

The applications of the neutron generator to practical neutron activation analysis are limited, and these limitations must be kept in mind when estimating the usefulness of a generator to a specific problem. These limitations are as follows:

1. Target life: As mentioned previously, the high neutron yield T–Zr or T–Ti targets deteriorate rapidly, so that short irradiations are desired.

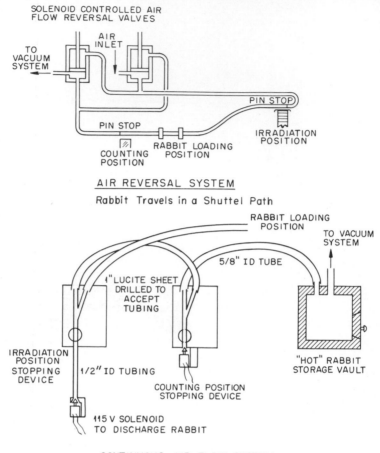

FIG. 3.8—Typical pneumatic rabbit systems.

2. Neutron flux: The usual small accelerator has a usable neutron flux of $2 \times 10^5$ to $\sim 5 \times 10^8$ 14-Mev neutrons/cm²/sec and $1 \times 10^5$ to $\sim 1 \times 10^8$ thermal neutrons/cm²/sec. Therefore only a few elements may be detected in the parts per million range.

3. Neutron energy: Whereas it is reasonable to expect monoenergetic fast neutrons, it is impossible to obtain a pure thermal neutron flux. This means that in all thermal activations one can expect to find $(n,p)$, $(n,\alpha)$, and $(n,2n)$ products from fast-neutron component activation.

4. Nonuniform neutron flux throughout the sample: This problem arises because of the geometric properties of a point source and scattering and absorption in the sample.

Although the list of problems seems formidable, there are a number of accurate analyses which may be performed using the neutron generator:

1. The limited interaction of fast neutrons is often a great advantage over conventional reactor-spectrum neutron activation through the elimination of high levels of matrix activity.
2. The low temperatures of the sample during irradiation and the lack of radiation damage within the sample are often advantageous.
3. Some sixty elements can be determined through short irradiation ($<10$ min) and counting, if present in macroquantities, whereas twenty elements may be detected if in quantities of 100 $\mu$g or more.[7] Table 3.4 summarizes some of the more sensitive elements and the 14-Mev reactions that are used in their detection.

Table 3.4—REACTIONS AND LOWER LIMITS OF DETECTION OF
SELECTED ELEMENTS 14-MEV NEUTRON IRRADIATION
FOR $\leq$10 MIN AT $10^8$ NEUTRONS/CM²/SEC

| Element | Reaction | Measured radiation* (3 × 3 in. NaI detector), Mev | $T_{1/2}$ | Practical† detection limit, $\mu$g |
|---|---|---|---|---|
| Nitrogen | $N^{14}(n,2n)N^{13}$ | 0.51 | 10.0 min | 200 |
| Oxygen | $O^{16}(n,p)N^{16}$ | 6.13 | 7.35 sec | 100 |
| Fluorine | $F^{19}(n,p)O^{19}$ | 0.2, 1.3 | 29.4 sec | 50 |
|  | $F^{19}(n,2n)F^{18}$ | 0.51 | 112 min | 40 |
| Aluminum | $Al^{27}(n,p)Mg^{27}$ | 0.83, 1.02 | 9.45 min | 100 |
| Silicon | $Si^{28}(n,p)Al^{28}$ | 1.78 | 2.3 min | 50 |
| Phosphorus | $P^{31}(n,\alpha)Al^{28}$ | 1.78 | 2.3 min | 100 |
| Chromium | $Cr^{52}(n,p)V^{52}$ | 1.44 | 3.8 min | 150 |
| Manganese | $Mn^{55}(n,\alpha)V^{52}$ | 1.44 | 3.8 min | 300 |
| Copper | $Cu^{63}(n,2n)Cu^{62}$ | 0.51 | 9.8 min | 50 |
| Yttrium | $Y^{90}(n,2n)Y^{89}$ | 0.92 | 16.1 sec | 100 |
| Molybdenum | $Mo^{92}(n,2n)Mo^{91}$ | 0.51 | 66 sec and 15.5 min | 200 |
| Niobium | $Nb^{93}(n,n\alpha)Y^{89}$ | 0.92 | 16.1 sec | 400 |

* Radiation of 0.51 Mev is from $\beta^+$ annihilation.
† Based on direct spectral measurement at a level of twice background.

Nothing has been said in regard to counting systems in this section since there are as many systems as there are installations, and the choice of counting equipment is dependent on the purpose of the installation. The most flexible instrument is a multichannel analyzer with NaI gamma detector and anthracene or plastic scintillation beta detector. This allows one to do both gamma and beta spectrometry as necessary to eliminate interferences.

### 3-1.8 Neutron Generator Installation Costs

The cost of a complete generator installation may vary from a low of about $2500 for the small pulsed, sealed sources with an average available 14-Mev neutron flux of $1 \times 10^5$ neutrons/cm²/sec, that require only stacked concrete block shielding, to the multimillion dollar installation complexes of the high-energy Van de Graaff or cyclotron sources that produce fluxes upward of $10^{11}$ neutrons/$cm^2$/sec. Intermediate in this range are the 100-kev–400-kev machines, which accelerate deuterons to produce $T(d,n)He^4$ neutrons with available fluxes of $10^9$ 14-Mev neutrons/$cm^2$/sec either continuously or with microsecond pulsing. The costs of these machines range from \$12,000 to \$35,000, depending on the individual features.

The total installation cost including radiation counting equipment will as a rule total twice the accelerator cost. For example, a typical breakdown of an installation cost will be:

| | |
|---|---:|
| Generator cost | \$30,000 |
| Shielding and building space | 12,000 |
| Counting equipment | 12,000 |
| Pneumatic rabbit system | 1,000 |
| Incidental and health physics instrumentation | 2,000 |
| | \$57,000 |

The wide range of use for these small neutron generators in activation analysis, flowing-stream analysis, and training in nuclear physics or radiochemistry will justify their application in many industrial and educational installations.

## 3-2 ISOTOPIC NEUTRON SOURCES

A third source of neutrons is the isotopic source in which the emitted radiation of the radioactive isotope interacts with a target material to produce neutrons. Two types of sources are presently in use. The first is the photoneutron source, which produces low-energy neutrons (<100 kev) through the interaction of >1.67-Mev gamma radiation with beryllium. The second source is the alpha–neutron source in which $\alpha$ particles interact with low $Z$ material to produce neutrons.

### 3-2.1 Photoneutron Sources

Although there is a wide variety of radionuclides that can be used for photoneutron sources, i.e., $Na^{24}$, $Mn^{56}$, $Y^{88}$, etc.,[8] two radionuclides are most often employed due to their long half-life and low cost. These two are $Sb^{124}$, with a 60-day half-life, and $Ra^{226}$, with a 1622-yr half-life. The properties of these two sources are summarized in Table 3.5.

Table 3.5—PROPERTIES OF $Sb^{124}$ AND $Ra^{226}$ PHOTONEUTRON SOURCES

| Source | Half-life | Neutrons/sec/curie* (actual yields) | Average neutron energy† | Gamma radiations/curie, rhm |
|---|---|---|---|---|
| $Sb^{124}$–Be | 60 day | $1.6 \times 10^6$ | 24 kev | 1.5 |
| $Ra^{226}$–Be | 1622 yr | $1.3 \times 10^6$ | 200 kev | 1 |

* Using beryllium as the radiator.
† Hughes and Egler, USAEC Report ANL-4476, Argonne National Laboratory, 1950.

The methods of fabrication of these photoneutron sources are shown in Fig. 3.9. Note that the Ra$^{226}$ source is so sealed as to be removable from the beryllium radiator, so it may be used as a pure gamma source independent of neutron production.

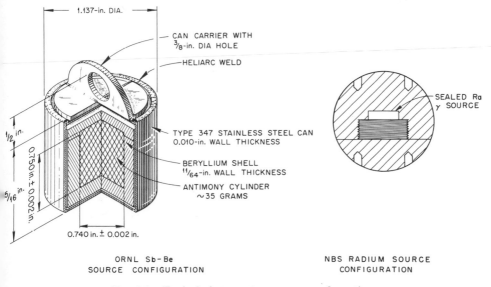

ORNL Sb–Be
SOURCE CONFIGURATION

NBS RADIUM SOURCE
CONFIGURATION

FIG. 3.9—Typical photoneutron source configuration.

The primary advantage of the photoneutron source for thermal neutron activation work is the low neutron energy and the relatively low cost of the Sb$^{124}$–Be sources. The major disadvantage is the intense gamma radiation associated with it which requires heavy lead shielding. The short half-lives of the less expensive isotopes (Sb$^{124}$, Na$^{24}$, Mn$^{57}$, etc.) also cause calibration difficulties.

### 3-2.2 Alpha-initiated Neutron Sources

Another type of source is the *alpha–neutron* source in which alpha particles emitted in the decay of a radionuclide are absorbed in several low $Z$ elements to produce neutrons.[1] Four alpha emitters are presently widely used as the radioactive alpha source. These nuclides, their nuclear properties, and the neutron energy and yield of beryllium sources are shown in Table 3.6.

Since the range of an alpha particle in most materials is only a few microns, the beryllium, boron, fluorine, or other target material must be intimately mixed with the alpha emitter to approach the theoretical neutron yield. The sketch of a typical alpha–neutron source is shown in Fig. 3.10. The size of the source will vary as a function of the radionuclide and number of curies employed.

The source is prepared by thoroughly blending the alpha emitter and the target element (beryllium, boron, fluorine, etc.). The usual atom ratio of target atom to alpha emitter is $>10$, with a theoretical maximum neutron yield at a

Table 3.6—TYPICAL ALPHA EMITTERS USED IN Be($\alpha,n$) SOURCES

| Isotope | $T_{1/2}$ | Curies/gram | Neutrons/sec/curie (actual yields) | Energy of emitted neutrons | |
| | | | | Maximum, Mev | Average, Mev |
| --- | --- | --- | --- | --- | --- |
| $Pu^{239}$ | 24,600 yr | 0.063 | $1.6 \times 10^6$ | 10.6 | 3–5 |
| $Am^{241}$ | 470 yr | 3.17 | $2.2 \times 10^6$ | 11 | 3–5 |
| $Po^{210}$ | 138 day | $4.5 \times 10^3$ | $2.5 \times 10^6$ | 10.8 | 4.2 |
| $Ra^{226}$ | 1620 yr | 1.0 | $1.04 \times 10^{7*}$ | 12 | 4.0 |

* Increased yield due to short-lived alpha-emitter daughters.

ratio of about 250. This mixture is then pressed into a pellet and sealed in the inner container. This inner container is leak-tested, cleaned, and sealed inside the outer container. The combination of double encapsulation and rugged construction makes these sources unusually resistant to physical damage.

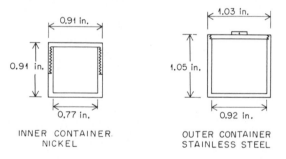

INNER CONTAINER.
NICKEL

OUTER CONTAINER
STAINLESS STEEL

FIG. 3.10—Container for a 2-curie $Am^{241}$–Be source (emission rate $4.23 \times 10^6$ neutrons/sec).

Table 3.7 is a comparison of some of the characteristics of sources using various target materials.[1]

Since the ($\alpha,n$) reaction on beryllium produces the most neutrons per curie of activity, it is the usual choice for most source applications. The lower energy neutrons may have an advantage for applications in which portability and small size is desired.

Table 3.7—COMPARISON OF NEUTRON YIELD AND ENERGY
WITH TYPICAL TARGET ELEMENTS

| Alpha emitter | Target material | Neutrons/sec/curie yield | Average neutron energy, Mev |
| --- | --- | --- | --- |
| $Po^{210}$ | Lithium | $8.8 \times 10^4$ | 0.4 |
| | Beryllium | $2.9 \times 10^6$ | 4.5 |
| | Boron | $8.2 \times 10^5$ | 3 |
| | Fluorine | $4.4 \times 10^5$ | 1.5 |

### 3-2.3 Spontaneous Fission Neutron Sources

The third type of isotopic neutron source is the spontaneous fission source. In this source no target material is required, as the radionuclide emits neutrons. An example of such a source is $Cf^{252}$, 1 mg of which will emit approximately $10^9$ neutrons/sec (a factor of $\sim 100$ greater than the most active presently available isotopic source). These spontaneous fission sources will be essentially point sources for many applications, but special problems will arise in cooling them. The short-range high-mass fission products will dissipate in the source large quantities of energy ($\sim 160$ Mev/fission) that must be removed through some type of cooling jacket. The energies of the neutrons emitted will be very probably of the same energy distribution as the unmoderated $U^{235}$ fission spectrum, with an average neutron energy between 1 and 2 Mev.

### 3-2.4 Radiation Safety

The health physics aspects of the isotopic sources vary depending upon the initiating radionuclide used and the total neutron output. In photoneutron

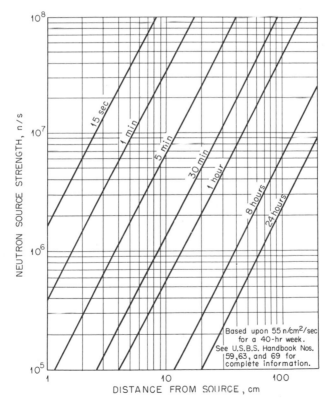

FIG. 3.11—Time and distance relationships to obtain the maximum permissible 8-hr whole-body dose.

sources using $Sb^{124}$ or $Ra^{226}$, the amount of gamma radiation emitted by the source is such that, if sufficient distance or shielding is employed to reduce the gamma radiation to an acceptable level, the neutron dose rate will be well within tolerance.  The alpha-neutron sources, with the exception of $Ra^{226}$ sources, emit very little gamma radiation relative to the number of neutrons.  For example, a 2-curie ($\sim 4.5 \times 10^6$ neutrons/sec) $Po^{210}$, $Pu^{239}$, or $Am^{241}$ (Ref. 9) source will produce only about 100 mrem/hr of $\beta^-$ and $\gamma$ radiation at contact.  Figure 3.11 may be used to determine the safe working time and distance for unshielded neutron sources.  Thus a source emitting $10^6$ neutrons/sec may be used unshielded at a distance of 38 cm for 8 hr a day for 5 days per week without exceeding the permissible exposure levels.

Figure 3.12 shows the effect of paraffin shielding on a 4.5-Mev neutron source.

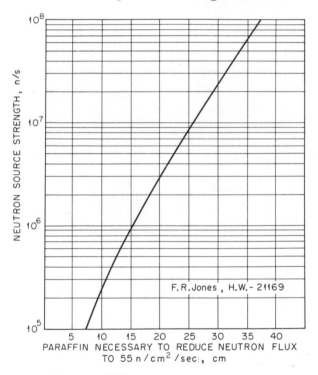

FIG. 3.12—Shielding of neutron sources with paraffin.

For example, if a neutron source ($Am^{241}$–Be) has a total neutron output of $10^6$ neutrons/sec, a 15.5-cm thickness of paraffin will reduce the surface neutron flux to 55 neutrons/cm²/sec, which is considered the permissible dose rate for a 40-hr wk.[6]

The gamma-ray spectrum from paraffin moderated Pu, Po, or $Am^{241}$–Be neutron sources consists of several photon peaks which cannot be associated with the radioactive source used. Figure 3.13 shows the gamma-ray spectrum obtained from such a source by use of a NaI (Tl) detector and analyzer.[9]

The high-energy photopeaks, 4.43 Mev photopeak and its 3.93 Mev and 3.48 Mev escape peaks (see Chap. 6, "Compton Scattering Phenomena") are associ-

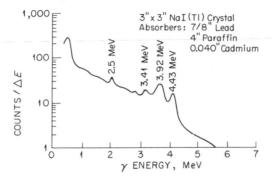

FIG. 3.13—Gamma-ray spectrum of an Am$^{241}$–Be neutron source.

ated with the decay of $C^{12*}$, produced in the $Be^9(\alpha,n)C^{12*}$ reaction, to the ground state, whereas the 2.5-Mev radiation is produced in the interaction of fast neutrons with hydrogen of the moderator. Although these high-energy gamma-rays present no biological hazard due to their low yield, they will cause counting difficulty if the NaI (Tl) gamma detector is located too near the source.

### 3-2.5 Installation and Shielding

The analytical use of isotopic neutron sources determines what size and shape neutron moderators (if any) will be used. If fast neutron activation is to be used exclusively, no moderator will be needed. If thermal activation is to be used, a hydrogenous moderator, such as water or paraffin, will usually be employed. Practical arrangements of source, moderator, and sample will depend on several factors.

1. Neutron source employed: Photoneutron sources and Ra$^{226}$-initiated sources that emit intense gamma radiations will require lead shielding. A typical radiation facility using a 2-curie Ra$^{226}$–Be neutron source is shown in Fig. 3.14.

Alpha–neutron sources do not require lead shielding and may be used in an appropriate paraffin cube.

2. The neutron energy produced by the source: This parameter will determine the optimum distance between the source and the sample. The Po$^{210}$, Pu$^{239}$, and Am$^{241}$ sources have an optimum thermal flux at a moderator distance of 4 to 5 cm, whereas the maximum thermal flux generated by a photoneutron source in a moderator is at the source surface. This is

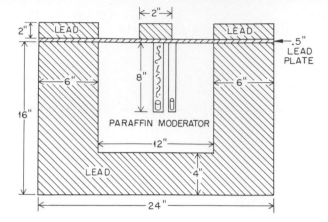

Fig. 3.14—Lead-shielded paraffin moderator for a 2-curie Ra²²⁶–Be neutron source.

explained by the difference in emitted neutron energy and results from a combination of slowing down length in the moderator and the geometrical considerations.

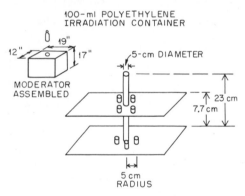

3. The type sample: If the sample is a hydrogenous sample, it is advantageous to place the sample in an annular container within the moderator so that the source is in the sample center. If the sample is a large non-hydrogenous solid, a possible arrangement is to place small sources in the moderator surrounding it, thus providing uniform flux over a large volume. A typical arrangement using eight 2-curie Am²⁴¹–Be neutron sources in a paraffin moderator is shown in Fig. 3.15.

Fig.  3.15—Paraffin  moderator  for  eight 2-curie Am²⁴¹–Be neutron sources.

The available thermal neutron flux that may be obtained from isotopic sources is illustrated in Table 3.8.

Table 3.8—AVAILABLE THERMAL NEUTRON FLUXES
FROM (α,n) NEUTRON SOURCES

| Two-curie source, (α,n) | Total neutron output, (neutrons/sec) | Max. thermal neutron flux,* (neutrons/cm²/sec) |
|---|---|---|
| Ra²²⁶–Be | $2.02 \times 10^7$ | $1.75 \times 10^5$ |
| Am²⁴¹–B | $1.29 \times 10^6$ | $8.6 \times 10^3$ |
| Am²⁴¹–Be | $4.54 \times 10^6$ | $2.4 \times 10^4$ |

* Monitored, using a dilute gold solution (2 mg/2-ml sample).

The eight-source array pictured in Fig. 3.15, when loaded with eight-$Am^{241}$–Be neutron sources with a combined neutron output of $2.9 \times 10^7$ neutrons/sec, produced a uniform thermal flux within a 183 cm$^3$ volume of 8 ($\pm$ 0.4) $\times 10^4$ neutrons/cm$^2$/sec.

## 3-2.6 Practical Applications of Isotopic Sources

The practical application of fluxes in the order of $10^5$ neutrons/cm$^2$/sec in neutron activation is clearly limited to the determination of macroelement concentrations. Table 3.9 lists some typical elements and their sensitivities of

Table 3.9—ISOTOPIC SOURCE ACTIVATION

| Element | Isotope produced | $T_{1/2}$ | Gamma energy, Mev | Irradiation time | Integral peak count, counts/min/mg |
|---------|---------|---------|---------|---------|---------|
| Hafnium | 189$m$ | 19 sec | 0.161 | 1 min | 8 |
| Scandium | 46 | 19.5 sec | 0.14 | 1 min | 12 |
| Tungsten | 183 | 5.5 sec | 0.105 | 1 min | 0.04 |
| Aluminum | 28 | 2.3 min | 1.78 | 5 min | 0.16 |
| Iodine | 128 | 25 min | 0.455 | 30 min | 0.32 |
| Silver | 108 | 2.3 min | 0.44 | 5 min | 0.8 |
| | | | 0.60 | | |
| Magnesium | 27 | 9.4 min | 0.84 | 10 min | 0.008 |
| Manganese | 56 | 2.58 hr | 0.845 | 60 min | 0.32 |
| Gold | 198 | 2.7 day | 0.412 | 2.6 day | 12 |

detection in terms of major photopeak area at a flux of $8 \times 10^4$ neutrons/cm$^2$/sec. A 3 $\times$ 3 in. NaI(Tl) detector was used to detect the gamma radiations.

Practical applications of neutron activation analysis with this 8-source array and large samples that have proved useful are listed in Table 3.10.

Additional qualitative analysis at this neutron flux ($8 \times 10^4$) has been used for the characterization of an unknown Hastelloy as either type $A$, $B$, $C$, or $D$. It is also possible to identify some nine different types of stainless steel on the basis of short (15 min) irradiation and gamma-ray measurements.

Sources of this intensity have also been used to generate short-lived activities in certain elements in a flowing stream, to determine either their concentration or the flow rate.

Two other techniques in which the low-intensity neutron source is successfully employed are neutron-absorption and neutron-transmission measurements.[9] Neutron absorption measurements are very sensitive in that total-neutron

Table 3.10—APPLICATION OF ISOTOPIC NEUTRON SOURCES IN ACTIVATION ANALYSIS

| Element | Sample | Irradiation time | Lower limit of detection (at $\pm20\%$ error level), % |
|---------|---------|---------|---------|
| Silicon | 50 g soil | 5 min | 1 |
| Aluminum | 50 g soil | 5 min | 0.2 |
| Hafnium | 50 g ZrO$_2$ | 1 min | 0.01 |
| Manganese | 50 g soil | 15 min | 0.01 |

absorption cross sections, rather than activation cross sections are employed, and the half-life of the isotope produced has no bearing on the sensitivity. The application and sensitivity of the technique is illustrated in Fig. 3.16. The neutron count ratio is the ratio of the unperturbed neutron density to the neutron density with the sample in place.

When a 2-curie $Am^{241}$–Be source ($4.5 \times 10^6$ neutrons/sec) is used, a neutron count ratio can be determined to 0.3% statistical accuracy in 100 sec. This same technique has in a similar manner been used for isotopic analysis of lithium, uranium, and boron. Neutron transmission is similar to absorption techniques except that the scattering cross section also enters into the measurement. Transmission measurements can be used to determine nondestructively high cross section materials in flat samples.

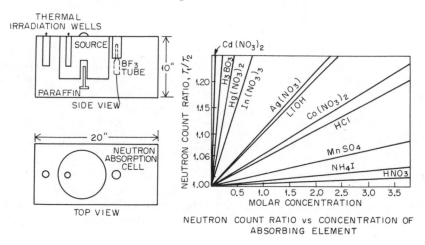

FIG. 3.16—Neutron absorption response curves and apparatus.

### 3-2.7 Isotopic Neutron Source Costs

Table 3.11 summarizes typical cost data for isotopic neutron sources (including fabrication).

Table 3.11—TYPICAL ISOTOPIC NEUTRON SOURCE COSTS
(Normalized to 1-curie Sources)

| Source | Type | Neutron emission (initial), neutrons/sec | % Output decrease in one year | Typical costs |
|---|---|---|---|---|
| $Sb^{124}$–Be | $(\gamma,n)$ | $2 \times 10^6$ | 98.5 | \$ 460 |
| $Ra^{226}$–Be | $(\alpha,n)$ | $1 \times 10^7$ | 0.0 | 17,000 |
| $Po^{210}$–Be | $(\alpha,n)$ | $2.8 \times 10^6$ | 84.0 | 800 |
| $Po^{210}$–B | $(\alpha,n)$ | $8 \times 10^5$ | 84.0 | 800 |
| $Am^{241}$–Be | $(\alpha,n)$ | $2.8 \times 10^6$ | 0.21 | 1,000 |
| $Pu^{239}$–Be | $(\alpha,n)$ | $1.06 \times 10^6$ | 0.0 | 700* |

* $Pu^{239}$ is not sold but is leased by the U. S. Government at a rate of 4%/yr considering the value of $Pu^{239}$ at \$30/g. For example, a 1-curie $Pu^{239}$–Be neutron source will contain 16 g $Pu^{239}$ and the lease charges will be \$19.20 per year.

### 3-2.8 Procedure for Ordering Neutron Sources

Persons other than those operating Commission-owned plants and laboratories for the Commission require a license to purchase and possess isotopic neutron sources. Application for a license is made to

>Isotopes Branch
>Division of Licensing and Regulation
>U. S. Atomic Energy Commission
>Washington 25, D. C.

All orders for sources are to be placed on AEC order forms. Federal Agencies use *Isotope Order Blank* Form AEC 375; all other agencies use *Isotope and Service Irradiation Order Form*, Form AEC 391. If acknowledgment of the order is desired, the order should be submitted in duplicate. These forms are available from either the Isotopes Branch at the above address or Mound Laboratory.

One copy of the license, together with the order, should be sent to (For Po$^{210}$ or Pu$^{239}$):

>Mound Laboratory
>Monsanto Research Corporation
>Miamisburg, Ohio
>Attention: Source Group

or (For Sb$^{124}$ or Am$^{241}$):

>Union Carbide Nuclear Company
>Oak Ridge National Laboratory
>Isotopes Sales Department
>P. O. Box X
>Oak Ridge, Tennessee.

### 3-2.9 Procedure for Ordering Plutonium Sources

A license to procure and possess fissionable material is required of persons other than those operating Commission-owned plants and laboratories for the Commission. Application for a license is made to:

>Licensing Branch
>Division of Licensing and Regulation
>U. S. Atomic Energy Commission
>Washington 25, D. C.

Upon approval of the request for plutonium, the requestor will furnish a purchase order on Form OR-640 to

>AEC Materials Leasing Officer
>Production Division
>U. S. Atomic Energy Commission
>Post Office Box E
>Oak Ridge, Tennessee.

He will also complete a lease agreement supplied by the AEC Materials Leasing Officer.

The Division of Licensing and Regulation will forward a copy of the license for plutonium and a copy of the Nuclear Draft (Form 437) to

> Dayton Area Office
> U. S. Atomic Energy Commission
> Miamisburg, Ohio.

## REFERENCES

1. J. B. Marion and J. L. Fowler, *Fast Neutron Physics*, Part I, Interscience Publishers, Inc., New York, 1960.
2. E. A. Burrill and J. Hirschfield, *Activation Analysis for Materials Testing and Research*, USAEC Report ANL-6515, Argonne National Laboratory, pp. 9–27.
3. R. S. Bender, F. G. Shoemaker, and J. L. Powell, *Phys. Rev.* **71**: 905 (1947).
4. J. B. Marion, *Nuclear Data Tables*, National Academy of Sciences, National Research Council, p. 107, 1960.
5. E. H. Arnold, Neutron Physics Division, Oak Ridge National Laboratory, private communication.
6. *Federal Register, Title 10*, Atomic Energy Part 20, Standards for Protection Against Radiation, Nov. 17, 1960.
7. A. S. Gillespie, Jr. and W. W. Hill, Sensitivities for Activation Analysis with 14-Mev Neutrons, *Nucleonics* **19** (11): 170 (1961).
8. A. Wattenberg, *Photo-Neutron Sources*, Report NP-1100, National Research Council, 1949.
9. J. E. Strain and G. W. Leddicotte, *The Preparation, Properties, and Uses of Americium-241, Alpha, Gamma, and Neutron Sources*, USAEC Report ORNL-3335, 1962.

# Chapter 4

## RADIOCHEMICAL SEPARATIONS

### HARLEY H. ROSS

It has been pointed out in earlier chapters that activation analysis can often be used as a nondestructive technique. This simply involves activity measurements on the irradiated sample without the use of chemical separations. With samples of any complexity, however, the number of radioactive products may be so large that activity measurements of a single component are impossible or, at best, very difficult.

The major types of counting interference are:

1. Nuclides in the sample exhibiting gamma-ray photopeaks which are so similar that they cannot be resolved using conventional counting equipment (see $Fe^{59}$ and $Co^{60}$).
2. Samples that contain one or more elements which, by virtue of their amounts, cross sections, and half-lives, become activated to such a high degree that they mask the activities of other elements present in the sample. (The determination of trace elements in a sodium matrix is an example.)
3. Mixtures of pure $\beta^-$ emitters whose maximum energies lie close to each other cannot be resolved with conventional $\beta^-$ counting equipment.

For these reasons and the fact that the ultimate in sensitivity and accuracy is obtained only after chemical isolation, separation techniques are routinely employed in many practical activation analysis problems.

Once it has been concluded that a chemical separation will be required for a given sample, one must decide if the separation is to be made before activation (preirradiation separation) or after activation (postirradiation separation). This decision usually creates no problem since in *all possible cases*, a postirradiation separation is the method of choice. This is true because one of the major advantages of activation analysis with a postirradiation separation (or without any separation) is that no reagent blank is involved. There are many instances in conventional methods of analysis where the reagents used in a procedure contain an appreciable quantity of the element to be determined. If these same reagents were used in a preirradiation separation, the sought element in both the sample and reagents would become activated and subsequently measured. A postirradiation separation completely avoids this problem.

There are some cases when a postirradiation separation is not feasible. In this situation a preirradiation separation is used, and results are compared to a reagent blank.

## 4-1 CHOICE OF A SEPARATION TECHNIQUE

The general analytical criteria of speed, efficiency, reliability, and ease of handling are always applied to the choice of a separation method for activation analysis. The additional factors that will affect this choice include:

1. The chemical and physical properties of the desired activity.
2. The sample matrix and presence of other activities.
3. The half-life of the desired activity.
4. The counting method chosen for the desired activity.
5. The degree of decontamination required in the counting sample.
6. The intensity of the radiation field caused by the active sample.

The chemical state of the desired activity is very important in the selection of a separation scheme. Under the conditions of a high irradiation flux, significant radiation decomposition (radiolysis) of the sample can occur. Thus the chemical state of an element before irradiation may not be the same as that after irradiation. A separation scheme that takes this fact into account is essential.

A recognition of the presence and types of other activities in the sample may dictate a particular separation method. It may not be necessary to separate the desired activity from all other activities in the sample but only from the major interference(s).

The half-life of the desired activity may be very short and, thus, require a rapid separation technique; a longer-lived nuclide may be separated after a period of days or even weeks.

The intensity of the radiation field due to the sample may necessitate the selection of a separation technique that is convenient to perform with remote handling equipment. High-intensity samples are frequently allowed to *cool* before separation procedures are attempted.

## 4-2 SEPARATION EFFICIENCIES

A major advantage of the separation schemes developed for activation analysis is that they need not be quantitative in order to obtain quantitative results. It is often the case that yield is purposely sacrificed in order to utilize a *cleaner* separation or one that is more rapid. These separations are possible since yield corrections are conveniently made with most systems. The two most widely used methods of yield correction are: (1) the addition of an isotopic carrier to the sample to act as a stable, bulk tracer of a particular element in the system, and (2) the addition of a radiotracer to the sample to determine recovery.

With either of these two methods of yield correction, it is most important to indicate that the carrier (or tracer) *must* be in the *identical* chemical form as the sought element in the sample. It is necessary, therefore, to add the carrier/tracer in all possible oxidation states, which may then be converted to the desired state for separation. Alternatively, the carrier/tracer may be added in one oxidation state only and the desired condition produced by oxidation and reduction before separation is attempted. Neglecting to recognize and correct differences in oxidation states of an element in a sample is the most usually encountered pitfall in radiochemical separations.

The addition of an isotopic carrier (a quantity of stable atoms of the same chemical species as the radioactive atoms) to a sample is the most widely used technique of separation yield correction. In this method, a known weight of carrier is added to the active sample before separation, and, if the weight of carrier is large (1000 X or more) compared to the weight of the sought element in the sample, the following type of calculation can be used to determine the activity before separation

$$A_x \text{ before separation} = A_x \text{ recovered} \left( \frac{W_x \text{ added}}{W_x \text{ recovered}} \right) \quad (4.1)$$

where $A_x$ = activity due to element X
$W_x$ = weight of element X

The weight of carrier added to the sample ($W_x$ added) must be known accurately. The recovered activity is measured by conventional counting techniques. The weight recovered ($W_x$) can be evaluated by any analytical technique: by direct weighing of a precipitate or by appropriate titrimetric, electrometric, or optical methods with subsequent conversion to weight units.

When the comparator technique is used for an activation analysis, an alternate method of yield correction is possible that eliminates the necessity of knowing the exact concentration of the added carrier solution. In this case, identical volumes of carrier solution are added to both the unknown and the comparator. The required separations are carried out, and the yields for both samples are compared. The amount of carrier added is unimportant since this term cancels itself in the calculation of the unknown amount.

The use of a radioisotopic tracer in a system is possible when a radionuclide of the sought element is available which is *different* from the activation analysis product. This is illustrated by the following example. In the analysis of iodine, the 127 isotope undergoes the reaction:

$$I^{127}(n,\gamma)I^{128}$$

which decays by $\beta^-$-$\gamma$ emission ($\gamma$:0.46, 0.54 Mev) with a 25-min half-life. If before the separation of the $I^{128}$ activity from the sample, a known *spike* of $I^{131}$ ($\gamma$:0.36, 0.64 Mev; $T_{1/2}$:8 day) is added, the following relation is true

$$A_{I^{128}} \text{ before separation} = A_{I^{128}} \text{ recovered} \left( \frac{A_{I^{131}} \text{ added}}{A_{I^{131}} \text{ recovered}} \right) \qquad (4.2)$$

where $A$ is activity.

Since $A_{I^{128}}$ recovered and $A_{I^{131}}$ recovered can be determined experimentally and $A_{I^{131}}$ added is known at the time of addition, the value of $A_{I^{128}}$ before separation can be calculated even though the isolation of the iodine activities was not quantitative. Obviously, the counting conditions (i.e., geometry, amount of absorbing materials, etc.) should be the same for the measurement made before and after irradiation.

## 4-3 SEPARATION METHODS

Separation methods that are used for conventional chemical systems can generally be applied to radiochemical systems. However, some radiochemical separation techniques are unique; isotope-exchange separations are only used when a radionuclide is present in a system. The following discussion of separation methods includes those which have found wide application to problems associated with activation analysis, although most are generally applicable to any chemical system.

### 4-3.1 Precipitation Separation

Separation by precipitation is one of the most commonly used classical methods of analytical chemistry. Radiochemical investigations of this technique indicate that all of the factors affecting the rate and completeness of precipitation in ordinary chemical systems are equally applicable in radiochemical systems. In activation analysis, one is usually looking for trace concentrations. This usually precludes the direct precipitation of an activity, since the concentration in solution before precipitation is generally too low to permit precipitation by exceeding the solubility product of a compound considered to be *insoluble*. For this reason trace activities are precipitated with the aid of carriers, which may be isotopic or nonisotopic. Isotopic carriers may be added to the sample solvent before the actual sample is dissolved or to the sample before precipitation. Nonisotopic carriers may be present already in the sample or may be added at the appropriate time.

The mechanism of isotopic carrying is the same as that which occurs in any direct precipitation process. Thus, in the trace determination of barium in a sample, one can add a known amount of $BaCl_2$ carrier to the sample and then precipitate $BaSO_4$. Since there is no chemical difference between the active barium and the inactive barium, both precipitate equally well; if 99.9% of the inactive carrier is precipitated, then 99.9% of the active barium will also precipitate.

If in the preceding example, the sample had also contained radioactive $Y^{90}$, the precipitate of barium sulfate would be appreciably contaminated with active $Y^{90}$. This contamination is due to physical entrainment and nonselective absorption of the yttrium on the barium sulfate during its formation. This type of contamination (absorption and entrainment on a solid substrate) can be reduced by the addition of an inactive analog of the interfering element to the sample before precipitation (called a *hold-back carrier*). Thus to reduce yttrium contamination in a barium sulfate precipitate, a large, i.e., 10 to 50 mg, quantity of stable yttrium hold-back carrier is added to the sample before separation.

It must be again emphasized that an isotopic carrier must not only be the same element as the sought element, but that both must be in the identical chemical form. ($SO_3^{2-}$ is not an isotopic carrier for $SO_4^{2-}$.)

Precipitation using nonisotopic carriers is frequently used in systems where

1. A stable isotopic carrier does not exist for a given element ($Fe^{3+}$ used as a carrier for protactinium).
2. A number of interfering activities are to be removed from a sample ($La^{3+}$ used as a carrier for a number of rare earths when precipitated as the fluoride; sometimes called scavenging).
3. The use of a nonisotopic carrier is more convenient (use of zirconium carrier for hafnium).

The mechanisms of nonisotopic carrying can be classified as either adsorption or isomorphic replacement processes.

## 4-3.2 Electrodeposition

Electrodeposition (especially controlled potential electrolysis) has been used for separations in activation analysis samples. This technique has the advantages of (1) being relatively fast for small amounts of material such as those concentration levels found in activation samples and (2) being almost completely free of contamination by adsorption from solution of microcomponents. The method is generally used for material which will undergo electrode reactions at a positive reduction potential such as $Au^{3+}$, $Pt^{2+}$, $Hg^{2+}$, $Ag^+$, $Cu^{2+}$, and $SbO^+$. In a number of cases, however, materials with a negative reduction potential have been separated by this method ($Pb^{2+}$, $Sn^{2+}$, $Ni^{2+}$ and $Co^{2+}$). Small amounts of isotopic carriers are necessary in the sample but yield corrections are frequently not needed, since quantitative recoveries are usually observed.

## 4-3.3 Solvent Extraction

Because solvent-extraction methods have the advantages of being fast, easy to use, often specific, and requiring little in the way of special equipment, they are often used in the isolation of trace materials in activation samples. Extraction systems have been developed for over 75 elements. The principle of solvent extraction is based on the partition of a solute between two solvents; in most cases, one of the solvent phases is an aqueous solution. The technique is ideally suited for use in remote handling facilities and is often the method of choice under these conditions.

### 4-3.4 Other Separation Methods

The techniques of volatilization, ion exchange, and chromatography are also recognized as useful methods in activation analysis. Their application in this area is usually no different than their use in ordinary chemical systems. A number of specialized references on these and other separation methods of importance are listed at the end of this chapter.

A separation technique that is peculiar to radiochemical systems is the isotope-exchange separation. Isotope exchange is a process whereby atoms of a given species will exchange with other atoms of the same species between chemical compounds. The exchange can occur in homogeneous systems or between various phases of multiphase systems. Thus

$$Ag^+ \text{ (active)} + AgCl \text{ (inactive)} \rightleftharpoons$$
$$Ag^+ \text{ (inactive)} + AgCl \text{ (active)}$$

If an amount of inactive silver chloride is added to a solution containing a small amount of active silver ion, the exchange reaction will occur with the activity being distributed between the solution and the solid. If the amount of AgCl added is large compared to the concentration of $Ag^+$ in solution, the majority of activity will be in the precipitate when equilibrium is reached. One need only collect the precipitate to isolate the activity. This type of separation can be very fast and specific. The technique has only recently been applied to activation samples and further work will probably be needed to indicate its general usefulness.

### 4-3.5 Conclusions

In conclusion it can be said that for routine applications, nondestructive analysis, if it is possible, is preferred to a postirradiation separation. When the utmost in sensitivity and accuracy is required, a postirradiation separation is necessary. Preirradiation separation techniques are considered only as a last resort.

The choice of a separation method depends upon the physical, chemical and nuclear properties of the sought element. Any conventional chemical separation technique can generally be applied to activation analysis systems. In these systems, one has the advantage that quantitative recoveries are not necessary, since yield corrections are easily determined.

The choice of a given technique over another will usually be a compromise in consideration of the various determining factors.

To aid workers in the field, the Subcommittee on Radiochemistry of the National Academy of Sciences has developed a series of monographs on the radiochemistry of the elements. This series has grown out of the need for up-to-date compilations of radiochemical information and procedures. Each monograph collects in one volume the pertinent information required for radiochemical work with an individual element or a group of closely related elements. All of the elements are covered in this series with the exceptions of hydrogen, helium, lithium, boron, and neon. These monographs are available at various prices from the Office of Technical Services, Department of Commerce, Washington 25, D. C.

## SUPPLEMENTARY REFERENCES

J. P. Cali, ed., *Trace Analysis of Semiconductor Materials*, Pergamon Press, (distributed by) Macmillan Co., New York, 1964.

F. Cramer, *Paper Chromatography*, 2d ed., St. Martin's, New York, 1954.

E. A. Burrill and J. Hirschfield, in *2nd Symposium on Physics and Nondestructive Testing Argonne National Laboratory*, Oct. 3, 1961, USAEC Report ANL-6515 Argonne National Laboratory, pp. 9–27.

Y. Kusaka and W. Meinke, *Rapid Radiochemical Separations*, NAS-NS-3104, Dec. 1961.

M. Lederer, *Introduction to Paper Electrophoresis and Related Methods*, Elsevier, Publishing Co., Inc., Houston, 1955.

F. L. Moore, *Liquid-Liquid Extraction with High-molecular-weight Amines*, NAS-NS-3101, Dec. 1960.

G. H. Morrison and H. Freiser, *Solvent Extraction in Analytical Chemistry*, John Wiley & Sons, Inc., New York, 1957.

O. Samuelson, *Ion Exchanges in Analytical Chemistry*, John Wiley & Sons, Inc., New York, 1953.

A. C. Wahl, and N. A. Bonner, *Radioactivity Applied to Chemistry*, John Wiley & Sons, Inc., New York, 1951.

J. C. White and W. J. Ross, *Separations by Solvent Extraction with Tri-n-Octylphosphine Oxide*, NAS-NS-3102, February 1961.

# Chapter 5

---

# RADIATION DETECTORS
# AND COUNTING STATISTICS

## Richard L. Hahn

---

Although $\gamma$-ray spectrometry is used quite extensively in activation analysis, it is often necessary to make use of gas-filled counters to detect the $\beta$ particles emitted by the nuclides being studied. For example, no $\gamma$ rays are emitted in the decay of such nuclides as $P^{32}$, $P^{33}$, $S^{35}$, and $Ca^{45}$; therefore $\beta$-particle detectors must necessarily be used in assays of these radionuclides. Also, it should be noted that determinations of nuclear parameters that are quite pertinent to activation-analysis investigations, such as half-lives and cross sections, are often-times performed with charged-particle detectors. Furthermore, an effective method for counting neutrons makes use of a gas-filled counter that detects the $\alpha$ particles from the reaction of $B^{10}$ with neutrons. Gas-filled proportional counters are also routinely used in the detection of low-energy photons and X rays.

All of these detection devices make use of the fact that charged particles interact with matter to form ion pairs. Thus, in principle, if an electric field can be established in the material to collect the ion pairs formed, the number of charged particles passing through the material can be determined. The first part of this chapter is a discussion of various gas-filled counters; the second part is a brief discussion of a new development in radiation detection, the semiconductor, or solid-state, detector. Finally, in the last section the statistical treatment of data from measurements of radioactive nuclides is discussed.

## 5-1 GAS-FILLED COUNTERS

### 5-1.1 Ionization Process in a Gas

Consider a detector consisting of two electrodes placed in a gaseous atmosphere.[1-4] If a constant number of charged particles per unit time passes through the gas, the number of ion pairs collected can be measured as a function of the d-c voltage applied to the electrodes. In Fig. 5.1, data from such measurements are shown. Curves for two particles, $a$ and $b$, with different specific ionization are presented. Because the ionizing ability of a charged particle depends on its charge and energy, $a$ and $b$ may either represent different particles, as $\alpha$ and $\beta$ particles, or identical particles with different kinetic energies.

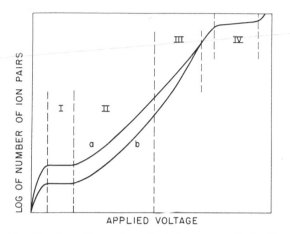

Fig. 5.1—Number of ion pairs collected versus applied voltage.

The striking point illustrated in Fig. 5.1 is that the curves change slope several times as the voltage is increased. These changes, as shown in regions I–IV in the figure, reflect differences in the details of the ionization process occurring in the gas and are the bases for the design and operation of the detectors, which are to be discussed in the following sections.

## 5-1.2 Ionization Chamber

As is seen in Fig. 5.1, no ion pairs are collected at zero voltage. Then, as the voltage is slowly raised, the number of ion pairs collected increases until a limiting value is attained where the number of ion pairs is independent of the applied voltage. This region of saturation, represented by I in the figure, is the operating region of the ionization chamber. The range of voltage over which saturation occurs is dependent upon the geometry and spacing of the electrodes, the pressure and type of filling gas, and the characteristics of the ionization process in the gas.

Approximately 30 ev are necessary to produce an ion pair in a gas; this value is essentially independent of the energy and type of charged particle. Then the number of such pairs at saturation will be equal to $NE/30$, where $N$ is the number of charged particles in the chamber, and $E$ is the average energy, in electron volts, lost by the particles in the chamber. Thus, in general, for two particles $a$ and $b$, different saturation values will be attained, as shown in Fig. 5.1. If the particles from two samples are identical in type and energy, then the ratio of their saturation values will be equivalent to the ratio of the activity levels of the samples.

The current produced by the ion pairs collected in the ionization chamber is quite small. To detect this current, one may produce a measurable voltage by use of appropriately selected resistors or capacitors. The resulting voltage level can be easily detected with an electrometer or by further electronic amplification. A schematic diagram of a parallel-plate ionization chamber is presented in Fig. 5.2. The direction of motion of the electrons and the positive ions in the

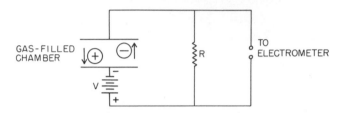

FIG. 5.2—Schematic diagram of a parallel-plate ionization chamber.

electric field of the chamber is indicated in the figure. The resistor, $R$, is used here to produce a potential drop that is detected by the electrometer.

Ionization chambers are widely used for detection of heavy charged particles, such as alpha particles or fission fragments. Neutrons can be detected by causing the neutrons to undergo nuclear reactions in the chamber; the resulting charged particle is then detected, as in the $B^{10}(n,\alpha)Li^7$ reaction. Beta and gamma rays can also be detected with an ionization chamber. In fact, the widely used *Cutie Pie* portable survey meter, which is sensitive to $\beta$, $\gamma$, and X radiation, is simply an ionization chamber filled with air at atmospheric pressure.

### 5-1.3 Multiplication Processes in a Gas

Regions II, III, and IV of Fig. 5.1 show that the number of ion pairs collected increases rapidly beyond the saturation level. This effect, called multiplication, is due to secondary ionization processes occurring in the gas; because of the high value of the electric field, electrons from the primary ionization process will have sufficient energy to initiate many additional ionization processes. In region II, the number of pairs collected will be proportional to the original ionization; thus the curve for particle $a$ is maintained at a constant value above the curve for particle $b$. Region II is accordingly termed the proportional region. As the voltage is further increased, the curves pass through region III, the region of limited proportionality. Here the number of secondary processes is increasing rapidly, and the relation between the number of initial and secondary ionization processes is no longer one of strict proportionality. It should therefore be noted that the curves for $a$ and $b$ approach each other. Finally, in region IV, the Geiger-Mueller region, an essentially constant number of ion pairs is collected, regardless of the primary ionization. Hence, a single primary electron will cause an avalanche of multiple ionization processes that propagates along the entire length of the collector electrode.

### 5-1.4 Proportional and Geiger-Mueller Counters

Because the operation of the proportional and G-M counters is based on the production of secondary ionization events in the gas, both will be described in this section. Since the use of the counters will primarily be for the assay of radioactive samples, the charged particles referred to below should be understood to be negative and positive electrons and $\alpha$ particles.

In counters that depend on multiple ionization, it is necessary to prevent the emission of secondary electrons from the negative electrode (cathode) caused by bombardment with positive ions of the gas, since these may initiate new multiplicative processes. This preventive measure is termed quenching. It may be performed by electronic means, or by the addition of small amounts of a polyatomic gas, usually $CH_4$ or a halogen, to the counter gas. Collisions of the ions of the counter gas, such as argon, with the polyatomic molecules will cause transfer of the ionic charge to the latter. These will then dissipate much of their energy by dissociation at the cathode. Consequently, no additional electrons will be produced to start new multiplication cycles. Because of the molecular dissociation, an organic quencher, such as $CH_4$, is eventually used up; the operating life of a G-M tube with such a quenching agent is about $10^9$ counts. Halogen atoms tend to recombine after dissociation occurs, so that halogen-quenched G-M tubes have lifetimes of perhaps $10^{11}$ counts.

Immediately after an avalanche of multiple ionization processes has taken place in the G-M counter, it is insensitive to new ionizing particles. The positive ions in the vicinity of the positive electrode (anode), left there after the collection of the electrons by the anode, depress the electric field and prevent new avalanches from occurring. These ions eventually migrate from the high field region to the cathode. The time it takes for the counter to become sensitive again to charged particles is termed the resolving time. The fraction of time that the counter is insensitive is then equal to $R\tau$, where $R$ is the observed counting rate and $\tau$ is the resolving time. One may determine $\tau$ of the counter by experimental means:[5] (1) Because of the greater counting losses at higher activity levels, the semilog plot of activity versus time, for a highly active, short-lived sample, will be concave downward at early times and linear at later times when the counting level is low. This behavior is illustrated in Fig. 5.3. The difference between the extrapolated and experimental curves at early times is just the counting loss due to $\tau$. (2) Again, because of the losses at higher counting levels, the counting rate for two samples assayed together will be less than the sum of the activities obtained by counting each sample alone. The resolving time, $\tau$, may then be calculated from the counting losses determined

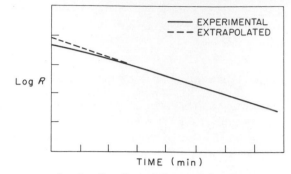

FIG. 5.3—Decay curve showing the effect of the resolving time, $\tau$, on counting rate, $R$.

by this two source method. Once $\tau$ has been determined, correction for counting losses may be made by use of the formula,

$$\frac{R}{R_o} = 1 - R\tau \qquad (5.1)$$

where $R_o$ is the true counting rate. In G-M counters, $\tau$ is generally of the order of a few hundred $\mu$sec. If $\tau = 300$ $\mu$sec $= 5$ $\mu$min, and $R = 2 \times 10^3$/min, then $R/R_o = 1-0.01 = 0.99$; that is, the observed rate will differ from the true rate by 1%. For proportional counters, the recovery time of the tube is extremely rapid because the multiplication process is localized to some small volume in the vicinity of the cathode and does not spread along the entire central wire. The resolving time of a proportional counting assembly is thus limited by the electronic equipment used. Many scalers have resolving times of the order of 1 $\mu$sec, so that the counting losses are negligible until $R$ is of the order of a few hundred thousand counts per minute.

The operating range of the proportional counter or G-M counter is determined by observing the rate of change of counting rate with increase in applied voltage. A region, called the plateau, is soon attained in which all of the charged particles produce pulses large enough to be detected. Thus, on the plateau, the counting rate is practically constant. The plateau for a proportional counter has a small slope, <0.2% per 100 volts, over a range of several hundred volts. In contrast to this, the plateaus obtained with G-M tubes have appreciable slopes. For an organically quenched tube, the plateau is about 200 to 300 volts long with a slope of some 1 to 2% per 100 volts; for a halogen-quenched tube, the plateau is about 100 to 200 volts long and has a slope of some 3 to 4% per 100 volts. The obvious advantage of operating on the plateau is that small voltage fluctuations, which are unavoidable, will not affect the counting data. The operating stability of a counter may be routinely checked by determining the counter background rate and the counting rate of a long-lived sample such as uranium. Large fluctuations in these counts from previous measurements may indicate electronic difficulties, or, in the case of a G-M counter, that the tube has exceeded its expected lifetime and should be replaced.

Because their response is proportional to the energy of the primary ionizing particle, proportional counters may be used for differential pulse height analysis. In this application, components of different energy are resolved from one another. This differential analysis may be applied to low-energy photons as well as to charged particles. In a proportional counter, 6-cm long and filled with argon at 1 atm, an X ray of 6 kev will be completely absorbed. The properties of the absorbing gas are important for the detection of photons, because the probability of a photoelectric event occurring is proportional to $\sim Z^4$, where $Z$ is the atomic number of the gas. Thus filling the counter with xenon will enable one to detect X rays of higher energy than is possible in an argon counter. The sensitive dependence of photon detection on the $Z$ of the absorbing gas also is important in the reduction of the background due to X rays and $\gamma$ rays in a counter that is used mainly for detecting $\beta$ particles. The photon detection efficiency for a typical end-window counter filled with P-10 gas (90% Ar, 10% $CH_4$) is of the order of 1 to 2%; changing the filling gas to a mixture of helium and $CH_4$ effectively reduces photon detection to zero.

It should be noted at this point that proportional counters, because of their proportional response to incident radiation, their low resolving time, long life, and approximately horizontal plateaus, offer distinct advantages over G-M counters. However, amplification of the proportional counter output is necessary. Various electronic units, consisting of a preamplifier, a linear amplifier, a scaler with decade scaling strips, a regulated high-voltage supply, a mechanical register, and a timer are commercially available for use with proportional counter tubes (see Ref. 6, for example). The price of such units, depending upon the specific characteristics of the system, lies in the range of about $1500 to $2500. The output of a G-M tube, on the other hand, does not require further amplification. Typical units for G-M counting, with a high-voltage supply, a timer, a mechanical register, and decimal or binary mode of addition, can be obtained for about $500 to $1000.

There is also a large variety of proportional and G-M counter tubes available. These tubes differ widely in their characteristics. Such properties as dimensions, window material, window thickness, cathode material, operating voltage, and slope and length of plateau will vary depending upon the intended use of the tube. For example, there are tubes that may be immersed in solutions, tubes that may be used to assay radioactivity in flowing gases or liquids, and tubes that may be used for portable survey work. For most work involving solid samples, end-window tubes are routinely used.

## 5-1.5 Use of Counters for the Assay of Radioactivity

A schematic representation of a typical end–window cylindrical counter assembly is shown in Fig. 5.4. The central wire serves as the anode, and the outer cylinder is the cathode. The window is made of a thin film (mica in many G-M tubes), so that low-energy particles can enter the tube. A plastic housing with shelves is often placed below the counter so that samples may be positioned in a reproducible manner with respect to the counter.  The entire assembly is then surrounded by a lead shield to reduce the background activity level. Radioactive samples are oftentimes prepared by depositing a small amount of precipitate onto filter paper, or by evaporating an aliquot of active solution onto a small watch glass or circle of plastic material.  These samples are then placed on cards made of cardboard or aluminum, which fit in the shelf arrangement shown in Fig. 5.4.

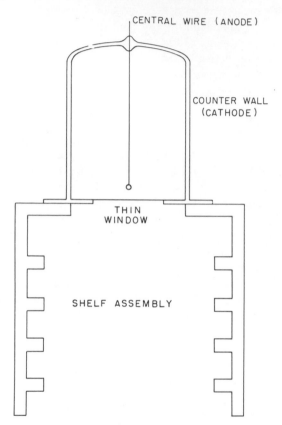

Fig. 5.4—Schematic drawing of an end-window cylindrical counter assembly.

Since in activation analysis work unknown samples are usually compared with known standards, it is not necessary to evaluate the various parameters that affect the counting rate observed for a sample.  However, it is important to have some knowledge of the nature of these various parameters so that a valid comparison between unknown and standard can be made.[7]  The geometry or position of the sample with respect to the counter window will, of course, affect the counting rate since the intensity of emitted radiation ideally decreases with the square of the distance from source to counter. Scattering and absorption of charged particles in the sample, the backing material, the air, the walls of the shelf assembly and shielding material, and in the counter window will also have an effect on the counting rate. Thus, in the comparison method, it is important that sample and standard be prepared in the same chemical form, be of similar weight (a correction for self-absorption[8] as a function of sample weight or thickness may have to be applied), and be mounted and counted in exactly the same way. If these conditions of sample preparation are satisfied, the total detection efficiency, $\epsilon$, which depends upon the various parameters mentioned above, will be the same for sample and standard. Then the weight of the unknown sample can be determined from Eq. 1.11b, in which relative counting rates instead of absolute disintegration rates are used.

If the absolute decay rate in an unknown is desired, instead of comparison with a standard that contains the same nuclide as the unknown, one may prepare a calibration curve of detection efficiency versus the energy of the charged particle by assaying different radioactive isotopes whose disintegration rates are known. The determination of absolute disintegration rates may be performed with a $4\pi$ beta counter[9] or by $\beta$-$\gamma$ coincidence counting.[10]

## 5-2 SEMICONDUCTOR DETECTORS OF RADIATION

### 5-2.1 Conductors, Insulators, and Semiconductors

Prior to discussing the use of semiconductors as radiation detectors, it will be helpful to describe some of the electrical properties of crystalline solids.[11-13] Figure 5.5 schematically presents electron-energy-level diagrams for (a) an

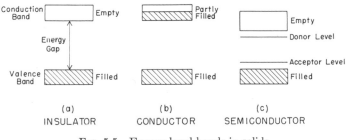

Fig. 5.5—Energy level bands in solids.

insulator, (b) a conductor, and (c) a semiconductor. Because of the interactions in the crystal lattice of neighboring atoms with one another, the closely spaced energy levels occur in groups called energy bands. In an insulator, Fig. 5.5(a), the lowest, or valence, band of electrons is completely filled, whereas the next, or conduction, band is empty. The energy gap between these bands is of the order of several electron volts; therefore electrons cannot be readily transferred from the valence band to the conduction band. The material thus will not conduct electricity, except in the presence of very high electrical fields. The energy of the electrons in a solid can also be increased by raising the temperature of the material. In fact, if the temperature is high enough in an insulator, some of the electrons will be raised to the conduction band. However, this phenomenon, termed intrinsic conduction, occurs in insulators at impractically high temperatures.

In contrast to the behavior of an insulator, the electrons in a conductor can rather easily move from one energy level to another. As seen in Fig. 5.5(b), a material acts as a conductor if the conduction band is partially filled. A solid whose conduction band is normally empty also conducts if the energy gap is zero, that is, if the full valence band and empty conduction band overlap.

Semiconductors, as seen in Fig. 5.5(c), display a behavior intermediate to that shown by insulators and conductors. The energy gap between the valence and conduction bands is small, $<3$ ev; therefore the material exhibits intrinsic conduction even at room temperature. The conductivity of a typical semiconducting material at room temperature is about $10^3$ to $10^{-6}$/ohm-cm; for insulators, the value is about $10^{-12}$/ohm-cm, whereas for a conductor, it is about $10^6$/ohm-cm. Because of the intrinsic conduction phenomenon, a semiconductor has the property that its conductivity increases as the temperature is raised. A conductor displays just the opposite behavior; its conductivity decreases with increasing temperature.

In addition to the intrinsic mode of conduction, a semiconductor exhibits impurity conduction, caused by the presence of impurity atoms in the crystal lattice. Thus, in a semiconductor made of quadrivalent germanium or silicon, pentavalent impurity atoms such as phosphorus, arsenic, or antimony act as electron donors. The material is an $n$ type or electron excess semiconductor, because the extra valence electrons are the carriers of charge. If, instead, trivalent impurity atoms such as aluminum, gallium, or indium are introduced into the crystal lattice, the material will be a $p$ type or electron defect semiconductor. Referring again to Fig. 5.5(c), one sees that the energy levels of the extra, or donor, electrons lie very close to the conduction band and these electrons may, indeed, be raised into the conduction band. The energy levels due to the missing electrons in the $p$ type material lie close to, and can accept electrons from, the valence band. The presence of electron vacancies, or holes, in the valence band also allows the material to conduct.

### 5-2.2 $p$–$n$ Junctions

A semiconductor crystal of $p$ type material, into which a small amount of electron donor has been diffused, contains a $p$–$n$ junction. As is seen in Fig. 5.6(a), the electrons and holes diffuse in the material so that the $p$ type region carries a net negative charge, and the $n$ type region, a net positive charge. In the vicinity of the $p$–$n$ junction, the diffusion of electrons from the $n$-region has filled all the acceptor sites and left the donor sites empty; a depletion layer has been formed. If an electric field is applied to the semiconductor, such that the $p$ type region is at a positive potential with respect to the $n$-region, as in Fig. 5.6(b), electrons and holes will flow across the junction; electrons toward the anode and holes toward the cathode. If the electric field is reversed, as in Fig. 5.6(c), so that the $p$-region is at a negative potential with respect to the $n$-region, the flow of current will stop. That is, since the $p$ type region does not contain excess electrons, there will not be a flow of electrons toward the $n$-region;

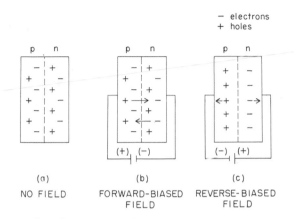

Fig. 5.6—$p$–$n$ Junctions showing the effect of an external d-c electric field.

therefore the semiconductor acts as a rectifier. The reverse-biased field then just serves to increase the extent of the depletion layer.

### 5-2.3 Semiconductor Particle Detector

A high electric-field intensity can thus be established in the depletion layer of the semiconductor. This layer acts analogously to a gas-filled ionization chamber in the detection of charged particles. A charged particle passing through the depletion layer produces ion pairs (electrons and holes) that are rapidly collected at the electrodes because of the high-electric field intensity. Moreover, the solid semiconductor radiation detector possesses several advantages with respect to a gas-filled counter: (1) its higher stopping power makes possible the fabrication of very small detectors, (2) a lower input voltage is required than for gas-filled counting tubes, and (3) the energy necessary to produce an ion pair is much lower, 3.5 ev in silicon as compared to ~30 ev in a gas. Thus, for a particle at a given energy, many more ion pairs are formed and collected in the semiconductor, which results in much higher resolution. It should be noted that depletion layers have also been produced in ion-drifted[14] and surface barrier[15] detectors.

The spectrum of $Cs^{137}$ obtained with a lithium-drifted semiconductor detector is shown in Fig. 5.7 (Ref. 16). Here, the $K$- and $L$-conversion electrons from the 0.662-Mev $\gamma$ ray are resolved from the continuous spectra of the 0.51- and 1.18-Mev $\beta$ particles. In addition to $\beta$-particle detection, semiconductor detectors have been used successfully in the counting of X rays, $\alpha$ particles, and fission fragments.

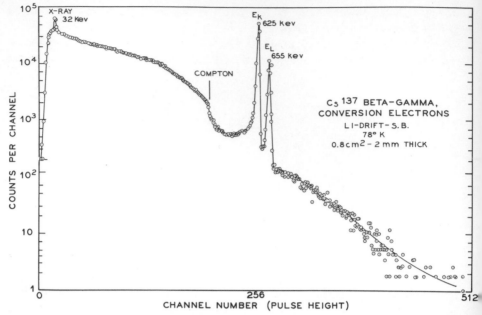

FIG. 5.7—Pulse-height distribution for Cs$^{137}$ obtained with a Li-drifted semiconductor detector. (From J. L. Blankenship, unpublished data.)

## 5-3 COUNTING STATISTICS

The following sections have been written for the activation analyst as an aid in understanding how the methods of statistics may be applied to data obtained in the laboratory. The treatment presented is neither rigorous nor complete; it only touches those points which, it is hoped, will be frequently used in work dealing with radioactive decay as applied to activation analysis. The literature on statistical analysis is quite extensive; therefore it should be consulted by workers who desire a greater degree of sophistication and thoroughness than that presented herein.[17–21]

### 5-3.1 Statistical Considerations

The radioactive decay process may be described by the laws of probability and statistics. Thus the exponential factor, $e^{-\lambda \Delta t}$, appearing in the expression for radioactive decay, where $\lambda$ is the radioactive decay constant and $\Delta t$ is the time interval, may be interpreted as representing the probability that an atom will not have decayed after time $\Delta t$ (Ref. 22). The probability that the atom has decayed is then equal to $1 - e^{-\lambda \Delta t}$. It then follows that the average number of atoms, $\bar{n}$, which have decayed in time, $\Delta t$, is given by

$$\bar{n} = N_o(1 - e^{-\lambda \Delta t}) \tag{5.2}$$

where $N_o$ is large and equal to the number of radioactive atoms present at the beginning of the said time interval.

For a set of data composed of $M$ values of a quantity, $m_i$, the average value, $\overline{m}$, may be defined as

$$\overline{m} = \frac{1}{M}(m_1 + m_2 + \ldots m_M) = \frac{1}{M}\sum_{i=1}^{i=M} m_i \tag{5.3}$$

The deviation of any of the individual values, $m_i$, from the average value is

$$d_i = m_i - \overline{m} \tag{5.4}$$

The average value of $d_i$ is just equal to zero; therefore the agreement between the various $m_i$ values is determined by taking the average of the squares of the deviations. This quantity is called the variance, $\sigma_m^2$; its square root is the standard deviation.

$$\sigma_m^2 = \frac{1}{M}\sum_{i=1}^{i=M} d_i^2 \tag{5.5}$$

Use of the definition of $d_i$ given in Eq. 5.4 then leads to the relation,

$$\sigma_m^2 = \overline{m^2} - \overline{m}^2 \tag{5.6}$$

That is, the variance is equal to the difference between the average value of the square of $m$ and the square of the average value of $m$.

The standard deviation associated with the average number of atoms, $\overline{n}$, given in Eq. 5.2, can now be determined. It can be shown[23] that

$$\overline{n^2} = N_o(1 - e^{-\lambda \Delta t})[(N_o - 1)(1 - e^{-\lambda \Delta t}) + 1] \tag{5.7}$$

Of course,

$$\overline{n}^2 = N_0^2(1 - e^{-\lambda \Delta t})^2 \tag{5.8}$$

Therefore

$$\sigma_n^2 = N_o(1 - e^{-\lambda \Delta t})e^{-\lambda \Delta t} = \overline{n}\, e^{-\lambda \Delta t} \tag{5.9}$$

An interesting conclusion may be drawn from Eq. 5.9. If the counting time, $\Delta t$, is long compared to the half-life, then $e^{-\lambda \Delta t} \rightarrow 0$, and $\sigma_n = 0$. In other words, if $\Delta t$ is long enough so that all $N_o$ atoms decay, then the number of disintegrations is exactly $N_o$. However, $\lambda \Delta t$ is usually small; that is, the counting interval, $\Delta t$, is much less than the half-life of the given nuclide. Then $e^{-\lambda \Delta t} \approx 1$, and

$$\sigma_n = \overline{n}^{1/2} \tag{5.10}$$

If $\overline{n}$ is large, it may be replaced by $N$, the number of recorded decays; so

$$\sigma_n = N^{1/2} \tag{5.11}$$

($N$ may be the number of decays recorded with any radiation detector; thus it may be the number of counts obtained with a $\beta$ counter or the area under a photopeak obtained with a $\gamma$-ray spectrometer.) Accordingly, if $10^4$ counts are recorded, the standard deviation of this measurement is $10^2$ or 1%. Similarly, for 100 counts, $\sigma_n = 10\%$; and for $10^6$ counts, $\sigma_n = 0.1\%$. The standard deviation for a given counting rate, $R$ (counts/min), can be determined from Eq. 5.11.

$$R = \frac{N}{\Delta t}$$

$$\sigma_R = \frac{N^{1/2}}{\Delta t} = (R/\Delta t)^{1/2} \tag{5.12}$$

If the Gaussian, or normal, probability distribution is applied to the problem of radioactive decay, it is possible to calculate the probability of finding an individual error, $e_i$, greater than $b\sigma$, where $b$ is a constant.[24] It is seen in Table 5.1 that the probabilities of observing errors that are greater or smaller than $0.6745\sigma$ are equal. The probability of obtaining an error greater than $\sigma$ is 0.3173. And for errors greater than $1.6449\sigma$ and $2.5758\sigma$, the respective probabilities of occurrence are 0.1000 and 0.0100. Although the standard deviation is most often given as a measure of the error in an experimental value, any of the measures of error named in Table 5.1 may be used. Graphs and nomographs, helpful in the determination of these errors, may be found in Jarrett's report on the use of statistical methods in radioactivity measurements.[25]

Table 5.1—THE PROBABILITY, $P$, THAT THE ERROR OF A
MEASUREMENT IS GREATER THAN $b\sigma$
(For radioactive decay, $e_i > bN^{1/2}$)

| Constant (b) | Probability (P) | Error |
|---|---|---|
| 0.0000 | 1.000 | |
| 0.6745 | 0.5000 | Probable error |
| 1.000 | 0.3173 | Standard deviation |
| 1.6449 | 0.1000 | Nine-tenths error |
| 1.9600 | 0.0500 | Ninety-five hundredths error |
| 2.5758 | 0.0100 | Ninety-nine hundredths error |
| 3.000 | 0.0027 | |
| 4.000 | 0.00006 | |

(Table from: Truman L. Kelley, *Fundamentals of Statistics*, p. 293, Harvard University Press, Cambridge, Mass., 1947.)

It is clear from Table 5.1 that the probability of obtaining errors greater than approximately $3\sigma$ is quite small. Thus the question of whether a series of measurements exhibits statistical behavior may be investigated. Also one may decide on the basis of the following criteria, that one of a series of measurements contains an unusually large error and so may be rejected. Graphically presented in Fig. 5.8 is the limiting value of the deviation from the mean of a single measurement plotted as a function of the number of measurements performed. When this limiting value, in units of the standard deviation, is exceeded, the given measurement may be rejected. This test of reliability of data is called Chauvenet's criterion for the rejection of suspected observations.[26] Specifically, consider a series of five determinations of the counting rate of a radioactive nuclide that had not decayed appreciably during the time the measurements were made. The rates obtained are 10100, 9900, 10050, 9950, and 10300. The mean of all five values is 10060; its standard deviation is $\pm(10060)^{1/2} = \pm100.3$. The deviation, equal to the difference between the mean and an individual measurement, is obtained and then divided by $\sigma = 100.3$. The ratios so obtained

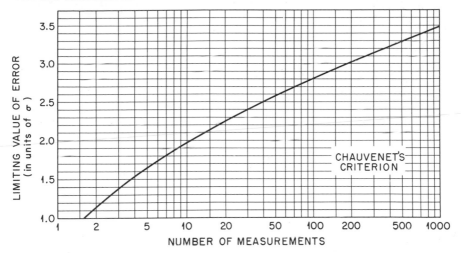

FIG. 5.8—Chauvenet's criterion for the rejection of suspected observations. (From A. G. Worthington and J. Geffner, *Treatment of Experimental Data*, p. 319, John Wiley & Sons, Inc., New York, 1946.)

for the first four values listed are all less than 1.6, whereas the ratio for the fifth measurement is equal to

$$\frac{10300 - 10060}{100.3} = 2.39$$

From Fig. 5.8, it is seen that the limiting value of this ratio, for five measurements, is 1.65. Thus only the last of the five values may be rejected. Then, taking the mean of the remaining four values, $10000 \pm 100$, it is seen that all of the four values fall within the limit of 1.63 and so are to be retained.

## 5-3.2 Propagation of Errors

Frequently two or more experimentally determined quantities, $x$ and $y$, are combined, as by addition, to give some new quantity, $f(x,y)$. The question naturally arises concerning the resulting error in $f$, namely, $e_f$. It should be emphasized that $e$ represents any measure of random error, such as the ones listed in Table 5.1. If $x \pm e_x$ and $y \pm e_y$ are the measured quantities then

$$e_f = (f_x^2 e_x^2 + f_y^2 e_y^2)^{1/2} \tag{5.13}$$

where $f_x$ and $f_y$ explicitly present the dependence of $f$ on $x$ and $y$, respectively. The following results may be easily obtained from Eq. 5.13 for the arithmetic operations of addition, subtraction, multiplication, and division of $x$ and $y$.

Addition: $\qquad f = x + y; e_f = (e_x^2 + e_y^2)^{1/2}$ $\qquad\qquad$ (5.14)

Subtraction: $\qquad f = x - y; e_f = (e_x^2 + e_y^2)^{1/2}$ $\qquad\qquad$ (5.15)

Multiplication: $\qquad f = xy; e_f = xy \left[ \left(\frac{e_x}{x}\right)^2 + \left(\frac{e_y}{y}\right)^2 \right]^{1/2}$ $\qquad$ (5.16)

Division: 
$$f = \frac{x}{y} \; ; e_f = \frac{x}{y}\left[\left(\frac{e_x}{x}\right)^2 + \left(\frac{e_y}{y}\right)^2\right]^{1/2} \tag{5.17}$$

For example, if the total number of counts, including background, collected in 1 min is 100, if the background for 1 min is 18 counts, and if $e$ is taken to be the standard deviation, then from Eq. 5.12,

$$R_T = 100 \pm (100)^{1/2} = 100 \pm 10$$

$$R_B = 18 \pm (18)^{1/2} = 18 \pm 4.2$$

The net counting rate for the sample is, from Eq. 5.15,

$$R_N = R_T - R_B = 100 - 18 \pm [(10)^2 + (4.2)^2]^{1/2}$$

$$= 82 \pm 10.9$$

It can be seen from this example that if the background rate is determined by counting over a long interval, then the error in the net counting rate will be that due solely to $R_T$. For, if the background is counted for 1 hr,

$$R_B = \frac{1080 \pm (1080)^{1/2}}{60} = 18 \pm 0.5$$

and

$$R_N = 82 \pm [(10)^2 + (0.5)^2]^{1/2} = 82 \pm 10.0$$

As a further example, the errors involved in comparing an unknown with a standard sample will now be considered. The weight of the standard is multiplied by the ratio of counting rates of unknown and standard to yield the weight of the unknown. Suppose the counting rates for unknown and standard are respectively $10000 \pm (10000)^{1/2}$ and $40000 \pm (40000)^{1/2}$ counts/min, the background as before is $18.0 \pm 0.5$ counts/min, and the weight of the standard, $W_s$, (obtained with an analytical balance) is $10.0 \pm 0.2$ mg. The net counting rates for standard, $R_s$, and unknown, $R_x$, will then be from Eq. 5.15,

$$R_s = 40000 - 18 \pm [40000 + (0.5)^2]^{1/2} = 39982 \pm 200$$

$$R_x = 10000 - 18 \pm [10000 + (0.5)^2]^{1/2} = 9982 \pm 100$$

Then, from Eq. 5.17,

$$\frac{R_x}{R_s} = \frac{9982}{39982} \pm \frac{9982}{39982}\left[\left(\frac{200}{39982}\right)^2 + \left(\frac{100}{9982}\right)^2\right]^{1/2} = 0.2500 \pm 0.0028$$

Using Eqs. 1.11b and 5.16 it follows that the weight of the unknown, $W_x$, is

$$W_x = \frac{R_x}{R_s} W_s = (0.2500 \pm 0.0028)(10.0 \pm 0.2)$$

$$= 2.500 \pm 2.500\left[\left(\frac{0.0028}{0.2500}\right)^2 + \left(\frac{0.2}{10.0}\right)^2\right]^{1/2}$$

$$= 2.500 \pm 0.058$$

Reviewing the calculation, one sees that the error in $R_x/R_s$ is 1.1%, whereas that in $W_s$ is 2%; the resulting error in $W_x$ is 2.3%.

If, instead, the unknown counting rate were $100.0 \pm (100)^{1/2}$ counts/min, then

$$R_x = 100.0 - 18.0 \pm [100 + (0.5)^2]^{1/2} = 82.0 \pm 10.0$$

and

$$\frac{R_x}{R_s} = \frac{82.0}{39982} \pm \frac{82.0}{39982} \left[\left(\frac{200}{39982}\right)^2 + \left(\frac{10}{82}\right)^2\right]^{1/2}$$

$$= 0.0205 \pm 0.0025$$

Then

$$W_x = (0.0205 \pm 0.0025)(10.0 \pm 0.2)$$

$$= 0.205 \pm 0.205 \left[\left(\frac{0.0025}{0.0205}\right)^2 + \left(\frac{0.2}{10}\right)^2\right]^{1/2}$$

$$= 0.205 \pm 0.025$$

Here, the large error in $R_x/R_s$ predominates in establishing the 12% error in $W_x$. It is therefore clear that the errors in $W_x$ due to counting can be minimized by the collection of sufficient counts for the known and unknown samples.

### 5-3.3 Relation Between Counting Interval and Sample Half-life

A final point concerning the counting rate and counting interval will now be considered. When the decay of a radioactive sample is followed as a function of time, the counting rate, $R = N/\Delta t$, is usually taken to represent the activity at the midpoint of the interval $\Delta t$. This approximation is quite good when $\Delta t \ll T_{1/2}$, because the rate of decay during $\Delta t$ is then small. However, the approximation fails when the counting interval is comparable to, or greater than, the half-life, for as $\Delta t$ increases, the fraction of radioactive nuclides present in the sample decreases exponentially. Hence, most of the decays occur during the first few half-lives. Obviously, then, for $\Delta t \geq T_{1/2}$, $R$ should represent the activity of the sample at some instant of time, $t_i$, which occurs earlier than the midpoint of the interval. In addition, the value of $t_i$ will depend upon the ratio, $\Delta t/T_{1/2}$. Consideration of the entries in Table 5.2 should help to clarify the above discussion.

Table 5.2—VARIATION OF COUNTING RATE WITH $\Delta t/T_{1/2}$
($T_{1/2} = 1$ min)

| $\Delta t/T_{1/2}$ | $N/N_o = F$ | $F/\Delta t$ |
|---|---|---|
| 1 | 1/2 | 1/2 |
| 2 | 3/4 | 3/8 |
| 3 | 7/8 | 7/24 |
| 4 | 15/16 | 15/64 |

The fraction of nuclei that have decayed, $F = N/N_o$, is calculated for various values of $\Delta t/T_{1/2}$. Then, if $T_{1/2} = 1$ min, it is seen that $F/\Delta t$, which is proportional to $R$, decreases as $\Delta t/T_{1/2}$ and $F$ both increase. In other words, when $\Delta t \geq T_{1/2}$, a larger fraction of decays per unit time occurs for smaller values of $\Delta t$ than for larger values. So, it follows that if $F/\Delta t$ is to correspond to some *true* counting rate at time, $t_i$, then $t_i$ must decrease as $\Delta t/T_{1/2}$ increases. Or, if $t_i = t_o + f\Delta t$, where $t_o$ is the beginning of the counting interval, and $0 \leq f \leq 1/2$, then $f$ will decrease as $\Delta t/T_{1/2}$ increases. The results of a calculation to determine $t_i$, or $f$, as a function of $\Delta t/T_{1/2}$ are shown in Fig. 5.9, where $f$ is plotted versus $\Delta t/T_{1/2}$.

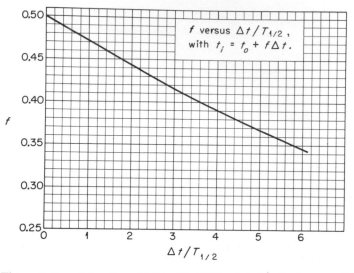

FIG. 5.9—The variation of $f = (t_i - t_o)/\Delta t$ with $\Delta t/T_{1/2}$, $t_i$ being the instant of time at which the counting rate, $R$, is equal to the *true* counting rate.

Indeed, if $\Delta t/T_{1/2} = 0$, then $f = 1/2$, but as $\Delta t$ increases beyond $T_{1/2}$, $f$ decreases. Thus, if $\Delta t = 5T_{1/2}$, the counting rate must be assigned to time $t_i = t_o + 0.368\Delta t$.

*REFERENCES*

1. G. Friedlander and J. W. Kennedy, *Nuclear and Radiochemistry*, pp. 224–236, John Wiley & Sons, Inc., New York, 1955.
2. E. Bleuler and G. J. Goldsmith, *Experimental Nucleonics*, pp. 16–32, 49–79, Rinehart & Company, Inc., New York, 1952.
3. I. Kaplan, *Nuclear Physics*, pp. 30–35, Addison-Wesley Publishing Company, Inc., Cambridge, 1955.
4. G. D. O'Kelley, *Detection and Measurement of Nuclear Radiation*, NAS-NS-3105, pp. 44–58, 75–87, 1962.
5. E. Bleuler and G. J. Goldsmith, *Experimental Nucleonics*, pp. 60–62, Rinehart & Company, Inc., New York, 1952.
6. Catalogs from Nuclear-Chicago Corporation, Radiation Counter Laboratories, Inc., Amperex Nuclear Products, etc.
7. E. P. Steinberg, Counting Methods for the Assay of Radioactive Samples, in *Nuclear Instrumentation and Methods*, pp. 306–366, John Wiley & Sons, Inc., New York, 1961.
8. W. E. Nervik and P. C. Stevenson, *Nucleonics* **10** (3): 18 (1952).
9. B. D. Pate and L. Yaffe, *Can. J. Chem.* **33**: 1656 (1955).
10. G. D. O'Kelley, *Detection and Measurement of Nuclear Radiation*, NAS-NS-3105, pp. 105–112, 121, 1962.

11. W. Crawford Dunlap, Jr., *An Introduction to Semiconductors*, pp. 1–55, John Wiley & Sons, Inc., New York, 1957.
12. J. S. Blakemore, *Semiconductor Statistics*, Pergamon Press, Oxford, 1962.
13. R. A. Smith, *Semiconductors*, Cambridge University Press, Cambridge, 1959.
14. E. M. Pell, *J. Appl. Phys.* **31**: 291 (1960).
15. J. L. Blankenship and C. J. Borkowski, *I.R.E. Trans.*, NS-7: 190 (1960).
16. J. L. Blankenship, unpublished data.
17. G. U. Yule and M. G. Kendall, *An Introduction to the Theory of Statistics*, Charles Griffin and Company, Ltd., London, 1948.
18. R. A. Fisher, *Statistical Methods for Research Workers*, Oliver and Boyd, Edinburgh, 1946.
19. A. G. Worthington and J. Geffner, *Treatment of Experimental Data*, John Wiley & Sons, Inc., New York, 1946.
20. T. B. Crumpler and J. H. Yoe, *Chemical Computations and Errors*, John Wiley & Sons, Inc., New York, 1940.
21. T. L. Kelley, *Fundamentals of Statistics*, Harvard University Press, Cambridge, 1947.
22. G. Friedlander and J. W. Kennedy, *Nuclear and Radiochemistry*, pp. 5, 252–269, John Wiley & Sons, Inc., New York, 1955.
23. G. Friedlander and J. W. Kennedy, *Nuclear and Radiochemistry*, p. 258, John Wiley & Sons, Inc., New York, 1955.
24. T. L. Kelley, *Fundamentals of Statistics*, Table VIII-C, p. 293, Harvard University Press, Cambridge, 1947.
25. A. A. Jarrett, *Statistical Methods Used in the Measurement of Radioactivity*, USAEC Report AECU-262 (Mon-P-126), pp. 6–17, 1946.
26. A. G. Worthington and J. Geffner, *Treatment of Experimental Data*, pp. 170–171, and Table III, p. 319, John Wiley & Sons, Inc., New York, 1946.

*Chapter 6*

# SCINTILLATION COUNTING TECHNIQUES

## James S. Eldridge

## 6-1 SCINTILLATOR AND ANALYZER TYPES

Modern scintillation counters were developed as high-gain photomultiplier tubes were made available. The discovery (by Hofstadter in 1948) of the scintillation characteristics of NaI activated with thallium caused a revolution in the techniques of gamma measurements and indirectly gave a tremendous impetus to the development of activation analysis.

### 6-1.1 Scintillation Process

The events responsible for the luminescence of inorganic solids such as NaI(Tl) are not completely understood, but a qualitative discussion is possible. The luminescence of NaI is primarily due to the presence of a thallium activator at a concentration of about 1%. A gamma photon interacts with the NaI(Tl) crystal by one of three processes: (1) photoelectric absorption, (2) Compton scattering, or (3) pair production. Each of these processes results in the production of high-energy electrons. It is these electrons that cause the luminescence. The electrons in slowing down lose their energy principally to electrons of the crystal. This results in excitation and ionization of the crystal constituents. The energy deposited in the crystal then migrates to an activator or luminescent center, from which a transition to the ground state occurs by the emission of a light photon or by a nonradiative transition that causes thermal excitation of the crystal.

The light output from a NaI(Tl) detector is essentially a linear function of the photon energy, over a wide energy range. The nonlinearity, for most applications in activation analysis, is negligible for all but a few specialized cases in which an energy calibration curve should be established.

### 6-1.2 Scintillation Detectors

To make a detector from a crystal of NaI(Tl), it is necessary to encase the crystal in a light- and air-tight enclosure and mount it on a suitable photomultiplier tube. The light sensitivity of the photomultiplier requires the light-tight enclosure, and the hygroscopic nature of NaI requires the air-tight enclosure. The combination of canned NaI crystal and photomultiplier tube is called a *detector*, whereas an assembly of detector, associated electronics, and readout devices is termed a *counter*. If the counter is capable of performing differential energy measurements, it is termed a *spectrometer*.

### 6-1.3 Photomultipliers

A photomultiplier is a light-measuring device consisting of a photocathode, several metal plates called dynodes, and a collector plate called an anode. The interaction of the incoming gamma ray produces in the crystal a flash of light that interacts with the photocathode and ejects electrons from the photocathode material. This is shown diagrammatically in Fig. 6.1. These electrons are drawn

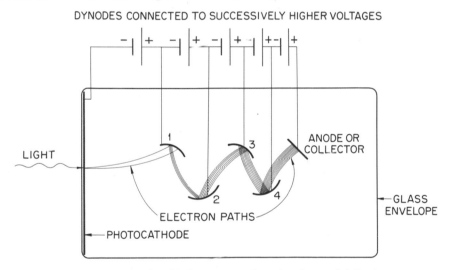

FIG. 6.1—A simplified representation of a photomultiplier.[8]

to the first dynode (labelled 1 in the diagram), where they strike hard enough to knock out two to four more electrons. This multiplication process continues down the entire string of dynodes (as many as ten or more) so that a very large resultant shower of electrons appears at the anode. The voltage pulses derived from the photomultiplier are feeble, but an electronic amplifier boosts these voltage pulses up to a level that will trigger a scaling circuit. The photocathode and dynode voltages in the photomultiplier are obtained from a precision high-voltage supply.

## 6-1.4 Organic Scintillators

There are several scintillating materials that can be classed as organic scintillators and have specialized applications in activation analysis. Anthracene and stilbene are used mainly as thin phosphors for detection of beta particles and the determination of their energies. The thin phosphor is generally used so as to minimize gamma-ray sensitivity. The energy response is essentially linear for betas above 150 kev. *Plastic* phosphors such as *p*-terphenyl in polyvinyl toluene can be made up into large sizes and pieces of any shape. Plastic scintillators have found applications as beta, gamma, and neutron detectors. Gardner and Meinke[1] have described the application of hollow plastic scintillators to beta-ray spectroscopy.

Another class of organic scintillator is the *liquid scintillator* system, which has been developed especially for tritium and $C^{14}$ determinations. These scintillators consist of a phosphor such as *2,5*-diphenyloxazole or *p*-terphenyl dissolved in an organic solvent such as xylene or toluene. When used as a detector for weak beta emitters, the liquid scintillator acts as a solvent for the radionuclide so that high efficiencies can be achieved. The efficiency of a liquid scintillation counter for $C^{14}$ has been as high as 90% and for tritium up to 40%. Modification of the solvent system, so as to make the scintillator miscible with aqueous solutions, results in a detector system that is adaptable to many activation analysis requirements where weak beta or X-ray emitters are involved. Large-volume liquid scintillators have been used as gamma detectors for many applications, including whole-body counting. The addition of a high cross-section element such as samarium, gadolinium, cadmium, boron or lithium-6 to the liquid scintillator makes it suitable as a neutron detector. Excellent texts on the general subject of liquid scintillation counting have been compiled.[2,3] Some instrument manufacturers provide useful technical bulletins describing the practical applications of liquid-scintillation counting techniques.[4-6]

## 6-1.5 Inorganic Scintillators

Some inorganic scintillators in current use include various alkali halides and ZnS(Ag), which is used for alpha detection. Lithium iodide activated with europium has been applied to problems of neutron detection and spectrometry. Cesium iodide has been applied to gamma-detection problems in specific instances where small detectors are advantageous. Sodium iodide activated with thallium is the most versatile scintillator for gamma detection. The major characteristics of NaI(Tl) that make it a suitable detector are its high conversion efficiency (effectiveness of conversion of radiation energy to light), high density, short luminescent decay time, and its crystal structure which permits the growth of large single crystals. Its major disadvantage is that it is hygroscopic and must be hermetically sealed.

Another class of detector which promises to have applications in activation analysis is the *semiconductor* radiation detector, which was discussed in Chap. 5.

## 6-1.6 Scintillation Counters

Owing to the exponential nature of the attenuation of gamma rays by matter, there is a probability that a portion of the gamma photons from a monoenergetic source reaching a detector will pass completely through the crystal, others will transfer only part of their energy to the crystal, and still others will be completely absorbed. With these energy variations within the crystal, there will consequently be a voltage distribution from the *detector*. These voltage pulses will have characteristic magnitudes and may be so classified as to their *pulse heights*. A plot of number of pulses vs. pulse height is called a pulse-height spectrum or gamma spectrum. Figure 6.2 is a typical pulse-height spectrum as usu-

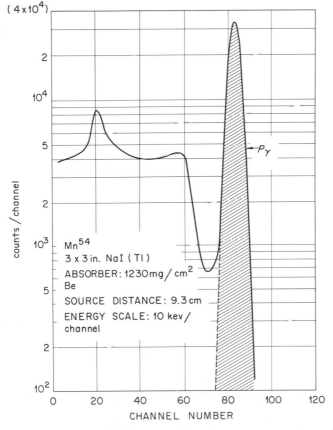

Fig. 6.2—Typical semilogarithmic presentation of gamma-ray spectrum of Mn⁵⁴.

ally represented on a semilogarithmic plot. The use of the semilogarithmic form of presentation accentuates the peaks that occur with low intensity relative to the high-intensity peaks and makes the graphical comparison of two spectra independent of counting rate. The peak occurring at Channels 75 to 95 is a peak due to the total or photoelectric absorption of the gamma ray and is called the *photopeak*. The remainder of the pulse-height distribution is due to incomplete absorption of the total γ-ray energy and is called the *Compton distribution*. Obviously, the gamma rays that pass through the crystal with no interaction cause no pulse-height distribution. The spread of pulses within the photopeak, which approximates a Gaussian distribution, stems from several sources. Among these are the process of conversion of energy of ionizing radiation into photons in the scintillator, electron emission from the photocathode, and electron multiplication at the dynodes. A term called *resolution* has been used to describe the quality of a scintillation detector. Resolution is defined as the photopeak full

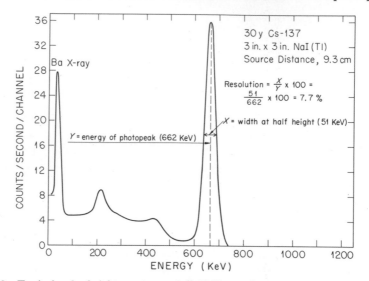

FIG. 6.3—Typical pulse height spectrum of Cs[137] illustrating measurement of resolution.

width at one-half maximum height ($X$ in Fig. 6.3) divided by the pulse height (or energy) at the photopeak center ($Y$ in Fig. 6.3). Thus

$$\text{resolution (in \%)} = \frac{X}{Y} \times 100 \qquad (6.1)$$

NaI(Tl) detectors are limited to an intrinsic crystal resolution that is approximately 6% for the 0.662-Mev gamma ray of Cs[137]. Carefully selected tube-crystal combinations have given resolutions for Cs[137] as low as 6.4%.[7] Detector resolution varies approximately inversely as the square root of the gamma-ray energy. A convenient rule-of-thumb is that detector resolution = $kE^{-1/2}$. A typical 3- by 3-in. detector with a 7.7% resolution for Cs[137] gamma rays might show resolutions of 16% for 0.081 Mev and 5.5% for 1.85 Mev gamma rays. Crystal size *per se* has little correlation with resolution.

Scintillation detectors of 3- by 3-in. size are commercially available with 7.5% or better resolution for Cs[137] gamma rays and with guaranteed stability of <1% drift per day at 1000 counts/sec.[7]

### 6-1.7 Gross Gamma Counters

A NaI scintillation counting system may be operated in several modes. One of the most common modes has been described as *Geiger-tube substitute scintillation counting*.[8] Figure 6.4 shows a block diagram of this type of counter. These

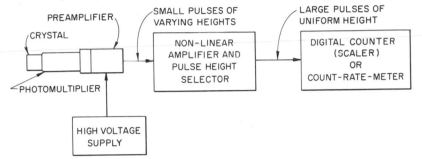

FIG. 6.4—Geiger-tube-substitute scintillation counter.[8]

counters are used in applications where the gross gamma counting rate from a sample is all the information that is required. An example of this type of counter is the *well*-type scintillation counter used for most tracer experiments with gamma-emitting nuclides. These counting systems may be used in activation-analysis procedures when radiochemical separations are used to give a pure radionuclide. A counting system of this type with a 2- by 2-in. well-type detector costs approximately $1200 for the detector, shield, and preamplifier, and approximately $1500–$2000 for a precision scaler, high-voltage supply, and nonlinear amplifier. A typical system will have the high-voltage supply, amplifier, and scaler in one chassis. Auxiliary lead shielding is usually required around the nominal 2-in. shield supplied with most systems to get background counting rates down to 200 counts/min. High-energy betas have a relatively high efficiency in these well detectors, therefore it is usually desirable to have an aluminum liner inserted in the well detector to reduce the beta contribution. Radioactive samples in test tubes are then placed in the aluminum liner. The amplifier is usually set at the factory at a level just above the noise level of the photomultiplier. To check day to day variations in the overall system, it is necessary to count a long-lived standard prepared so as to give reproducible geometry in the well detector. Standards are usually made of natural uranium or other long-lived radionuclides. Natural uranium is a useful standard because of the wide range of energies of gamma rays in the spectrum of the aged uranium.

### 6-1.8 Scintillation Spectrometers

A scintillation spectrometer differs from the Geiger-substitute counter in that a *linear* amplifier is used and additional discriminatory circuits are added. The output pulses from the photomultiplier, which are proportional to the energy of the incident gamma ray, are feeble pulses and must be amplified before they will cause the other circuits to function properly. These are amplified with a *linear* amplifier. Hence, there is linearity in the entire system from the crystal interaction through the preamplifier and linear amplifier. The electronic components of a scintillation spectrometer are termed pulse-height analyzers or kick-sorters. The energy increments into which a pulse-height distribution is divided are called *channels*.

### 6-1.9 Single-channel Analyzers

The simplest pulse-height analyzer consists of a *single* channel, whereas those more sophisticated may have thousands of channels. Single-channel analyzers have a linear amplifier, two pulse-height selectors, and an anticoincidence network, as shown in Fig. 6.5.

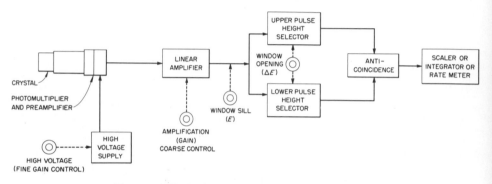

FIG. 6.5—Block diagram of single-channel analyzer.[8]

As stated previously, a pulse-height analyzer may be used to examine pulses from a scintillation detector and sort these voltage pulses into groups corresponding to the original gamma-ray distribution reaching the detector. By setting the proper high-voltage value on the photomultiplier tube and a suitable gain on the amplifier, a single-channel analyzer can be adjusted so that the entire gamma-ray spectrum will fall within the usual 1000 divisions on the pulse-height dial (lower pulse-height selector). The window opening ($\Delta E$) covers that portion of the spectrum between the lower and upper pulse-height selectors. Voltage pulses smaller than those selected by the lower pulse-height selector will be rejected by this discriminator. Pulses large enough to exceed both the lower and upper pulse-height selectors are rejected by the anticoincidence circuit. Therefore, only those voltage pulses that occur *between* the values given by the lower and upper pulse-height selectors will reach the scaler or rate meter. By varying the position of the window opening in relation to a lower pulse height just above electronic noise, the entire pulse-height distribution from a scintillation detector can be determined. Harris *et al.*,[8] give detailed instructions for the various spectrometer adjustments necessary in setting up a single-channel analyzer.

The cost of a single-channel analyzer is approximately twice that of a gross gamma counter. However, the analyzer system allows one to determine gamma-ray energies and hence perform qualitative identification tests as well as to do quantitative counting. The major limitation of the single-channel analyzer is the long time required to determine the one hundred or so data points necessary to define a gamma-ray spectrum. Single-channel analyzers with a motorized pulse-height selector are available that greatly facilitate the collection of data from a gamma-ray distribution. The output from such an analyzer is fed to a rate meter and then to a strip-chart recorder where a permanent record of the gamma spectrum is obtained. A motorized or *scanning* single-channel analyzer requires a counting period of approximately 15 min to cover an entire spectrum from a moderately intense source of radioactivity with correspondingly greater times required for weaker sources. Transistorized versions of the single-channel analyzer are available and are to be preferred over vacuum tube types.

Many activation analyses may be performed with equipment no more elaborate than a scanning single-channel spectrometer. For the smaller laboratory, this equipment would be recommended over a gross counting system. If the size of the program is large enough, then a multichannel spectrometer system is recommended.

## 6-1.10 Multichannel Analyzers

To reduce the time necessary to accumulate gamma-ray spectrum data, analyzers with a greater number of channels were perfected. Radio-activation analysis, in which the measurement of short-lived nuclides is essential, has benefited from the rapid development of *multichannel* analyzers. There is not only a great increase in speed and convenience when all the data points for a spectrum are accumulated in a single counting interval, but there is improvement in precision of data due to minimization of instrumental drifts. A 20-channel analyzer built up on the principle of 20 single-channel analyzers stacked together was an early successful version of a multichannel instrument. The major disadvantage of this instrument was the slow read out and relatively small number of channels. Each of the 20 channels had a scaler and mechanical register or glow-tube register that had to be read out and recorded manually.

Utilizing digital computer techniques for data storage and an *analog-to-digital converter*, which converts pulse heights to a train of pulses, electronic engineers at Argonne National Laboratory perfected a new type of multichannel analyzer which has revolutionized the fields of gamma-ray spectrometry and activation analysis. The original vacuum-tube designs have now given way to completely transistorized versions with large numbers of channels and many read-out modes. Figure 6.6 indicates the relationship of subassemblies and accessory equipment in a multichannel pulse-height analyzer of the Argonne type.[9] Components of this type of system are discussed in greater detail in the sections to follow on the characteristics of an analyzer system for instrumental analyses.

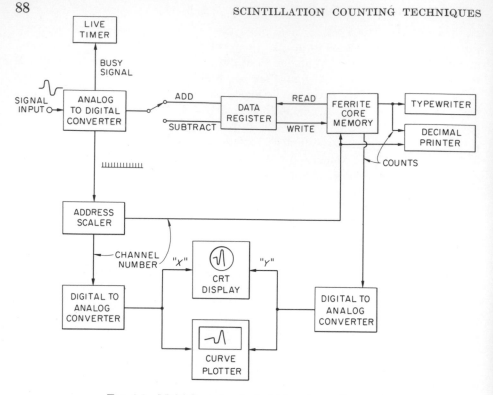

FIG. 6.6—Multichannel pulse-height analyzer diagram.[9]

## 6-2 GAMMA-RAY SPECTRA INTERPRETATION

### 6-2.1 Photoelectric Absorption and Escape Peaks

The processes by which gamma rays interact with matter are important to the design consideration of a detection system and hence will be reviewed in a general way. The process of *photoelectric absorption* is the most important process occurring in sodium iodide for gamma spectrometry applications. In this process, a gamma ray imparts all of its energy to an electron, which is then called a photoelectron. These short-range photoelectrons are stopped in the crystal and give up all their energy to the crystal; this results in a *total absorption* or *photoelectric* peak. These peaks are the characteristic photopeaks that make gamma spectrometry a useful tool. The original gamma-ray interaction with the crystal takes place in an iodine atom. The photoelectron produced leaves a vacancy in the iodine atom which then emits a characteristic iodine X ray of 28 kev. If the interaction takes place near the surface of the crystal, then the iodine X ray has a chance of leaving the crystal without detection. This phenomenon is illustrated in Fig. 6.7, which shows a pulse-height distribution for a Cd[109] source. The peak at ~80 pulse-height units is the total absorption peak from the

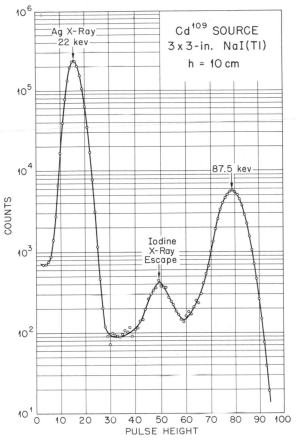

Ag X-Ray
22 kev

Cd$^{109}$ SOURCE
3 x 3 - in. NaI(Tl)
h = 10 cm

87.5 kev

Iodine
X-Ray
Escape

COUNTS

PULSE HEIGHT

FIG. 6.7—Spectrum of 87.5-kev gamma rays and 22-kev X rays from a Cd[109] source.[9]

87.5-kev gamma ray. The peak at 50 pulse-height units is due to the escape of the iodine X ray, and the energy at the peak is $87.5 - 28$ or 59.5 kev. The peak at 22 kev arises from the total absorption of Ag X rays emitted by the Cd[109] source. The phenomenon of iodine X-ray escape diminishes as the energy of the gamma rays increase. This feature of a gamma-ray spectrum is not observed above about 170 kev.

## 6-2.2 Compton Scattering Phenomena

In Fig. 6.8 are shown the total and partial absorption coefficients in NaI(Tl) for gamma rays as a function of energy.[10] It can be seen that at energies below about 300 kev, the photoelectric process is most probable, but the Compton effect dominates in the intermediate energy region. The *Compton effect* is the interaction that occurs when the incident gamma ray strikes an electron of an atom and shares part of its energy. The resultant electron and degraded (in energy) gamma ray recoil from the atom. The energy of the recoiling electrons

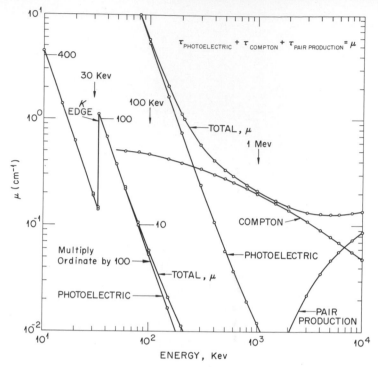

Fig. 6.8—Linear absorption coefficient vs. photon energy for sodium iodide, including partial absorption coefficients. (From P. R. Bell, in K. Sieghbahn, ed., *Beta- and Gamma-ray Spectroscopy*, p. 153, North Holland Publishing Company, Amsterdam, 1955; Interscience Publishers, Inc., New York, 1955.)

will have values from essentially zero up to a maximum cutoff point called the Compton edge, which represents the maximum energy transfer between the photon and a recoil electron. This point in a gamma-ray spectrum is given by

$$E_c = \frac{E_\gamma}{1 + (0.511/2E_\gamma)} \qquad (6.2)$$

where $E_c$ is the energy of the Compton edge and $E_\gamma$ is the energy of the incident photon in million electron volts. Large-angle Compton processes (180°) cause a characteristic spectral feature called the backscatter peak which looks quite like a photopeak at an energy of about 200 kev. The Compton distribution and the shapes of backscatter peaks are shown in Fig. 6.9, taken from Heath.[11] Figure 6.9 may also be used to illustrate the effect of crystal size on the gamma-ray spectrum of a monoenergetic gamma ray. It can be seen that as the size of the detector increases, the fraction of all pulses falling in the photopeak increases. This is evidenced by the height of the photopeak relative to that of the Compton distribution. This high photopeak fraction for the 3- by 3-in. detector is the reason that this size detector is used for most spectrometry applications. Heath[11]

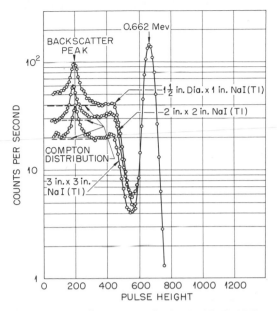

FIG. 6.9—Gamma-ray spectra of a Cs[137] source obtained with NaI(Tl) spectrometers of three crystal sizes.[11]

has compiled extensive response functions for this size detector. Crouthamel[12] has compiled a catalog of spectra made with a 4- by 4-in. detector.

The energy of the backscatter peak is given by

$$E_b = \frac{E_\gamma}{1 + (2E_\gamma/0.511)} \tag{6.3}$$

where $E_b$ is the energy of the backscatter peak in million electron volts. The magnitude of the backscatter peak may be decreased by increasing the distance from the shielding material to the detector. For spectrometer shields with large central cavities, one may achieve spectra with essentially no backscatter peak.

## 6-2.3 Shielding Effects

Another anomaly that complicates gamma-ray spectra interpretation is the production of lead X rays in the usual lead shield walls by a photoelectric interaction. This X ray arises from the same type process as discussed in section 6-2.1 on iodine escape. The lead X ray causes a peak to appear in the experimental spectrum at 72 kev. Since this peak arises from the shield material and not from the source, it is desirable to remove this contribution. This may be accomplished by the use of a *graded* liner for the spectrometer shield. Figure 6.10, taken from O'Kelley,[9] is a diagram of a typical spectrometer shield and detector assembly showing detail of the graded liner, which essentially removes the lead X ray contribution. Figure 6.11 shows the reduction of lead X rays by

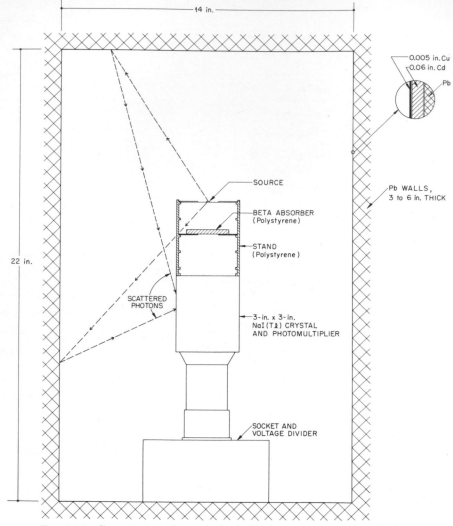

FIG. 6.10—Cross section of a typical scintillation spectrometer installation.[9]

the addition of a thin cadmium liner to the spectrometer shield for a $Cr^{51}$ spectrum. Heath[11] has shown that a shield made of lead yielded a backscatter peak much smaller than when an iron shield was used. This effect is shown in Fig. 6.12.

### 6-2.4 Pair Production and Escape Peaks

The final type of gamma-ray interaction that produces characteristic spectral features is the *pair-production* process. The pair process has a threshold at 1.02 Mev, but the effect of this process is not evident below about 1.5 Mev.

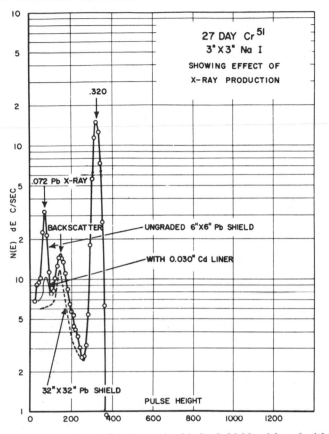

FIG. 6.11—Gamma-ray spectra of Cr[51] determined in lead shields with and without a cadmium liner.[11]

This process occurs when a photon interacts with the nucleus of an atom and expends all of its energy in producing an electron–positron pair. The resultant positron usually annihilates in the crystal, producing two 0.511-Mev photons, which are emitted in opposite directions. If one of these photons escapes the crystal without interaction, then a peak called the *single-escape* peak is produced. If both photons escape undetected, then a *double-escape* peak arises. The energy of the single-escape peak is found to be 0.511 Mev below the total-absorption peak, and the double-escape peak is found to be 1.02 Mev below the total-absorption peak. This may be illustrated in Fig. 6.13, which shows the gamma-ray spectra of Na[24] from two detector sizes. Sodium-24 emits gamma rays of 2.76 and 1.38 Mev. The single-escape peak at 2.25 Mev and the double-escape peak at 1.74 Mev can be seen. These latter peaks are caused by pair production from the 2.76-Mev gamma ray. There is no detectable escape peak due to the 1.38-Mev gamma ray.

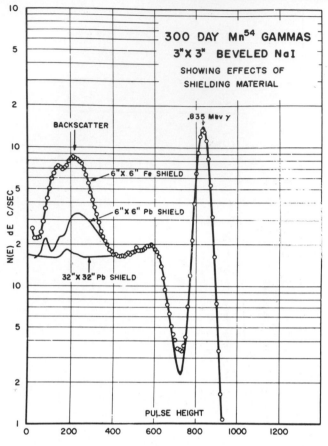

FIG. 6.12—Gamma-ray spectra of Mn⁵⁴ illustrating the magnitude of backscatter peaks with different shields.[11]

### 6-2.5 Bremsstrahlung Effects

Internal bremsstrahlung produced in a source and external bremsstrahlung emitted when beta rays are stopped in an absorber will cause a characteristic response in a scintillation detector up to the maximum energy of the beta particles. The quantitative measurement of gamma rays in the presence of intense beta activity is difficult, and the comparative measurement of two sources may be in considerable error if one has a large quantity of beta activity present and the other does not. Figure 6.14 shows the spectrum of Y⁹¹ which has a 1.2-Mev gamma with only 2% abundance (but 100% yield of beta particles). The contribution to the spectrum from the bremsstrahlung can be clearly seen.

For spectrometry applications, it is desirable to stop beta particles or electrons from the source before they reach the detector. The use of a beta absorber such as is shown in Fig. 6.10 accomplishes this. The absorber should have a sufficient

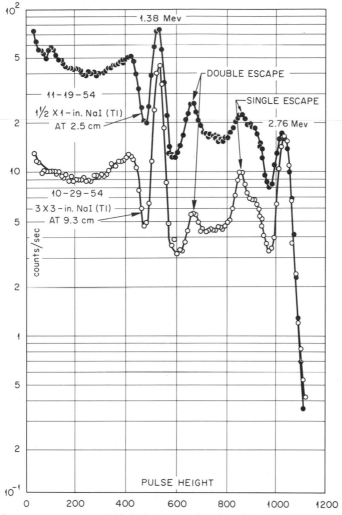

Fig. 6.13—Gamma-ray spectra of Na²⁴ from two detector sizes illustrating escape peaks due to pair production.[9]

surface density or thickness to stop the most energetic beta particles from the source. For general applications, a polystyrene absorber of 1.25 g/cm² is usually used. This thickness of absorber is sufficient to stop 2.5-Mev beta particles. The absorber material should be a low $Z$ material such as beryllium, polystyrene, or aluminum, in order to keep bremsstrahlung production to a minimum. For certain precise applications, it is desirable to cover the sides of the detector with the beta absorber as well. A compilation of tables and data useful in calculating absorber thicknesses or other parameters may be found in the Radiological Health Handbook.[13]

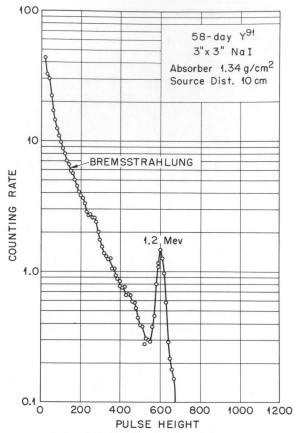

FIG. 6.14—Gamma-ray spectrum of 58-day $Y^{91}$, showing the bremsstrahlung spectrum characteristic of a source for which the beta-to-gamma intensity ratio is very large.[11]

## 6-3 CHOICE OF MULTICHANNEL ANALYZER

All of the foregoing features of a spectral response curve will be present whether or not the data are collected with a single-channel or multichannel spectrometer. The response will be characteristic of the source-detector-shield configuration only.

Before the development of modern multichannel analyzer systems and techniques of scintillation spectrometry, radiochemical separations were usually necessary for activation analysis measurements. Use of purely instrumental techniques or instrumental techniques coupled with a minimum amount of chemical separation has made activation-analysis techniques considerably simpler and sometimes more reliable. The possibility of rapid data collection and processing has extended activation-analysis techniques to elements producing radionuclides with half-lives measured in minutes or less. Data-handling techniques such as computer spectra-resolution and electronic spectrum stripping have greatly influenced the choice of an instrumental system. Therefore, characteristics of analyzer systems affecting instrumental methods should be considered when an analyzer purchase is contemplated.

## 6-3.1 Number of Channels and Memory Subgroupings

The number of channels in a transistorized multichannel analyzer is governed by the capacity of the analyzer *memory* consisting of ferrite cores. For flexibility of usage and an adaptability to computer data processing, it is recommended that an analyzer with a memory capacity of either 400 or 512 channels be used. A channel capacity of $10^6$ counts is recommended. All modern analyzers have memory units that may be broken down into 1, 2, 4, and sometimes 8 subgroups. By simple switching, various regions of the memory may be utilized. Hence, it is possible to accumulate up to 8 spectra before any type of read out is necessary. Since read-out time is sometimes comparable to the half-life of many short-lived nuclides, it is an obvious advantage to be able to accumulate several spectra before stopping to read out any data points. For computer spectra resolution, it is desirable to use 200 or 256 channels for each spectrum with the other 200 or 256 channels available for other data-reduction applications.

## 6-3.2 Analog-to-digital Converter

The analog-to-digital converter (ADC), which is the heart of the system, should have a *differential linearity* of better than 2%. This differential linearity is a measure of the deviation in channel widths. The *integral linearity*, which governs the deviations of linearity between input pulse height and channel number, should be better than 0.5%. The system should include a suitable amplifier and high-voltage supply to permit achievement of the above specifications with the ADC. The ADC should be capable of accepting pulses of varying shapes and magnitudes, such as single- and double-delay line clipped pulses as well as the more common RC clipped pulse. O'Kelley[9] gives a useful discussion of amplifiers and pulse shapes.

## 6-3.3 Live Timer and Cathode-ray-tube Display

Since the modern analyzer systems use memory-cycle storage times that are relatively long (10 to 20 $\mu$sec), they incorporate a device called a *live timer* that automatically corrects for the time when the analyzer is busy and cannot accept additional pulses. A typical analyzer might have a 15-$\mu$sec memory cycle and a 0.5-$\mu$sec spacing between address pulses; this leads to an analysis time for each pulse (during which the analyzer is *dead* or incapable of recording any further pulses) of $(15 + 0.5\,n)$ $\mu$sec, where $n$ is the channel number. This dependence of dead time on channel number shows that the average dead time is a function of the spectrum under measurement. It can be shown that the spectrum shape is undistorted under these conditions, and it is only necessary to correct for the dead time to obtain accurate counting rates. The live timer should have an accuracy of $\pm 0.2\%$ for input counting rates up to 30,000 pulses per second.

The analyzer system should have a cathode-ray-tube (CRT) display so that features of the spectrum may be observed visually before any read out is performed. It is recommended that the CRT have both linear and logarithmic displays. For clear readability the CRT should consist of a 5-in. oscilloscope. It is often desirable that the spectral data be visible while accumulating. This is called *live display*.

### 6-3.4 Read-out Devices

The other requirement for a minimum system is that it have a suitable read-out device so that channel-by-channel decimal information will be available on a permanent record. Devices to perform this read out consist of decimal printers or electric typewriters. A complete minimum system may consist of a 400–512 channel memory, linear amplifier, high-voltage power supply, CRT display, and typewriter read out. Such a system is commercially available at prices ranging from \$10,000 to \$14,000.

### 6-3.5 Accessory Equipment

In addition to the cathode-ray-tube and typewriter read-out modes, there are other features of the modern transistorized analyzer that greatly speed up the collection and processing of data. These include the use of punched-paper or magnetic-tape systems for data read out. Most analyzers have provisions for taking the data from magnetic or punched-paper tape and returning this information to the memory of the analyzer. At the same time, it is usually possible to multiply the data by suitable factors and add or subtract these data to data previously stored in the analyzer memory. Photoelectric readers are available at most computer centers for direct handling of data on punched-paper tape.

The paper-tape format, i.e., the physical lay-out of punched holes on the paper tape, varies from one analyzer manufacturer to another. Some formats include the channel number as well as digital data from each channel, whereas others include only the channel data. In addition, some formats include a *parity* check. Depending on whether an even or odd number of holes is punched at each level, a special punch is inserted on the paper tape indicating even or odd parity. Parity information is used by the computer to find tape-punching errors. A typical paper-tape format should include a parity check, channel identification as well as channel data, and a special symbol at the end of the tape. This end of tape symbol is needed so that computer data-handling codes can recognize the end of one spectrum and the beginning of the next.

Magnetic-tape systems for all but the most sophisticated analyzer systems are of the home recorder type and are not suitable for computer data processing.

At least three commercial manufacturers can supply systems that have the provision for combining spectra stored in different portions of the memory by computer principles, i.e., without the use of external paper or magnetic-tape systems. These systems allow one to add or subtract two or more experimental spectra for purposes of spectra resolution.

Quantitative measurements of gamma-ray intensities are generally made by integration of the area under the photoelectric peak for that particular gamma ray. This can be accomplished by summation of the channel by channel information in the photopeak from the decimal data recorded on typewriter or decimal printer sheets. One of the latest features to be added to an analyzer system is the spectrum integrator. With this device it is possible to sum counts between any two selected channels in the pulse-height spectrum by internal circuit applications. The sum of counts in the selected interval is automatically transferred to a given channel so that one channel read out is all that is necessary to obtain the integrated area.

Digital information stored in the memory of an analyzer can be converted to analog voltages that will drive an $X$-$Y$ curve plotter or strip-chart recorder. It is desirable to make $X$-$Y$ point plots on the same 3-decade format as used in Heath's[11] catalog for ease in identification purposes or graphical resolution procedures. For specific information concerning a particular analyzer system, the reader is referred to the literature available from various instrument manufacturers.[14-19] Figure 6.15 is a photograph of a modern 512-channel

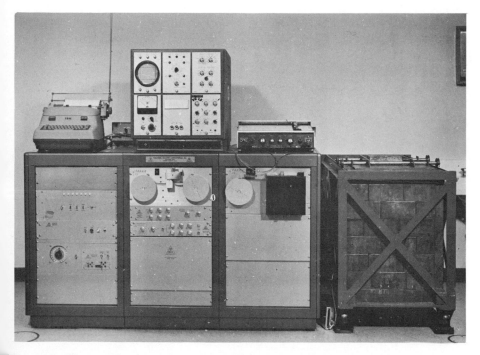

FIG. 6.15—Photograph of transistorized multichannel analyzer system with complete data reduction capabilities.

analyzer system used in the author's laboratory. Shown in the photograph on top of the console is the electric typewriter read out, the 512-channel analyzer with its oscilloscope, and an $X$-$Y$ point plotter. Also shown are the paper-tape punch mechanism, as well as the paper-tape reader for taking information from paper tape back into the analyzer memory or directly to the typewriter. Other control circuitry governs the integration device and the circuitry for spectrum resolution by the *spectrum-stripping* technique. The spectrometer shield is shown just to the right of the console. This shield is 30 in. long by 30 in. wide by 32 in. high and has 4-in.-thick walls. A 3- by 3-in. NaI(Tl) detector is housed in the shield.

## 6-4 APPLICATION OF THE MULTICHANNEL ANALYZER TO ACTIVATION ANALYSIS PROBLEMS

Multichannel analyzers have increased the utility of the activation-analysis technique to the extent that it is commonplace for product activities with half-lives in the range of a few minutes to be used for many applications. There are many examples whereby the use of short-lived product nuclides will increase the sensitivity of activation analysis, or will substantially reduce the irradiation time necessary for analysis. An example of this may be found in the case of $Co^{60}$ and $Co^{60m}$ (see Table 2.3 in Chap. 2). With instrumental techniques, a greater sensitivity for the analysis of cobalt may be achieved by measuring the 10.5-m $Co^{60m}$ produced after a 1 min bombardment than can be achieved with a 1-wk bombardment and measuring the 5.3-yr $Co^{60}$ activity.

### 6-4.1 Absolute Gamma Measurements

Techniques of absolute gamma measurements, as developed by Lazar[20] and Heath[11] may be performed efficiently with spectral data collected with a multichannel analyzer. In this application, it is necessary to know the probability that a gamma ray from the source will strike the crystal and the probability that an incident gamma ray will cause a response in the full energy peak (photopeak). The former probability is given simply by the solid angle ($\Omega$) for the particular source-to-detector geometry and the latter is called the *intrinsic peak efficiency*, $\epsilon_p(\gamma)$. Values of $\epsilon_p(\gamma)$ may be read from Lazar's data presented in Fig. 6.16. The number of gamma rays of a given energy emitted from the source $N_{(\gamma)}$ may be determined from

$$N_{(\gamma)} = \frac{P_{(\gamma)}}{\Omega \epsilon_p(\gamma) A_{Abs.}} \tag{6.4}$$

where $P_{(\gamma)}$ is the total integrated area within the photopeak (obtained by summation of data in channels encompassing the photopeak and corrected for background and distributions caused by other gamma rays), $\Omega$ is the solid angle, $\epsilon_p(\gamma)$ is the intrinsic peak efficiency from Fig. 6.16, and $A_{Abs.}$ is a correction for absorption in any absorbing material present between the source and detector

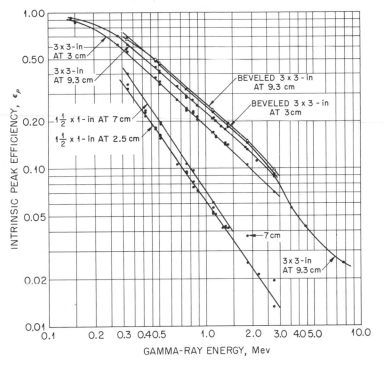

FIG. 6.16—Measured intrinsic peak efficiency of various NaI(Tl) crystals.[20]

$(A_{Abs.}$ is the term $e^{-\mu d}$ in Eq. 1.9a). Measurement of $P(\gamma)$ is illustrated in Fig. 6.2. Heath[11] uses a similar expression, but changes the product $\Omega \times \epsilon_p(\gamma)$ into $\epsilon_t(\gamma) \times P_t(\gamma)$, where $\epsilon_t(\gamma)$ is the calculated value of the total detection efficiency of the gamma ray and $P_t(\gamma)$ is an experimentally determined *peak-to-total ratio*. The product of $\Omega \times \epsilon_p(\gamma)$ and $\epsilon_t(\gamma) \times P_t(\gamma)$ in the two notations give identical values. Heath[11] gives detailed instructions for use of the absolute method. To determine the absolute disintegration rate of a particular nuclide, it is only necessary to divide the value of the number of gamma photons emitted from the source by the number of those gamma rays per disintegration. Thus

$$A_t = \frac{N_{(\gamma)}}{\gamma/d} \tag{6.5}$$

where $A_t$ is the disintegration rate in the same units as $N_{(\gamma)}$. Values of $\gamma/d$ for a particular nuclide may be obtained from such tabulations of nuclear data as Nuclear Data Sheets.[21]

Two factors must be considered in applying absolute gamma spectrometry to the determination of positron disintegration rates. The first factor is that the annihilation of a positron results in the production of *two* gamma photons of 0.511 Mev. The second is that it is necessary for all the positrons to be annihilated at or in the source, if the geometry factor, $\Omega$, is to apply. This annihilation may be accomplished by making a sandwich of the source between two absorbers of sufficient thickness to stop the positrons.

### 6-4.2 Comparative Gamma Measurements

Comparative measurements are made simply by comparing the photopeak area of a given gamma ray from an unknown sample with the photopeak area from that same gamma ray in the spectrum of a comparator sample. Obviously, the same gamma ray must be present in the spectrum of both the comparator and unknown samples, and the photopeak areas compared must be free of contributions from gamma rays of a similar energy.

Photopeak areas are determined by summing individual channel data over the entire photopeak region (typically 10 to 12 channels). In many cases the photopeaks compared are not the highest energy peaks in the spectra. Under these circumstances, corrections must be made to the photopeak area. This may be accomplished with the graphical technique described in section 6-5.1. Another less-accurate method consists in constructing a *base* to the peak by connecting the two minima of the spectrum on either side of the photopeak. The area under the photopeak less the area under the *base* is used in comparing two samples. For semiquantitative work, peak-height comparisons may be made.

### 6-4.3 Half-life Determinations

The determination of half-lives of short-lived nuclides may be accomplished with the multichannel analyzer in two ways: (1) multiple spectra determinations and (2) scaler-time operation of the analyzer. In the first method, the analyzer memory is broken down into as many subgroups as possible, and the spectrum of the activity is recorded in each of the subgroups in turn with a suitable delay period between each determination. If the half-life is long enough to permit read out of the data between determinations, then a single subgroup may be used. The area of one of the characteristic photopeaks in the sample is then plotted versus time of spectrum accumulation in order to determine the half-life. In the second method, a single channel gate is set on one of the photopeaks, and counts are recorded in channel one for a preset time. At the end of this period, the analyzer automatically switches the counts to channel two, etc., up to the capacity of the analyzer memory. In this fashion, a cathode-ray tube display of the decay curve of the nuclide is directly obtained. If the gamma activity is from a pure source, a semilogarithmic display of the data will show a straight line, and a knowledge of the preset time will allow a quick computation of the half-life. Mixtures may be resolved by graphical techniques. Cumming[22] has described an IBM-7090 program that greatly facilitates decay-curve analyses with a least-squares technique.

### 6-4.4 Identification of Unknown Nuclides

The identity of an unknown radionuclide may be made by the determination of its half-life and by the energy of its characteristic radiations. For rapid identification of photopeak energies, it is desirable to calibrate the coarse-gain control on the multichannel analyzer so that there is a convenient multiplying factor which will convert channel number to kilo electron volts. This may be accomplished by adjusting the overall gain of the system (using high-voltage control and fine-gain controls) so that the usual four coarse settings on the amplifier correspond to 20, 10, 5, and 2.5 kev per channel. Most measurements may be made on the 10 kev per channel scale. Hence, with the zero-level control set so that zero energy falls in channel zero and with the multiplier at 10 kev per channel, any gamma-ray energy between approximately 0.03 Mev and 2 to 2.5 Mev may be determined directly with a single counting-interval. Since many nuclides emit characteristic X rays in their decay, it is important to examine the low-energy regions of the spectrum at the same time higher-energy gammas are recorded. For this reason, it is desirable that the analyzer be capable of sorting low-energy pulses in the presence of higher-energy ones. That is, the analyzer should have no more than 1 or 2 initial channels that contain no information. Very useful tables of gamma-ray energies and abundances as well as characteristic X-ray energies are given in Appendix IV of Crouthamel.[12] Comparison of unknown spectra with those of Heath[11] is sometimes a great aid in identification. Table 6.1 lists some useful calibration source energies.

Table 6.1—STANDARD GAMMA LINES[23,24]

| Nuclide | Energy of gamma ray, kev | Energy of $K$ conversion electron, kev |
|---|---|---|
| $Hg^{203}$ | 279.12 ± 0.05 | 193.59 ± 0.05 |
| $Au^{198}$ | 411.80 ± 0.03 | 328.68 ± 0.03 |
| Annihilation line | 510.976 ± 0.007 | |
| $Bi^{207}$ | 569.7 ± 0.2 | 481.7 ± 0.2 |
| $Cs^{137}$ | 661.65 ± 0.10 | 624.21 ± 0.10 |
| $Y^{88}$ | 898.4 ± 0.7 | |
| $Bi^{207}$ | 1063.9 ± 0.25 | 975.9 ± 0.25 |
| $Co^{60}$ | 1172.8 ± 0.5 | 1164.5 ± 0.5 |
| $Na^{22}$ | 1277 | |
| $Co^{60}$ | 1332.6 ± 0.3 | 1324.3 ± 0.3 |
| $Na^{24}$ | 1368.7 ± 1.0 | |
| $Y^{88}$ | 1835.5 ± 1.5 | |
| $Tl^{208}$ | 2614.4 ± 0.4 | 2526.4 ± 0.4 |
| $Na^{24}$ | 2755.7 ± 1.0 | |

It is extremely important, for all but the most routine applications, to determine with certainty the identity of a measured radioactivity. A commonly mistaken pair of nuclides is $Cr^{51}$ and $Pa^{233}$; both emit 0.3-Mev gamma rays. It is difficult to identify these nuclides by a measurement of only the 0.3-Mev gamma ray. The presence of a 0.1-Mev uranium X ray in the spectrum will establish the activity as being $Pa^{233}$. Decay measurements, coupled with energy determinations, will aid in eliminating difficulties arising from improper interpretation of gamma-ray spectra.

## 6-5 GAMMA-RAY SPECTRA RESOLUTION

The ability to resolve gamma-ray spectra by several means has been the basis for the success of instrumental activation analysis procedures. These resolution techniques may be described as graphical, instrumental, and computer techniques.

### 6-5.1 Graphical Technique

A number of techniques have been developed to unscramble complicated gamma-ray spectra. One of these, described by Heath,[11] is the successive response-function subtraction technique. This is illustrated in Fig. 6.17. The

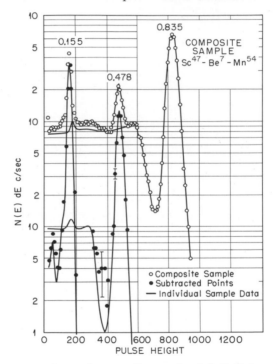

FIG. 6.17—Gamma-ray spectrum of composite sample of $Sc^{47}$, $Be^7$, and $Mn^{54}$ illustrating technique of graphical resolution.[11]

procedure involves the fitting of the response function for the most energetic gamma to the experimental points at the full-energy peak and then drawing in the entire response function under the remainder of the spectrum. Channel by channel subtractions are then made, and the residual values are plotted. This first step is accomplished, in Fig. 6.17, by fitting the response function for a pure sample of $Mn^{54}$ to the peak at 0.835 Mev. The residual points at the region of the 0.478-Mev peak are then fitted with a $Be^7$ response function. The final step involves the subtraction of both the $Mn^{54}$ and $Be^7$ contribution at the 0.155-Mev peak to get the contribution from the $Sc^{47}$ portion. In general, then, the process involves the peeling off of successive contributions until the complete spectrum has been resolved. A requirement for this technique to be successful is that the response functions must be determined under conditions identical with those under which the unknown was measured. Only in this manner will all spectra have the same spectral distortions, such as those which arise due to scatter phenomena. These methods can be extremely tedious if complicated spectra are routinely encountered.

### 6-5.2 Instrumental Techniques

Commercial analyzer accessory equipment is now available in which a variable amount of a standard spectrum may be subtracted from or added to a pulse-height distribution stored in the memory of the multichannel analyzer. This process has been called *electronic spectrum unfolding* or *spectrum stripping*.

With this equipment, it is possible to algebraically combine spectra in separate halves of the analyzer memory. A background spectrum stored in one half of the analyzer memory may be subtracted from an experimental spectrum stored in the other half. It is not necessary to have the two spectra collected for equal live times. It is sometimes desirable to count the background for a longer period of time than the sample to reduce the statistical uncertainty associated with the former. The difference in live times may be corrected by internally multiplying the background by a suitable fraction before the algebraic combination.

Use of a magnetic or paper-tape read-in device is another means of normalization of background correction. An experimental spectrum stored in the analyzer memory may be successively *unfolded* by repeated subtractions of standard spectra stored on tape. The only limitation is that each must have identical energy calibrations and identical zero-energy intercepts. Changes in amplifier gain in the experimental spectrum compared to that of the standard will cause errors in the resultant spectrum when the subtraction is accomplished.

Other techniques of instrumental data-reduction have been described. Among these are the *complement-subtraction* methods described by Lee[25] and Olson.[26] These methods consist in using the *live-display* feature of an analyzer in a subtract mode. The unknown spectrum stored in the analyzer memory is observed on the CRT, while a standard source of one of the constituents is allowed to subtract until its contribution to the spectrum is nullified. If the time required for complete removal and disintegration rate of the standard are known, the amount of that nuclide in the unknown spectrum can be calculated. Individual components in a four-component mixture can be determined with precisions ranging from $\pm 1$ to $30\%$. Precision is found to be poor for low-energy components in mixtures and is affected by the complexity of the spectral data.

### 6-5.3 Computer Applications

Computer resolution of gamma-ray spectral data promises to become one of the most useful adjuncts for activation analysis problems since the development of the modern multichannel analyzer. Activation analysis problems have proved amenable to application of computer techniques. The efforts of a large group at Texas A & M in applying these principles to a fully automatic analysis system are noteworthy.[27,28] A recent conference[22] has discussed many applications of computer usage in radiochemical problems. A detailed account of applications of the method of least-squares data reduction to the analysis of spectral data from activation analysis determinations is given in the work of Trombka.[29] He applied computer techniques and multiple spectral data to a nondestructive analysis of a complex mixture of 10 elements and achieved good agreement with their known amounts. Trombka points out that the least-squares analysis is only as good as the set of response functions available for the least-squares fit. For this reason, it is imperative to expend as much effort as practicable in obtaining a set of response functions for all components in the unknown pulse-height distributions. This should include bremsstrahlung spectra for expected beta distributions. Trombka and other workers have pointed out the difficulties that arise from unexpected contaminants in the standard spectra. A typical contaminant of this type is due to the activation of air entrapped in the comparator standard or in its container. The result of this activation is the production of 110-m $Ar^{41}$ which decays by the emission of a 1.29-Mev gamma ray.

### 6-5.4 Gain Shift Phenomena

Gain shift phenomena that occur during the course of measurements offer serious limitations to the application of instrumental techniques in gamma spectral resolution. Though these shifts may arise from several sources, the most usual cause is changes in the photomultiplier tube. Such shifts occur as a consequence of high counting rates and in a given detector might involve photopeak drifts of many channels. These gain changes show a hysteresis effect, so that the gain does not immediately return to its normal value when the high activity sample is replaced with a low one. Detectors with guaranteed stability to counting rate effects are now available commercially.[7] Several gain shift correction devices have been proposed. Many of these problems are discussed fully in the proceedings of a recent conference.[30]

*REFERENCES*

1. D. G. Gardner and W. W. Meinke, *Intern. J. Appl. Radiation Isotopes* **3**: 232 (1958).
2. C. G. Bell and F. N. Hayes, eds., *Liquid Scintillation Counting*, Pergamon Press, New York, 1958.
3. G. H. Daub, F. N. Hayes, and E. Sullivan, eds., *Proceedings of the University of New Mexico Conference on Organic Scintillation Detectors*, USAEC Report TID-7612, August 1960.
4. *Packard Technical Bulletins*, Packard Instrument Company, La Grange, Ill.
5. *Nuclear-Chicago Technical Bulletins 11 and 13*, Nuclear-Chicago Corporation, Des Plaines, Ill.
6. E. T. Bush, *Liquid Scintillation Counting*, Report BK-328, Nuclear-Chicago Corporation, Des Plaines, Ill., August 1961.
7. The Harshaw Chemical Company, Cleveland, Ohio.

8. C. C. Harris, D. P. Hamblen, and J. E. Francis, *Basic Principles of Scintillation Counting*, USAEC Report ORNL-2808, Oak Ridge National Laboratory (December 1959).

9. G. D. O'Kelley, *Detection and Measurement of Nuclear Radiation*, NAS-NS-3105, April 1962.

10. P. R. Bell, in *Beta- and Gamma-Ray Spectroscopy*, North Holland Publishing Company, Amsterdam, 1955.

11. R. L. Heath, *Scintillation Spectrometry–Gamma-Ray Spectrum Catalogue*, USAEC Report IDO-16408, Phillips Petroleum Company, July 1957.

12. C. E. Crouthamel, ed., *Applied Gamma-Ray Spectrometry*, Pergamon Press, New York, 1960.

13. *Radiological Health Handbook*, PB-121784R, September 1960, U. S. Department of Health, Education, and Welfare, Public Health Service, Division of Radiological Health, Washington 25, D. C.

14. Nuclear Data Incorporated, 100 W. Golf Rd., Palatine, Ill.

15. Radiation Counter Laboratories, Inc., 5121 West Grove Street, Skokie, Ill.

16. Radiation Instrument Development Laboratory, Inc., 4501 West North Ave., Melrose Park, Ill.

17. Technical Measurement Corp., 441 Washington Ave., North Haven, Conn.

18. The Victoreen Instrument Company, 5857 W. 95th St., Oaklawn, Ill.

19. Packard Instrument Company, Inc., La Grange, Ill.

20. N. H. Lazar, R. C. Davis, and P. R. Bell, *IRE Trans. Nucl. Sci.* NS-3(4) 136 (1956); *Nucleonics* **14**(4) : 52 (1956).

21. K. Way *et. al.*, *Nuclear Data Sheets*, Nuclear Data Group, National Academy of Sciences, National Research Council, 2101 Constitution Ave., Washington 25, D. C.

22. J. B. Cumming, in *Applications of Computers to Nuclear and Radiochemistry*, NAS-NS-3107, 1963.

23. A. H. Wapstra *et al.*, *Nuclear Spectroscopy Tables*, North Holland Publishing Co., Amsterdam, 1959.

24. *Proceedings of the Total Absorption Gamma-Ray Spectrometry Symposium, Gatlinburg, Tennessee, May 10–11, 1960.* USAEC Report TID-7594, p. 173.

25. W. Lee, *Anal. Chem.* **31**: 800 (1959).

26. D. G. Olson, *Quantitative Gamma-Ray Spectrometric Analysis of Nuclide Mixtures—Consecutive Standard Sources Nullification*, USAEC Report IDO-14495, Phillips Petroleum Company, November 1959.

27. W. L. Kuykendall and R. E. Wainerdi, *Computer Techniques for Radioactivation Analysis*, USAEC Report ORO-307, Texas Engineering Experiment Station, 1960.

28. L. E. Fite, D. Gibbons, and R. E. Wainerdi, *Computer-coupled Automatic Activation Analysis*, USAEC Report TEES-2671-1, Texas Engineering Experiment Station, 1961.

29. J. I. Trombka, *Least-square Analysis of Gamma-Ray Pulse Height Spectra*, Report JPL-TR-32-373, Jet Propulsion Laboratory, Pasadena, Calif., 1962.

30. *Proceedings, 1961 International Conference, Modern Trends in Activation Analysis*, A & M College of Texas, 1961.

# Chapter 7

## PRESENT BYWAYS AND FUTURE TRENDS
## IN ACTIVATION ANALYSIS

### William S. Lyon, Jr.

## 7-1 OTHER NUCLEAR METHODS OF ANALYSIS

Neutron activation analysis (in which the radioactive capture product is measured) has been the most successful and most applied technique of nuclear analysis. However, there are a number of other specialized applications of these methods that have been proposed, studied, and in many cases adopted for analytical purposes. This chapter briefly describes several of these techniques that have had unusual success, interest, or effort attached to them.

### 7-1.1 Miscellaneous Applications of Neutrons

(a) *Use of capture gamma rays.* When a nucleus undergoes a neutron-capture reaction, the energy released appears in the form of prompt gamma rays, i.e., the gamma rays are emitted simultaneously ($< 10^{-14}$ sec) with the capture event. Several investigators have suggested that measurement of these capture gamma rays might be used to identify the element capturing the neutron. Considerable work has been done in accumulating capture gamma-ray spectra from a number of elements; of particular interest are the experiments carried out at the Illinois Institute of Technology.[1] At this institution, a library of capture gamma-ray spectra has been collected, and efforts have been made to use these spectra for analytical purposes. Because the capture gamma-ray spectrum of each element usually consists of a number of gamma rays ranging in energy from tens of kilovolts to about 10 Mev, the use of these spectra for identification purposes has not proved easy. Nevertheless several unique applications, particularly in fuel element technology,[2] have appeared. The method has the advantage that a flux of only $10^6$ is generally satisfactory.

(b) *Neutron Scattering.* The high neutron-scattering cross section for hydrogen has been made the basis of methods that attempt to evaluate the relative amounts of hydrogen in organic samples. At Brookhaven,[3] for example, neutrons (3 to 5 Mev) from a plutonium–beryllium source were allowed to pass through various solutions of hydrocarbons, and the fraction of the neutrons transmitted was related to hydrogen content. Neutrons at three other energies, 0.273, 0.0700, and 0.0326 ev, were obtained from a graphite reactor with a beryllium crystal spectrometer. Data from all four neutron experiments agreed as to hydrogen content of the liquids. Typical data from Brookhaven are shown in Fig. 7.1. It

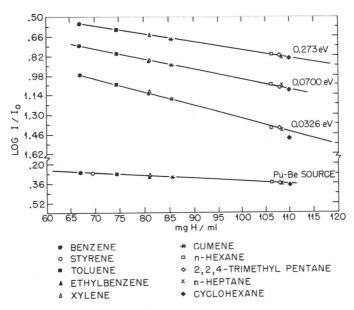

FIG. 7.1—Use of neutron scattering to determine hydrogen. Log fraction transmission vs. hydrogen content for hydrocarbons. [From H. L. Finston and E. Yellin, *Anal. Chem.* **35**: 336 (1963).]

is apparent that for this particular application, neutron transmission adequately determined hydrogen concentration.

### 7-1.2 Proton Activation Analysis

Machine-accelerated protons have been used in activation analysis by allowing them to impinge upon a Zr–T target to produce neutrons, as discussed in an earlier chapter. Additionally, protons may be used as bombarding particles themselves; the main nuclear reactions observed are $(p,n)$, $(p,2n)$, $(p,3n)$, $(p,\alpha)$, $(p,pn)$, $(p,2p)$, $(p,t)$, $(p,d)$, $(p,\gamma)$, and $(p,\text{He}^3)$. Of these reactions, the first five are probably most common.

Proton activation analysis has been confined almost exclusively to the light elements, primarily because neutron activation methods are not feasible for many of these elements. Charged-particle irradiations are, in general, considerably more difficult to perform and reproduce than reactor irradiations. Sensitivity for analyses is not as great by these reactions due in part to the lower cross sections for proton reactions when compared to neutron interactions. A proton will require a kinetic energy of about 5 Mev to produce even the simplest proton reaction $(p,n)$; hence, the need for high-energy charged-particle accelerators. Machines capable of producing protons for analytical purposes are the Cockcroft-Walton, Van de Graaff, and linear accelerators and the cyclotron. All these machines are essentially installations for physical research, and, consequently, analytical applications of the machines have been limited. Flux monitoring and reproducing the irradiation conditions from experiment to experiment are but two of a number of practical difficulties encountered in machine activations. The particle energy is degraded in traversing matter, and, consequently, products produced by lower-energy proton reactions constitute a progressively greater proportion as the penetration depth increases. Thus protons may interact to produce a number of nuclear reactions and the result is often a number of different product nuclides. Often undesired reactions may be minimized or eliminated by judicious choice of an operating parameter, such as the particle energy. Nevertheless, most proton irradiations result in the production of a number of different radionuclides through a variety of nuclear reactions.

Since protons interact on and near the surface of solids, preirradiation preparation and handling of samples become important. Usually the sample is etched both before and after irradiation. For example, Gill,[4] in the determination of submicro amounts of boron in silicon, etched the sample in concentrated NaOH prior to irradiation. After exposure in the Harwell cyclotron, the sample was re-etched with an HF–HNO$_3$ mixture. The principal reactions were

$$Si^{30}(p,n)P^{30} \quad (T_{1/2} \ 2.5 \ min)$$
$$B^{11}(p,n)C^{11} \quad (T_{1/2} \ 20.4 \ min)$$

The silicon $(p,n)$ reaction was used as the flux monitor, and the counting was performed immediately after irradiation. The C$^{11}$ was separated by chemical methods, and decay measurements were made by use of a gamma counter. Sensitivities down to 0.01-ppm boron in silicon have been obtained.

Because proton activations are so strongly a function of the accelerator, experimental assembly, irradiation conditions, and type of sample, no general listing of reaction cross sections, etc., is particularly meaningful as far as sensitivity for analytical purposes is concerned. Some reactions that have been employed include C$^{12}(p,\gamma)$N$^{13}$ for analysis of carbon in iron at a concentration level of $\sim$10 ppm[5] and O$^{18}(p,n)$F$^{18}$ for determination of oxide film thickness on metals.[6] Albert[7] presents a tabulation of possible proton applications and experimental conditions for light-element determinations. Oxygen at the level of 1 ppm has been determined in aluminum by the O$^{18}(p,n)$F$^{18}$ reaction at the Orsay Synchrocyclotron. Here, protons of about 20 Mev were used. As mentioned previously, however, availability of such complex machines is severely limited, and for the majority of analytical chemists, methods involving accelerator use lie beyond their reach.

### 7-1.3 Activation with He³ Ions

As discussed previously, proton reactions require that kinetic energy be supplied to the bombarding particle. He³ ions, however, undergo a number of nuclear reactions with light elements in which energy is released; hence, little or no additional acceleration or energy is required to bring about these reactions once the particle has penetrated the coulomb barrier of the nucleus. The reaction $O^{16}(He^3,p)F^{18}$ has been most studied, because of the great interest in oxygen analysis. This reaction has a maximum cross section of $\sim$400 mb, and produces the easily separated and measurable nuclide $F^{18}(T_{1/2}$ 111 min). A set of experimentally determined values for the cross section of a reaction as a function of particle energy is called an excitation function. Figure 7.2 shows the excitation

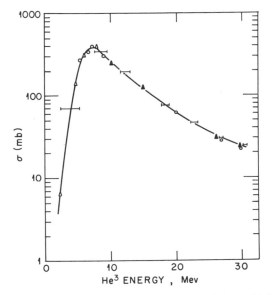

FIG. 7.2—Excitation function for the reactions $O^{16}(He^3,p)F^{18} + O^{16}(He^3,n)Ne^{18}$ [From S. S. Markowitz and J. D. Mahony, *Anal. Chem.* **34**: 329 (1962).]

function for the reaction $O^{16}(He^3,p)F^{18} + O^{16}(He^3,n)Ne^{18}$. This latter reaction leads directly to $F^{18}$ since the $Ne^{18}$ decays to $F^{18}$ by positron emission ($T_{1/2}$ 1.6 sec). A *desk-type cyclotron* has been suggested that would accelerate He³ ions up to 8 Mev; as seen in Fig. 8.2, this would be in the region of maximum cross section for the oxygen analysis. Markowitz and Mahony[8] at the Lawrence Radiation Laboratory have proposed a cyclotron that would have a 15-kilogauss field and require a radius of 9.2 in. The maximum energy of the He³ ion would be about 8 Mev; because of the increase with $Z$ of the coulombic barrier in the nucleus, this would limit the elements undergoing reaction to those below $Ca^{48}$. Such a machine would produce ions capable of penetrating only a few mils into the surface of a sample. This major limitation of all particle activation techniques, that the reaction permits primarily only a surface analysis, is advantageous in some instances, such as metal surface studies. Where the interior composition is important, sectioning with careful surface preparation as described above can often be used. Ultimate sensitivity would appear to approach 1 ppb. If such a *desk-top cyclotron* were to be made available, many of the difficulties in technique mentioned in connection with accelerators might be reduced or eliminated. The problems of identical positioning of both sample and standard and reproducibility of flux might be more easily solved with a smaller, specifically designed, analytical instrument. The method appears to have considerable application to many current problems.

### 7-1.4 Gamma Photon Activation

The use of bremsstrahlung to bring about photon induced reactions has been used successfully for oxygen analysis. Sensitivities down to 1 ppm for oxygen have been claimed by workers[9] who used the Stanford University linear accelerator which produces 40-Mev gamma photons.

French scientists[10] have used 24-Mev gamma photons produced from a betatron in an effort to determine carbon, nitrogen, and oxygen, but the flux obtained was too low. Another group using the accelerator at Saclay[7] has demonstrated 1-ppm sensitivity for oxygen. In the U.S.A., attempts to use activation by photons have been quite limited. Table 7.1 presents data of

Table 7.1—SENSITIVITY OF PHOTOACTIVATION ANALYSIS

| Element | Required* activity at irradiation end, counts/min | Specific activity in 1 hr irradiation, counts/min/g | Minimum weight determinable, mg | Minimum concentration determinable, ppm |
|---|---|---|---|---|
| Selenium | 460 | 140,000 | 3.3 | 110 |
| Strontium | 32 | 10,000 | 3.2 | 110 |
| Yttrium | 460 | 6,000 | 77 | 2,600 |
| Rhodium | 50 | 800 | 62 | 2,100 |
| Silver | 300 | 100,000 | 3.0 | 100 |
| Cadmium | 64 | 65,000 | 1.0 | 33 |
| Indium | 32 | 150,000 | 0.21 | 7.0 |
| Tin | 32 | 10 | 3,200 | 110,000 |
| Barium | 160 | 800 | 200 | 6,700 |
| Erbium | 3,000 | 300,000 | 10 | 330 |
| Lutecium | 32 | 5,000 | 6.4 | 210 |
| Hafnium | 440 | 4,000,000 | 0.11 | 3.7 |
| Iridium | 1,300 | 1,000,000 | 1.3 | 43 |
| Platinum | 32 | 500 | 64 | 2,100 |
| Gold | 1,000 | 400,000 | 2.5 | 83 |
| Mercury | 74 | 2,000 | 37 | 1,200 |

* For 10% standard deviation in sample count.

(Table from H. R. Lukens, Jr., J. W. Otvos, and C. D. Wagner, Formation of Metastable Isomers by Photoactivation with the Van de Graaff Accelerator, *Intern. J. Appl. Radiation Isotopes* **11**: 30 (1961).

Lukens, Otvos, and Wagner[11] who studied the possible application of bremsstrahlung from a 3-Mev accelerator. It is apparent for even the *best elements* that sensitivity is quite poor. The very small cross sections for photon reactions militate against their use as an analytical tool.

A technique that has seen considerable analytical service is the photoneutron method for beryllium and deuterium. The method is based upon the fact that the neutron binding energies in beryllium and deuterium are 1.67 and 2.23 Mev, respectively. Thus, when a radioactive nuclide with a gamma energy greater than these values is placed near these materials, the production of neutrons will occur through the reactions

$$Be^9 + \gamma \rightarrow Be^8 + n$$
$$D^2 + \gamma \rightarrow H^1 + n$$

These reactions have been used as methods to produce neutrons for isotopic sources as discussed in Chap. 3. It is clear that the number of neutrons produced is directly proportional to the amount of beryllium or deuterium present. A number of applications of this method have been made; these include the determination of beryllium in geological samples, ores, and beryllium metal, and the determination of deuterium in water.

Portable instruments have been designed and are commercially available for beryllium prospecting. It is obviously advantageous to use a gamma source with as long a half-life as possible. The most commonly used radionuclides (and their half-lives) have been $Sb^{124}$ (60 days) and $Y^{88}$ (87 days) for beryllium, and $Th^{228}$ (1.90 yr) for deuterium. Beryllium has been determined at levels below 60 ppm;[12] deuterium has been measured at a level of 0.02 vol. % $D_2O$ (Ref. 12). $Na^{24}$, when used as a source, gives greater sensitivity for deuterium determination, but the short half-life (15 hr) makes it difficult to use routinely.

## 7-2 FUTURE TRENDS IN ACTIVATION ANALYSIS

### 7-2.1 Responsibility of the Chemist

No discussion of activation analysis would be complete without some attempt to anticipate the future. Activation analysis has had a spectacular and rapid period of growth, but it obviously must soon begin to level off. As the previous authors have emphasized, activation analysis is a technique—but as in the case with any technique, activation must compete with other methods. For some applications, especially those which require high sensitivity and nondestructiveness, activation may be ideally suited. For other applications there may exist more useful methods; indeed, better methods are constantly being devised by the analytical chemist to meet new problems. What is to be expected in the future is what is already occurring: a re-evaluation of the technique of activation analysis and critical appraisal of what it can and can not do. Because activation analysis is built upon chemical and nuclear physics research, it is to these areas that the practitioner must look for improvements, innovations, and refinements of nuclear analysis techniques. Although few activation analysts will have the privilege of conducting research in these basic areas, all should be aware of the importance of such research and follow the literature in the field. Certainly future successes in activation analysis depend to a large extent upon successful research in chemistry and nuclear physics and the consequent application of these findings to improvements in activation technique. Results of past research, such as NaI spectrometry, fast chemical separations, and discovery of new radioactive species, are examples of the types of findings that can contribute to analytical methods. To keep current in the literature and to improve the technique are two fundamental requirements for the activation analyst.

## 7-2.2 Areas for Future Application

Activation analysis has already been applied in a great diversity of problems. Areas in which it can be particularly useful are those in which unusual specific sensitivity, rapid determination, and nondestructiveness are prerequisites. Coupled with modern-electronic data processing systems, it is useful for remote analysis. The proposals to analyze the surface of the moon by activation are already well publicized; there are a number of other space applications where nuclear analysis can be effective: analysis of very-high-purity materials, measurement of the types and magnitudes of radiation in space, control of purity of electronic components used in vehicles, etc.

There are a number of problems of national interest to which this technique may be successfully applied. In forensic science, activation shows promise of being a useful investigative tool: paints, drugs, physical evidence, hair, etc., have all been studied by use of nuclear analysis. These applications should increase. Tracing of opium and other seized drugs may be facilitated through trace-element identification.

Activation analysis offers promise of contributing information concerning trace-element behavior in living systems to the biologist and medical researcher. Stable-isotope addition followed later by analysis by activation makes possible many previously difficult experiments in life sciences where the presence of radioactive material during the experiment would be either undesirable or impossible. This general method of stable tracing may prove of use to a number of investigators in other scientific areas.

## 7-2.3 Conclusions

The prospects for future application of nuclear-analysis techniques appear promising indeed, particularly in the life sciences where the sheer volume of work necessitates the maximum of automation. Activation analysis is ideal for the rapid analysis of a selected group of sensitive elements in an organic matrix and here automation can be effectively applied. Problems involving the analysis of ultrapure materials will certainly increase with the accelerating demands of solid-state technology. Fundamental developments in solid-state detectors leading to better resolution of photon spectra, the possibilities of charged-particle activation, and reactions leading to superior neutron sources are examples of fundamental developments of which the activation expert must be aware. The challenge to the future practitioner of nuclear analysis is clear: to relate these advances in science to successful and useful applications of activation analysis.

## REFERENCES

1. R. C. Greenwood and J. Reed, in *Proceedings, International Conference Modern Trends in Activation Analysis*, A & M College of Texas, 1961.
2. *Isotopes Technology Development Program*, USAEC Report TID-7681, pp. 6–7, 1963.
3. H. L. Finston and E. Yellin, *Anal. Chem.* **35**: 336 (1963).
4. R. A. Gill, British Report AERE-C/R-2758, 1958.
5. J. J. Point, in *Proceedings of the International Conference on Radioisotopes in Scientific Research*, Paris, 1957, Vol. II, p. 180, Pergamon Press, 1958.
6. Barbara A. Thompson, *Anal. Chem.* **33**: 583 (1961).
7. P. Albert, in *Proceedings, International Conference, Modern Trends in Activation Analysis*, A & M College of Texas, 1961.
8. S. S. Markowitz and J. D. Mahony, *Anal. Chem.* **34**: 329 (1962).
9. D. Beard, R. H. Johnson, and W. G. Bradshaw, *Nucleonics* **17**: No. 7, 90 (1959).
10. R. Basile, J. Hure, P. Leveque, and A. Schuhl, *Comp. Rend.* **239**: 422 (1954).
11. H. R. Lukens, Jr., J. W. Otvos, and C. D. Wagner, *Intern. J. Appl. Radiation Isotopes* **11**: 30 (1961).
12. G. Goldstein, *Anal. Chem.* **35**: 1620 (1963).
13. C. P. Haigh, *Proc. Radioisotope Conf. 1954, Vol. II: Physical Sciences and Industrial Applications*, J. E. Johnston, ed., London (1954).

# Chapter 8

## PRACTICAL EXAMPLES OF ACTIVATION ANALYSIS

### E. Ricci

The following examples illustrate the main problems that are frequently found in activation-analysis practice, i.e., (1) counting interferences in nondestructive testing, (2) spurious nuclear-reaction interferences, and (3) self-shadowing effects in a high cross-section matrix. The standard procedure of activation analysis (irradiation, chemical separation—if needed—counting, and calculation) is explained in detail at the same time and followed in each of these examples.

Listed below are several constants, formulas, and conversion factors that may be useful in nuclear calculations:

$N_{Av.}$ = Avogadro's number = $(6.02308 \pm 0.00040) \times 10^{23}$
1 barn = $10^{-24}$ cm$^2$

Time: 1 yr = 8760 hr = $5.256 \times 10^5$ min = $3.1536 \times 10^7$ sec
1 day = 1440 min = 86,400 sec

Decay correction (Eq. 1.7c)

$$R_t = R_o e^{-\frac{0.693t}{T_{1/2}}}$$

(See p. 3)

Radioactivity production (Eq. 1.10c)

$$A = N\sigma\phi \left(1 - e^{-\frac{0.693t_i}{T_{1/2}}}\right)$$

(See p. 9)

Relation between mass and count rate (Eq. 1.11b)

$$W_x = \frac{W_s R_x}{R_s}$$

(See p. 10)

Chemical yield correction (Eq. 4.1)

$$A_x \text{ before separation} = A_x \text{ recovered} \left(\frac{W_x \text{ added}}{W_x \text{ recovered}}\right)$$

(See p. 57)

Resolving time correction (Eq. 5.1)

$$R = R_o(1 - R\tau)$$

(See p. 66)

## 8-1 DETERMINATION OF SODIUM IN CADMIUM NITRATE (SELF-SHADOWING EFFECT)

### 8-1.1 Discussion

This example shows precautions that must be taken when the results of an activation analysis may be altered by the neutron self-shadowing of the matrix.

Sodium can be determined by the reaction $Na^{23}(n,\gamma)Na^{24}$. Cadmium has a very high thermal cross section ($\sigma_o$), due mostly to its stable isotope $Cd^{113}$ (see p. 25). If a sample of cadmium and a sodium comparator are irradiated in a reactor, thermal neutrons are absorbed at such a high rate by cadmium that an actual depression of the thermal flux results inside the cadmium sample. No flux depression occurs, however, in the sodium comparator. Therefore, since the fluxes seen by the sample and the comparator are different, their resulting $Na^{24}$ specific activities ($Na^{24}$ activity per unit weight of sodium present) will be different, and Eq. 1.11b will no longer be valid. Figure 8.1 illustrates this effect.[1]

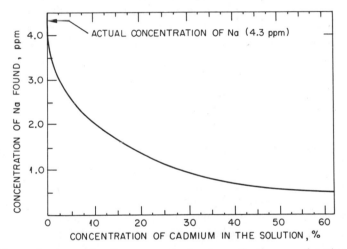

FIG. 8.1—Change in observed sodium concentration by activation, as a function of cadmium content of the sample.

Several samples of 1 ml of solution containing 4.3 ppm of sodium each, but increasing concentrations of cadmium, were analyzed for sodium by comparison with a sodium standard free of cadmium. The results of the activation analyses are plotted vs. concentrations of cadmium in the samples. These data show the large errors that may be introduced in this kind of analysis.

Some general ways to solve this problem are listed below:

1. Reactor irradiation of the sample and the standard, both prepared in the same chemical and physical form, as mentioned on page 31. Although the self-shadowing effect is not avoided in this procedure, the flux depressions in the

sample and the standard are made equal. Therefore, Eq. 1.11b can be used in the calculations. This method is described in detail below.

2. Use of reactor fast neutrons in the activation of the sought impurity. The sample and the comparator are irradiated in a cadmium shield, which is transparent to resonance and fast neutrons. Here, a fast-neutron reaction is used in the activation analysis. Since the cross sections for fast-neutron reactions on most elements (including cadmium) are small, self-shadowing does not affect this kind of experiment. Although this method can be very useful in the analysis of many trace elements in self-shadowing matrices (see p. 27), it becomes difficult in this example. The usable fast-neutron reactions on sodium are: $Na^{23}(n,p)Ne^{23}$, $Na^{23}(n,\alpha)F^{20}$, and $Na^{23}(n,2n)Na^{22}$. $Ne^{23}$ (38 sec) and $F^{20}$ (11 sec) are too short-lived to be separated successfully from other radioactive impurities before counting. The threshold of the third reaction (13.0 Mev) is too high compared with the energies of most reactor fast neutrons (see Fig. 2.1, Chap. 2). The concept of threshold is discussed on p. 20. It is interesting to point out, however, that in this particular example the resonance activation of $Na^{23}$ ($I_o = 0.30$ b; see Table 2.4 and p. 26), in a cadmium-covered irradiation of the cadmium sample and the standard, can be used in the activation analysis of sodium. The absorption of resonance neutrons by cadmium is very small, and, therefore, there is no self-shadowing of resonance neutrons inside the cadmium sample. However, the reactor irradiation (point No. 1 above) makes use of both the thermal and the resonance neutrons and, thus, is inherently more sensitive than a method that uses only the resonance activation.

3. Use of a 14-Mev neutron generator. The cross sections of 14-Mev neutron reactions are generally small. Consequently, self-shadowing does not occur when the cadmium sample and the comparator are irradiated with a neutron generator. The disadvantages of fast-neutron activation analysis of sodium have been pointed out in point No. 2 above. The reaction $Na^{23}(n,2n)Na^{22}$ can be produced by 14-Mev neutrons ($\sigma_{14\,Mev} \cong 14$ mb); however, the long half-life of $Na^{22}$ (2.60 yr) and the relatively low fluxes (see p. 42) of neutron generators work against the attainment of a practical activity of $Na^{22}$ for activation analysis. In general, however, a large number of elements can be analyzed by fast-neutron activation (see Chap. 3, particularly, *Practical Applications of Neutron Generarators*; see also Section 8-4 of this chapter). It must be recalled that each problem in activation analysis has its own characteristics and, therefore, its own solution. In this particular example, the choice obviously points to the method given in point No. 1.

## 8-1.2 Procedure

The chemical purification of sodium may be performed according to procedures 4 to 10 given in *The Radiochemistry of Sodium* (Ref. 2). Assume that final precipitates of NaCl (as in procedure 8) are obtained for the sample and the standard.

To avoid the self-shadowing error caused by the cadmium matrix, the standard must be prepared by mixing a known amount of sodium standard solution with a concentrated solution of spectrographically pure cadmium in $HNO_3$. This acid must be free of sodium (distilled). The above mixture is evaporated to dryness* before the irradiation. The cadmium concentration of this standard must be the same as that of the cadmium nitrate sample. Now, the pure cadmium may contain small but finite amounts of sodium. Since a massive quantity of pure cadmium is used in the standard, this spurious sodium content of the comparator must also be determined. Then, for comparison purposes, a blank is prepared by dissolving the same amount of pure cadmium as before in sodium-free distilled $HNO_3$ and by evaporating this solution. Assume that the following specimens are irradiated under the same conditions in a reactor:

Sample: 1.099 g of $Cd(NO_3)_2 \cdot 4H_2O$ (containing 400.0 mg of cadmium), dried after weighing.

Standard: Dried residue of a nitric solution containing 400.0 mg of pure cadmium plus 2.00 $\mu g$ of sodium (pipetted from a previously calibrated solution).

Blank: Dried residue of a nitric solution containing 400.0 mg of pure cadmium.

It can be seen that, after the irradiation, the activity of $Na^{24}$ corresponding to the known 2.00 $\mu g$ of sodium of the standard may be obtained by subtracting the $Na^{24}$ activity of the blank from that of the standard. Meanwhile, the $Na^{24}$ activity of the sample is representative of the sought amount of sodium in the cadmium nitrate.

After a 30-hr irradiation, the three specimens are dissolved in water, and 1.0 ml of a sodium carrier solution containing 20.0 mg sodium per milliliter is added to each of them. Then the chemical purification of $Na^{24}$ is performed. The final precipitates of NaCl corresponding to the sample, the standard, and the blank are dried, weighed, and their $\beta$ or $\gamma$ rays are measured by gross $\beta$ or $\gamma$ counting or with a single-channel or multichannel analyzer. If a pulse-height analyzer is used, the area under the 2.76 Mev photopeak of $Na^{24}$ may be measured.[3] Practical details of $\gamma$ spectrometry are presented in Sections 8-3 and 8-4 of this chapter. If a gross $\gamma$ counter is used, the measurements are performed as in $\beta$ counting. (See Section 8-2.)

### 8-1.3 Experimental Results

Assume that the following data have been obtained in an experiment:

Irradiation length: 30 hr (2 half-lives of $Na^{24}$)
End: 09 hr 30 min 00 sec (or 09.30.00)
Thermal flux: $4.2 \times 10^{12}$ neutrons/$cm^2$ sec (a flux depression of a factor of 6 is assumed). Then the actual average thermal flux is $7.0 \times 10^{11}$ neutrons/sec $cm^2$

---

* An evaporation is made because the reaction $Cd^{113}(n,\gamma)Cd^{114}$, with its high thermal cross section, results in the fast release of large amounts of heat. Thus a sealed liquid sample might explode due to excessive pressure.

Resonance flux: $1.4 \times 10^{11}$ neutrons/cm$^2$ sec
Length of chemical separation = 3 hr
Counting efficiency = 0.01 (or 1%)

These data are not needed in the calculations, but they are included to enable the reader to correlate them with the count rates listed below, and thus have an estimation of the sensitivity in this particular analysis. Table 8.1 shows weighing and counting results for the three specimens.

Table 8.1—WEIGHING AND COUNTING OF NaCl PRECIPITATES

| Specimen | Time | Count rate,* counts/min | Weight NaCl, mg |
|----------|------|-------------------------|------------------|
| Sample | 12.40.00 | 11,130 | 38.1 |
| Standard | 12.43.00 | 8,520 | 41.7 |
| Blank | 12.46.00 | 2,400 | 40.1 |

\* Background: 53 counts/min (time 12.49.00).

## 8-1.4 Calculations

(a) *Correction of the count rates.* The decay of Na$^{24}$ during the time spent in the measurements is only 0.5%; therefore no decay corrections are necessary.* The background is very low, compared with the first two count rates; it will only be subtracted from the count rate of the blank. Then the net count rate of the blank becomes $2,400 - 53 = 2,347$ counts/min. Since a chemical separation is involved in this procedure, a chemical yield correction must be applied. The amount of NaCl, which corresponds to the previously added 20.0 mg of sodium carrier, is 50.8 mg. Then, by making calculations similar to those given in Section 8-2, p. 126, the corrected count rates (C.R.) are:

$$\text{(Sample C.R.)} = 11,130 \text{ counts/min} \left(\frac{50.8 \text{ mg}}{38.1 \text{ mg}}\right) = 14,850 \text{ counts/min}$$

$$\text{(Standard C.R.)} = 8,520 \text{ counts/min} \left(\frac{50.8 \text{ mg}}{41.7 \text{ mg}}\right) = 10,390 \text{ counts/min}$$

$$\text{(Blank C.R.)} = 2,347 \text{ counts/min} \left(\frac{50.8 \text{ mg}}{40.1 \text{ mg}}\right) = 2,974 \text{ counts/min}$$

(b) *Application of Eq. 1.11b.* The values of $R_x$, $R_s$, and $W_s$ (defined in Eq. 1.11b) must be obtained first. As shown above, $R_x$ is simply the corrected count rate for the sample (14,850 counts/min), whereas $R_s$ is equal to the difference:

$$R_s = \text{(Standard C.R.)} - \text{(Blank C.R.)}$$
$$= 10,390 - 2,974 = 7,416 \text{ counts/min}$$

Since $W_s$ is known to be 2.00 $\mu$g sodium, Eq. 1.11b can now be applied:

---

\* A counting method which does not require resolving-time correction is assumed.

$$W_x = \frac{W_s R_x}{R_s} = \frac{2.00\ \mu g \times 14{,}850\ \text{counts/min}}{7{,}416\ \text{counts/min}} = 4.0\ \mu g\ \text{of sodium}$$

This amount of sodium is present in 1.099 g of $Cd(NO_3)_2 \cdot 4H_2O$. Thus the concentration of sodium in the sample of cadmium nitrate is

$$\frac{4.0\ \mu g}{1.099\ g} = 3.6\ \mu g/g,\ \text{or 3.6 ppm, or 0.00036\%}$$

(c) *Remarks.* It is interesting to note that the unknown concentration of sodium in the pure cadmium can also be calculated from the data of Table 8.1. Here, the values of $R_s$ and $W_s$ are obviously the same as before, but the count rate of $Na^{24}(R_x')$ corresponding to the sodium content of the pure cadmium $(W_x')$ in the blank is

$$R_x' = (\text{Blank C.R.}) = 2{,}974\ \text{counts/min}$$

Then, by Eq. 1.11b:

$$W_x' = \frac{W_x R_x'}{R_s} = \frac{2.00\ \mu g \times 2{,}974\ \text{counts/min}}{7{,}416\ \text{counts/min}} = 0.80\ \mu g$$

Since there were 400.0 mg of cadmium in the blank, the sodium concentration in the pure cadmium metal is

$$\frac{0.80\ \mu g}{0.4000\ g} = 2.0\ \mu g/g,\ \text{or 2.0 ppm, or 0.00020\%.}$$

It may be pointed out here that a sodium concentration of 2 ppm in pure cadmium may be frequently observed; therefore, if the expected concentration of sodium in the analyzed sample is of the order of 1 to 10 ppm, the necessity for a blank is obvious.

To know the concentration of sodium in the pure cadmium may be useful if a series of analyses of the same kind are to be performed at different times and reactor sites. With this concentration known, the cadmium metal itself, or its prepared derivatives, may provide excellent self-shadowing sodium standards for further analyses. Then the use of a blank and the addition of a known amount of comparator solution to the standard specimen are no longer needed.

The calculation of the statistical errors of the results is discussed in Chap. 5.

## 8-2 DETERMINATION OF PHOSPHORUS IN SKIN TISSUE (INTERFERING NUCLEAR REACTIONS)

### 8-2.1 Discussion

This example shows a case where a chemical separation followed by $\beta$ counting must be applied. It also illustrates the effect of interfering nuclear reactions in activation analysis.

Table 8.2 shows typical values obtained by standard chemical procedures for the analysis of dried skin.

Table 8.2—MINERAL ELEMENTS IN DRIED SKIN (MAN)

| Element | Concentration, % | Element | Concentration, % |
|---|---|---|---|
| Boron | 0.017 | Potassium | 0.28 |
| Cadmium | 0.046 | Silicon | 0.09 |
| Chlorine | 1.10 | Sodium | 0.94 |
| Copper | 0.019 | Sulfur | 0.34 |
| Iodine | 0.0002 | Zinc | 0.020 |
| Iron | 0.0059 | Phosphorus | 0.030 |
| Nitrogen (total) | 14.5 | | |

The reaction $P^{31}(n,\gamma)P^{32}$ is used in the activation analysis for phosphorus. From Table 8.2 it is clear that many other radioactive nuclides besides $P^{32}$ will be formed in a reactor irradiation of skin tissue. Furthermore, no $\gamma$-spectrometric technique can be used because $P^{32}$ is a pure $\beta$-emitter. Therefore $P^{32}$ has to be purified by chemical separation and counted on a G-M tube or a proportional counter. The half life of $P^{32}$ is 14.3 days.

The different steps for the activation analysis of biological samples for phosphorus may be found in procedures 3, 7, and 8 of *The Radiochemistry of Phosphorus* (Ref. 4).

The chemical procedure can separate $P^{32}$ from other radioactive nuclides, but it cannot separate the $P^{32}$ induced in the phosphorus content of the sample from the $P^{32}$ which originates in sulfur and chlorine by the interfering reactions

$$S^{32}(n,p)P^{32} \quad \text{and} \quad Cl^{35}(n,\alpha)P^{32}$$
(See reactions 2.17, page 30)

The first of these reactions can only be produced by fast neutrons, e.g., fission neutrons in a reactor (see p. 20), because its threshold energy is positive ($E_T = 0.95$ Mev) (Ref. 5). The second reaction has a negative threshold energy ($E_T = -0.92$ Mev); therefore it releases energy and can take place even with thermal neutrons.

This interference, though serious, can still be overcome. If a bare sample and a cadmium-covered sample of skin tissue are irradiated under the same conditions in a reactor, the total induced $P^{32}$ activities ($A$ and $A_r$, respectively) will be given by the following equations (see also p. 18):

$$A = (A_{P,th} + A_{P,r}) + (A_{Cl,th} + A_{Cl,r} + A_{Cl,f}) + A_{S,f} \qquad (8.1)$$

$$A_r = A_{P,r} + (A_{Cl,r} + A_{Cl,f}) + A_{S,f} \qquad (8.2)$$

where

$A_{P,th}$ and $A_{P,r}$ = activities of $P^{32}$ produced by the reaction $P^{31}(n,\gamma)P^{32}$ with thermal and resonance neutrons, respectively.

$A_{Cl,th}$, $A_{Cl,r}$, and $A_{Cl,f}$ = interfering activities of $P^{32}$ produced by the reaction $Cl^{35}(n,\alpha)P^{32}$ with thermal, resonance and fast neutrons, respectively.

$A_{S,f}$ = interfering activity of $P^{32}$ produced by the reaction $S^{32}(n,p)P^{32}$ with fast neutrons.

An estimation of the interferences can be made by calculating these activities (according to Eqs. 1.10a, 1.10b, and 1.10c, and Eqs. 2.1, 2.2, and 2.5) for a 30-min irradiation of 100 mg of skin tissue. The data are:

Stable isotopes: $P^{31}$ (100%)     Atomic wt.: P = 30.97
$\qquad\qquad\qquad$ $Cl^{35}$ (75.53%)     Atomic wt.: Cl = 35.46
$\qquad\qquad\qquad$ $S^{32}$ (95.02%)     Atomic wt.: S = 32.07

Reactions: $P^{31}(n,\gamma)P^{32}$     $\sigma_o = 0.21$ barn*
$\qquad\qquad\qquad\qquad\quad$ $I_o = 0.10$ barn (see Table 2.4, Chap. 2)
$\qquad\quad$ $Cl^{35}(n,\alpha)P^{32}$     $\sigma_o = 0.05$ mb (Ref. 6)
$\qquad\qquad\qquad\qquad\quad$ $I_o = 0.45 \times \sigma_o = 22.5$ $\mu$b (Ref. 7) (because the cross section of this reaction is proportional to 1/v at resonance energies)[8]
$\qquad\qquad\qquad\qquad\quad$ $\bar{\sigma} = 3.0$ mb (Ref. 8)
$\qquad\quad$ $S^{32}(n,p)P^{32}$     $\bar{\sigma} = 65$ mb (see Table 2.2, Chap. 2)

Assumptions: Weight of sample: 100 mg
$\qquad\qquad\quad$ Type of sample: dried skin tissue (Table 8.2)
$\qquad\qquad\quad$ Irradiation length = 30 min
$\qquad\qquad\quad$ $\phi_{th} = 6.0 \times 10^{13}$ neutrons/$cm^2$ sec (see Fig. 2.1, Chap. 2)
$\qquad\qquad\quad$ $\phi_r = 2.3 \times 10^{12}$ neutrons/$cm^2$ sec
$\qquad\qquad\quad$ $\phi_f = 1.6 \times 10^{13}$ neutrons/$cm^2$ sec

$$A_{P,th} = \overset{N_{P^{31}}}{\frac{(3.0 \times 10^{-5}\text{ g})(6.02 \times 10^{23})}{30.97\text{ g}}} \overset{\phi_{th}}{(6.0 \times 10^{13}\text{ cm}^{-2}\text{ sec}^{-1})}$$

$$\overset{\sigma_o}{(0.21 \times 10^{-24}\text{ cm}^2)} \left\{ 1 - \exp\left[ -\left( \overset{\text{Saturation factor}}{\frac{0.693 \times 30\text{ min}}{14.3 \times 24 \times 60\text{ min}}} \right) \right] \right\}$$

$$= (5.82 \times 10^{17})(6.0 \times 10^{13}\text{ cm}^{-2}\text{ sec}^{-1})(0.21 \times 10^{-24}\text{ cm}^2)(1.01 \times 10^{-3})$$
$$= 7.41 \times 10^3\text{ sec}^{-1} \text{ (or dis/sec)}$$

$$A_{P,r} = \overset{N_{P^{31}}}{(5.82 \times 10^{17})} \overset{\phi_r}{(2.3 \times 10^{12}\text{ cm}^{-2}\text{ sec}^{-1})} \overset{I_o}{(0.10 \times 10^{-24}\text{ cm}^2)}$$

$$\overset{\text{Saturation factor}}{(1.01 \times 10^{-3})} = 150\text{ dis/sec}$$

$$N_{Cl^{35}} = 1.41 \times 10^{19}$$

$$A_{Cl,th} = \frac{(1.10 \times 10^{-3}\text{ g})(6.02 \times 10^{23})(0.7553)}{35.46\text{ g}} \overset{\phi_{th}}{(6.0 \times 10^{13}\text{ cm}^{-2}\text{ sec}^{-1})}$$

$$\overset{\sigma_o}{(5 \times 10^{-29}\text{ cm}^2)} \overset{\text{Saturation factor}}{(1.01 \times 10^{-3})}$$
$$= 42.7\text{ dis/sec}$$

---

* The symbols $\sigma_o$, $I_o$, $\bar{\sigma}$, $\phi_{th}$, $\phi_r$, $\phi_f$, etc., are defined in Chap. 2. Since the difference between $\sigma_o$ and $\sigma_{th}$ is small for $P^{31}$ and $Cl^{35}$, $\sigma_o$ values for these two nuclides have been used in the calculation of $A_{P,th}$ and $A_{Cl,th}$.

$$\overset{N_{Cl^{35}}}{\phantom{x}} \qquad \overset{\phi_r}{\phantom{x}} \qquad \overset{I_o}{\phantom{x}} \qquad \text{Saturation factor}$$

$$A_{Cl,r} = (1.41 \times 10^{19})(2.3 \times 10^{12} \text{ cm}^{-2} \text{ sec}^{-1})(22.5 \times 10^{-30} \text{ cm}^2)(1.01 \times 10^{-3})$$
$$= 0.74 \text{ dis/sec}$$

$$\overset{N_{Cl^{35}}}{\phantom{x}} \qquad \overset{\phi_f}{\phantom{x}} \qquad \overset{\bar{\sigma}}{\phantom{x}} \qquad \text{Saturation factor}$$

$$A_{Cl,f} = (1.41 \times 10^{19})(1.6 \times 10^{13} \text{ cm}^{-2} \text{ sec}^{-1})(3.0 \times 10^{-27} \text{ cm}^2)(1.01 \times 10^{-3})$$
$$= 683 \text{ dis/sec}$$

$$\overset{N_{S^{32}}}{\phantom{xxxxxxxxxxxxxxxxxxxxxxxx}} \qquad \overset{\phi_f}{\phantom{x}}$$

$$A_{S,f} = \frac{(3.40 \times 10^{-4} \text{ g})(6.02 \times 10^{23})(0.9502)}{32.07 \text{ g}} (1.6 \times 10^{13} \text{ cm}^{-2} \text{ sec}^{-1})$$

$$\overset{\bar{\sigma}}{\phantom{xxxxx}} \qquad \text{Saturation factor}$$

$$(6.5 \times 10^{-26} \text{ cm}^2)(1.01 \times 10^{-3})$$
$$= 6.36 \times 10^3 \text{ dis/sec}$$

It is clear from the above calculations that 43.4% of the total activity of $P^{32}$ ($A$) induced in the bare sample is due to the sulfur content of the tissue, and that another 5.0% is produced by chlorine. However, the $P^{32}$ activity, corresponding only to the phosphorus content of the sample, can be calculated by subtracting Eq. 8.2 from Eq. 8.1:

$$A - A_r = A_{P,th} + A_{Cl,th} \cong A_{P,th} \qquad (8.3)$$

In this example $A_{Cl,th}$ is only 0.58% of $A_{P,th}$, and thus $A_{Cl,th} \ll A_{P,th}$. In fact, $A_{Cl,th}$ could still be neglected if the ratio chlorine/phosphorus in the tissue were twice as large. Only a few $(n,p)$ and $(n,\alpha)$ reactions can occur with thermal neutrons. So, in general, the activity of the measured nuclide, which is formed only by thermal activation will be exactly obtained by subtracting the activity of this nuclide induced in the cadmium-covered sample from the activity of the same nuclide induced in the bare sample. Two conclusions may be drawn from Eq. 8.3:

1. Since $A_{P,th}$ does not include the $P^{32}$ activity induced by resonance neutrons in $P(A_{P,r})$, two phosphorus comparators must also be irradiated: one bare and the other cadmium shielded. The count rates of the induced $P^{32}$ in these must be subtracted in a manner similar to that described for the tissue sample.

2. If $A$ and $A_r$ are large numbers and $A_{P,th}$ is of the order of their statistical error, obviously no significant results can be obtained by this method. In this case, the determination can be made by irradiating the sample and the standard in a pure thermal-neutron flux (*thermal column*).

### 8-2.2 Procedure

Two samples (one bare and one cadmium covered) and two standards (one bare and one cadmium covered) were irradiated under the same conditions. The standards consisted of $(NH_4)_2HPO_4$ and weighed 17.1 mg each; after irradiation, they were dissolved in water and diluted. Aliquots representing 1/100th of the original weights for each of the standards were taken. One milliliter of a solution containing 20.0 mg/ml of phosphorus carrier was added to each of the four specimens; then, procedure 3 of Ref. 4 was performed on each of them, after destroying the organic matter of the skin tissue. The final weighing form is $MgNH_4PO_4 \cdot 6H_2O$. The dried and weighed filter discs with the final precipitates were mounted on counting cards and measured on a G-M counter assembly (see Fig. 5.4 and related text, and part D of Ref. 4). It is a good practice to check the purity of $\beta$ sources by counting them with a $\gamma$ spectrometer; only bremsstrahlung photons should be registered during this check. If the measurements of $P^{32}$ are taken within a few hours, decay corrections are unnecessary because of the long half-life of $P^{32}$.

## 8-2.3 Experimental Results

Type of sample: dried skin tissue
Irradiation time: 30 min
Reactor flux: $\phi_{th}$, $\phi_r$, and $\phi_f$ as given on p. 123

1. For the bare tissue sample:
   Weight of irradiated sample = 102.3 mg
   Weight of final $MgNH_4PO_4 \cdot 6H_2O$ (or MgNP) precipitate = 135.4 mg
   Count rate = 20,400 counts/min
2. For the cadmium-covered tissue sample:
   Weight of irradiated sample = 98.7 mg
   Weight of final MgNP precipitate = 126.2 mg
   Count rate = 9,850 counts/min
3. For the bare phosphorus comparator:
   Weight of irradiated standard = 17.1 mg of $(NH_4)_2HPO_4$
   Weight of final MgNP precipitate = 153.0 mg
   Count rate = 15,970 counts/min (for 1/100th aliquot)
4. For the cadmium-covered phosphorus comparator:
   Weight of irradiated standard = 17.1 mg of $(NH_4)_2HPO_4$
   Weight of final MgNP precipitate = 156.7 mg
   Count rate = 377 counts/min (for 1/100th aliquot)
   Natural background = 22 counts/min

## 8-2.4 Calculations

(a) *Corrections applied to the count rates.* Before treating the count-rate data, according to Eq. 8.3, they must be corrected for G-M resolving-time losses and for chemical yields. If a proportional counter had been used, the resolving-time correction would not be necessary (p. 66).

*Resolving-time losses.* Assume a resolving time $\tau = 280$ $\mu$sec (Chap. 5) for the G-M counter used in the measurements. The true counting rate, $R_o$, can be calculated by Eq. 5.1:

$$R_o = \frac{R}{1 - R\tau}$$

where $R$ is the experimental counting rate. Then, for the bare sample:

$$R_o = \frac{20,400 \text{ counts/min}}{1 - (20,400 \text{ counts/min} \times 4.67 \times 10^{-6} \text{ min})} = 22,480 \text{ counts/min}$$

because $\quad \tau = 280 \ \mu\text{sec} = \dfrac{2.80 \times 10^{-4} \text{ sec}}{60 \text{ sec/min}} = 4.67 \times 10^{-6} \text{ min}$

For the cadmium-covered sample:

$$R_o = \frac{9,850 \text{ counts/min}}{1 - (9,850 \text{ counts/min} \times 4.67 \times 10^{-6} \text{ min})} = 10,335 \text{ counts/min}$$

and for the bare comparator:

$$R_o = \frac{15,970 \text{ counts/min}}{1 - (15,970 \text{ counts/min} \times 4.67 \times 10^{-6} \text{ min})} = 17,245 \text{ counts/min}$$

The count rate of the cadmium-covered standard is low and needs no correction for resolving-time losses. However, the natural background count rate is significant in this case and must be subtracted. For the cadmium-covered comparator, then: True count rate $= 377 - 22 = 355$ counts/min.

*Chemical yield corrections.* The amount of MgNP, which corresponds to the added 20.0 mg of phosphorus carrier, is

$$\text{Maximum MgNP precipitate weight} = 20.0 \text{ mg} \left(\frac{\text{mol. wt. MgNP}}{\text{at. wt. P}}\right)$$

$$= 20.0 \text{ mg} \left(\frac{245.5}{30.97}\right) = 158.6 \text{ mg MgNP}$$

Therefore, by Eq. 4.1, the count rate now also corrected for chemical yield (or totally corrected count rate) is

$$\text{Corrected count rate} = (\text{True count rate}) \left(\frac{158.6 \text{ mg MgNP}}{\text{weight MgNP precipitate}}\right)$$

Then, for the bare sample:

$$\text{Corrected count rate} = 22,480 \text{ counts/min} \left(\frac{158.6 \text{ mg}}{135.4 \text{ mg}}\right) = 26,350 \text{ counts/min}$$

For the cadmium-covered sample:

$$\text{Corrected count rate} = 10,335 \text{ counts/min} \left(\frac{158.6 \text{ mg}}{126.2 \text{ mg}}\right) = 12,980 \text{ counts/min}$$

For the bare comparator:

$$\text{Corrected count rate} = 17,245 \text{ counts/min} \left(\frac{158.6 \text{ mg}}{153.0 \text{ mg}}\right) = 17,880 \text{ counts/min}$$

For the cadmium-covered comparator:

$$\text{Corrected count rate} = 355 \text{ counts/min} \left(\frac{158.6 \text{ mg}}{156.7 \text{ mg}}\right) = 360 \text{ counts/min}$$

(b) *Calculation of $R_x$ and $R_s$.* As defined on p. 10, $R_x$ and $R_s$ are the $P^{32}$ count rates of the sample and the standard, respectively, to be used in Eq. 1.11b.

Both count rates can be obtained by applying Eq. 8.3 (see also point No. 1, p. 124). From the corrected count rates of the two comparators, then

$$R_s = 17,880 - 360 = 17,520 \text{ counts/min}$$

Since the two tissue samples differ in weight, the bare and the cadmium-shielded count rates per unit weight of tissue must be calculated before substituting them in Eq. 8.3:

$$R_x = \frac{26,350 \text{ counts/min}}{102.3 \text{ mg}} - \frac{12,980 \text{ counts/min}}{98.7 \text{ mg}}$$

$$= 257.7 \text{ counts/min/mg} - 131.5 \text{ counts/min/mg} = 126.0 \text{ counts/min/mg}$$

(c) *Application of Eq. 1.11b.* From the data, $W_s$ in Eq. 1.11b is the amount of phosphorus contained in a 1/100th aliquot of 17.1 mg of $(NH_4)_2HPO_4$:

$$W_s = \left(\frac{17.1 \text{ mg}}{100}\right)\left(\frac{\text{at. wt. P}}{\text{mol. wt. } (NH_4)_2HPO_4}\right)$$

$$= (171 \ \mu g)\left(\frac{30.97}{132.1}\right) = 40.1 \ \mu g \text{ P}$$

Then:

$$W_x = \frac{W_s R_x}{R_s} = \frac{(40.1 \ \mu g)(126.0 \text{ counts/min/mg})}{(17,520 \text{ counts/min})}$$

$$W_x = 0.288 \ \mu g \text{ P/mg dried tissue}$$

The concentration of phosphorus in the sample of dried skin tissue is then 288 ppm or 0.0288%.

The statistical treatment of errors has been discussed previously beginning on p. 75.

## 8-3 ANALYSIS OF VANADIUM IN AN IRON MATRIX (NONDESTRUCTIVE $\gamma$-RAY SPECTROMETRY)

### 8-3.1 Discussion

This example shows details and problems inherent to a nondestructive method which uses a short-lived nuclide.

The determination of vanadium is done by direct $\gamma$ spectrometry of $V^{52}$ in the irradiated iron sample. The main requirement of this analysis is that the $V^{52}$ $\gamma$ rays be resolved from those emitted by other radionuclides. It is assumed that no interferences (other than iron and manganese radionuclides that originate from the matrix) are found in the measurements. Reactor irradiations of iron produce $Fe^{59}$ by $(n,\gamma)$ reactions with thermal and resonance neutrons and $Mn^{56}$ by an $(n,p)$ reaction with fast neutrons. $Fe^{55}$, produced by neutron capture in $Fe^{54}$ emits only a 6-kev X ray and therefore presents no interference. $Mn^{54}$ produced by the reaction $Fe^{54}(n,p)Mn^{54}$ is a possible interference. It is not important, however, since $Mn^{54}$ only emits $\gamma$ rays of 0.83 Mev. In addition, the low abundance of $Fe^{54}$ (5.84%), the small cross section for the $(n,p)$ reaction ($\bar{\sigma} = 65$ mb; see Ref. 8, Chap. 2), and the long half-life of $Mn^{54}$ (314 days) all work against production of significant amounts of $Mn^{54}$.

By using sensitivity calculations similar to those in Chap. 1, the activities of $V^{52}$, $Fe^{59}$, and $Mn^{56}$ ($A_{V^{52}}$, $A_{Fe^{59}}$, and $A_{Mn^{56}}$) formed in a 4-min irradiation can be obtained. The length of the irradiation is usually made less than or equal to the half-life of the nuclide to be measured.

The data are:

Reactions: $V^{51}(n,\gamma)V^{52}$      $\sigma_o = 5.1$ barn*
$\qquad\qquad\quad Fe^{58}(n,\gamma)Fe^{59}$      $\sigma_o = 0.98$ barn*
$\qquad\qquad\quad Fe^{56}(n,p)Mn^{56}$      $\bar{\sigma} = 0.71 \times 10^{-3}$ barn

Stable elements: Atomic weights      $V = 50.95$
$\qquad\qquad\qquad\qquad\qquad\qquad$ Fe $= 55.85$
$\qquad\qquad\qquad$ Abundances $\qquad\quad$ $V^{51} = 99.76\%$
$\qquad\qquad\qquad\qquad\qquad\qquad$ $Fe^{58} = 0.31\%$
$\qquad\qquad\qquad\qquad\qquad\qquad$ $Fe^{56} = 91.68\%$

Radioactive nuclides:

$V^{52}$     $T_{1/2} = 3.76$ min     $E_\gamma$(Mev) $= 1.44$ (100%)
$Fe^{59}$     $T_{1/2} = 45.1$ days     $E_\gamma$(Mev) $= 1.10$ (57%); 1.29 (43%);
$\qquad\qquad\qquad\qquad\qquad\qquad\qquad\quad$ 0.191 (2.8%)
$Mn^{56}$    $T_{1/2} = 2.58$ hr     $E_\gamma$(Mev) $= 0.845$ ($\sim$100%); 1.81 ($\sim$30%);
$\qquad\qquad\qquad\qquad\qquad\qquad\qquad\quad$ 2.13 ($\sim$20%)

Assumptions: Concentration of V in iron matrix $= 1$ ppm
$\qquad\qquad\quad$ Irradiation length $= 4$ min
$\qquad\qquad\quad$ Thermal flux ($\phi_{th}$) $= 10^{13}$ neutrons/cm$^2$ sec
$\qquad\qquad\quad$ Fission flux ($\phi_f$) $= 3 \times 10^{12}$ neutrons/cm$^2$ sec (taken to be
$\qquad\qquad\qquad$ one-third of thermal flux; this is illustrated in Fig. 2.1).

Activities: From Eq. 1.10a to 1.10c (at irradiation end), for 1 $\mu$g of vanadium:

$$A_{V^{52}} = \overbrace{\frac{(10^{-6} \text{ g})(0.9976)(6.02 \times 10^{23})}{50.95 \text{ g}}}^{N_{V^{52}}} \overbrace{(5.1 \times 10^{-24} \text{ cm}^2)}^{\sigma_o}$$

$$\underbrace{(10^{13} \text{ cm}^{-2} \text{ sec}^{-1})}_{\phi_{th}} \left\{ 1 - \exp\left[ -\left( \overbrace{\frac{0.693 \times 4 \text{ min}}{3.76 \text{ min}}}^{\text{Saturation factor}} \right) \right] \right\}$$

$A_{V^{52}} = 3.14 \times 10^5$ sec$^{-1}$ (i.e., disintegrations/sec)

For 1 g of iron:

---

* Since only an approximate estimation of the activities is required, thermal (or 2200 m/sec) cross sections and thermal flux are used. A more rigorous calculation can be made by using Eq. 2.2.

$$A_{Fe^{59}} = \frac{\overset{N_{Fe^{58}}}{(1\ g)(0.0031)(6.02 \times 10^{23})}}{55.85\ g} \overset{\sigma_o}{(0.98 \times 10^{-24}\ cm^2)} \overset{\phi_{th}}{(10^{13}\ cm^{-2}\ sec^{-1})}$$

$$\overset{\text{Saturation factor}}{\left\{1 - \exp\left[-\left(\frac{0.693 \times 4\ min}{45.1 \times 24 \times 60\ min}\right)\right]\right\}}$$

$$A_{Fe^{59}} = 1.40 \times 10^4\ dis/sec$$

From Eq. 2.5 and for 1 g of iron:

$$A_{Mn^{56}} = \frac{\overset{N_{Fe^{56}}}{(1\ g)(0.9168)(6.02 \times 10^{23})}}{55.85\ g} \overset{\bar\sigma}{(0.71 \times 10^{-27}\ cm^2)}$$

$$\overset{\phi_f}{(3 \times 10^{12}\ cm^{-2}\ sec^{-1})} \overset{\text{Saturation factor}}{\left\{1 - \exp\left[-\left(\frac{0.693 \times 4\ min}{2.58 \times 60\ min}\right)\right]\right\}}$$

$$A_{Mn^{56}} = 3.73 \times 10^5\ dis/sec$$

It is clear, from the above calculations, that 53.2% of the total activity induced in iron, after a 4-min irradiation, is due to $Mn^{56}$. The activity corresponding to $Fe^{59}$ is 2.0%. Since the measurements will be made by $\gamma$ spectrometry, the actual interferences depend on the relative amounts and energies of the $\gamma$ rays of $V^{52}$, $Mn^{56}$, and $Fe^{59}$ present at the end of the irradiation. Figure 8.2 shows the $\gamma$-ray spectrum of this mixture of radionuclides with the relative intensities calculated above. The interference of $Fe^{59}$ in the determination of $V^{52}$ is small since (1) the absolute amount of $Fe^{59}$ present is low, and (2) the gamma branching in $Fe^{59}$ is only 43% for the interfering gamma ray.[9-11] Consequently, the 1.29-Mev gamma-ray photopeak only slightly overlaps the $V^{52}$ 1.44-Mev gamma-ray photopeak. However, $Mn^{56}$ interference is significant, and its relative value increases as $V^{52}$ decays. Therefore the $Mn^{56}$ activity must be subtracted in the counting.

## 8-3.2 Procedure

To estimate the weight of iron to be irradiated, assume that 2 min will have elapsed before counting ($e^{-\lambda t} = 0.6915$) and that the counting efficiency ($\epsilon$) is 4% (see below). From the above sensitivity calculations, it can be shown that a 50-mg iron sample will provide a suitable count rate ($R_{V^{52}}$), if the conditions are the same as in Fig. 8.2:

$$R_{V^{52}} = A_{V^{52}} \times (\epsilon) \times e^{-\lambda t} \times (\text{grams of iron})$$

where

$$A_{V^{52}} = 3.14 \times 10^5\ dis/sec/\mu g\ V^{52}\ (\text{or dis/sec/g iron})$$

Then

$$R_{V^{52}} = (3.14 \times 10^5\ dis/sec/g)(0.04)(0.6915)(0.050\ g)(60\ sec/min)$$
$$= 26{,}056\ counts/min$$

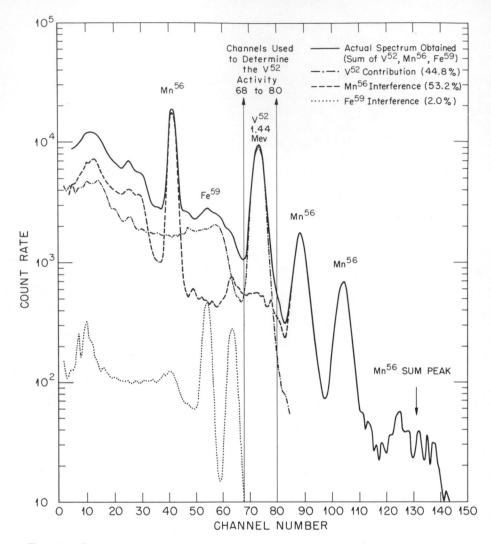

FIG. 8.2—Gamma-ray spectrum of an iron sample containing 1 ppm of vanadium at the end of a 4-min reactor irradiation. Relative interferences of $Mn^{56}$ and $Fe^{59}$ in the gamma spectrometry of $V^{52}$ are shown. Detector: 3- by 3-in. NaI(Tl) crystal and multichannel analyzer. Source distance: 10 cm. Energy scale: 20 kev/channel.

$R_{V^{52}}$ corresponds to only 0.05 $\mu$g of vanadium, and is an example of the high sensitivity of activation analysis under usual conditions. The standard will be obtained by evaporating an aliquot of a previously prepared solution of vanadium in a small plastic vial. Assume that the comparator contains 0.03 $\mu$g of vanadium. The iron sample and the vial of standard are irradiated close together (to insure an equal neutron flux) in a reactor pneumatic facility for 4 min.

After the irradiation, the iron sample and the comparator are directly mounted on counting cards (see p. 68); their $\gamma$ rays can be measured with a single-channel or multichannel analyzer. A suitable $\gamma$-ray detector installation is shown in Fig. 6.10. The two sources must be counted at exactly the same geometry, and at some distance from the detector in order to minimize their differences in shape and size; a distance of 2 cm, resulting in an efficiency of 3.7%, is considered adequate in this case. If a multichannel analyzer is used, the total counts due to the 1.44-Mev $\gamma$ of $V^{52}$ can be obtained from the $\gamma$-ray spectrum by adding the counts of each channel in the 1.44-Mev photopeak (channels 68 to 80 in Fig. 8.2). This is equivalent to measuring the area under this peak (see p. 102). To subtract the $Mn^{56}$ interference, the spectrum of $Mn^{56}$ is measured in the sample, after $V^{52}$ has decayed out. The counts in the same channels as before are added, and this sum (or area) is then corrected for decay of $Mn^{56}$ back to the time of $V^{52}$ measurement, and subtracted from the formerly measured $V^{52}$ 1.44-Mev peak area. It is not convenient to obtain a $\gamma$-ray spectrum with a single-channel analyzer because of the short half-life of $V^{52}$; however, the measurement can still be made. The pulse-height selector (see p. 86) is set to a voltage known to correspond to the 1.44-Mev peak, from a previous energy calibration. The channel width is opened in order to include the whole peak. The measurements and subtractions are made with counts read from the single-channel analyzer scaler.

### 8-3.3 Experimental Results

Assume that the following data have been obtained in this experiment:

Sample: 50 mg of iron
Comparator: 0.03 $\mu$g of V
Irradiation (4 min): end 10 hr 13 min 00 sec (or 10.13.00)
Counting: See Table 8.3.

Table 8.3—RADIOACTIVITY MEASUREMENTS

| Measurement | Time | | Total counts | Count rate, counts/min | True time* |
| | Start | End | | | |
|---|---|---|---|---|---|
| $V^{52}$ in iron | 10.15.00 | 10.16.00 | 43,306 | 43,306 | 10.15.29 |
| Std. aliquot | 10.17.00 | 10.19.00 | 20,540 | 10,270 | 10.17.58 |
| Natural bckgd. | 10.20.00 | 10.30.00 | 1,350 | 135 | † |
| $Mn^{56}$ in iron | 11.05.00‡ | 11.07.00 | 22,200 | 11,100 | 11.06.00 |

* Calculated by using Fig. 5.9.
† The natural background count rate changes only slowly with time. It has been obtained by the same channel-addition procedure as explained for $V^{52}$ and $Mn^{56}$.
‡ At this time the $V^{52}$ count rate is only about 0.03% of that of $Mn^{56}$.

### 8-3.4 Calculations

(a) *Subtraction of $Mn^{56}$ interference from gross $V^{52}$ count rate.* The $Mn^{56}$ count rate (11,100 counts/min) must first be corrected for background and then corrected for decay back to time 10.15.29. The first of these steps gives a net count rate of

$$11,100 - 135 = 10,965 \text{ counts/min}$$

Since 50 min and 31 sec (50.52 min) have elapsed from 10.15.29 to 11.06.00, by Eq. 1.7c the count rate is

$$(\text{Mn}^{56} \text{ C.R. at } 10.15.29) = \frac{10,965 \text{ counts/min}}{\exp\left(-\dfrac{0.693 \times 50.52 \text{ min}}{2.58 \times 60 \text{ min}}\right)} = 13,743 \text{ counts/min}$$

Therefore, for the iron matrix at 10.15.29

$$\overset{\substack{(\text{gross} \\ \text{V}^{52} \text{ C.R.})}}{R_x = 43,306} - \overset{\substack{(\text{Mn}^{56} \\ \text{interference})}}{13,743} = 29,563 \text{ counts/min}$$

$R_x$ has been defined in Eq. 1.11b and is the net count rate of the $\text{V}^{52}$ in the sample. The background has not been subtracted from the gross $\text{V}^{52}$ count rate because it is only 0.3% of this value.

(b) *Decay times of sample and comparator.* In order to obtain $R_s$, count rate of $\text{V}^{52}$ in the standard (defined in Eq. 1.11b), the count rate of the standard (10,270 counts/min) will be corrected first for background and then for decay back to the time of the measurement of the sample (10.15.29). The net count rate of the comparator at 10.17.58 is

$$10,270 - 135 = 10,135 \text{ counts/min}$$

Since the time elapsed from 10.15.29 to 10.17.58* is 2 min 29 sec (or 2.48 min), by Eq. 1.7c:

$$R_s = \frac{10,135 \text{ counts/min}}{\exp\left(-\dfrac{0.693 \times 2.48 \text{ min}}{3.76 \text{ min}}\right)} = 16,011 \text{ counts/min}$$

(c) *Application of Eq. 1.11b.* The value $W_s$ to be used in Eq. 1.11b is the amount of vanadium present in the standard, i.e., 0.03 μg. Therefore

$$W_x = \frac{W_s R_x}{R_s} = \frac{0.03 \text{ μg} \times 29,563 \text{ counts/min}}{16,011 \text{ counts/min}}$$

$$W_x = 0.055 \text{ μg of V in 50 mg of iron}$$

The concentration of vanadium in the iron sample is, then:

$$\frac{0.055 \text{ μg}}{0.050 \text{ g}} = 1.1 \text{ μg/g, or } 1.1 \text{ ppm, or } 0.00011\%.$$

---

* It is worth pointing out here that the difference between these two times must be kept small in order to minimize any error caused by uncertainty of the half-life data in the literature and introduced into the decay factor.

The statistical treatment of Eq. 1.11b has been previously discussed with examples beginning on p. 75.

## 8-4 DETERMINATION OF OXYGEN, PHOSPHORUS, AND NITROGEN IN A TYPICAL PHOSPHINE OXIDE DERIVATIVE (A NEUTRON GENERATOR METHOD)

### 8-4.1 Discussion

This is an example of the use of a neutron generator in the rapid, nondestructive analysis for three of the main elements present in an organic sample. Background material is given in Chap. 3. Assume that a sample has been synthesized to have the concentrations of phosphorus, oxygen, and nitrogen according to the formula:

$$OP(CH_2 \cdot CH_2 \cdot CO \cdot NH_2)_3$$
$$P = 11.69\%$$
$$O = 24.25\%$$
$$N = 15.88\%$$

The purpose of the analysis is then to determine the actual concentration of these elements and to ascertain if the synthetic product satisfies the proposed formula. It is advantageous here to irradiate the sample and the standard with fast neutrons from a 14-Mev neutron generator for several reasons:

1. High spurious activities are avoided due to the absence of the high-thermal and resonance neutron fluxes which are present in nuclear reactors and cause trace impurities to be activated by $(n,\gamma)$ reactions (see p. 43). The need for a chemical separation in the reactor activation analysis for phosphorus has been mentioned in Section 8-2 (p. 122). The same applies to oxygen determination by reactor irradiation.[12]

2. Although three nuclear reactions may be used to analyze nitrogen by reactor irradiation, i.e., $N^{15}(n,\gamma)N^{16}$, $N^{14}(n,p)C^{14}$, and $N^{14}(n,2n)N^{13}$, none of them are satisfactory. All these reactions have low yields. In the first, the abundance of $N^{15}$ is low (0.365%), and its thermal-neutron cross section is small ($2.4 \times 10^{-5}$ barn). In the second the long half-life of $C^{14}$ ($5.3 \times 10^3$ yr) results in a small saturation factor to be used in Eq. 1.10c. The third has a threshold energy of 10.5 Mev; thus the number of reactor neutrons capable of producing this reaction is relatively small (see Fig. 2.1 and p. 20). However, the $(n,2n)$ reaction can be produced with 14-Mev neutrons, and it is this reaction that will be used in this example.

3. The organic sample is not damaged by heat or radiation as it might be in a reactor.

4. Despite the relatively low neutron flux of the neutron generator (see p. 42), this disadvantage is partially compensated by the large concentrations ($> 10\%$) of the sought elements in the sample.

The above considerations make it possible to analyze phosphine oxide samples for phosphorus, oxygen and nitrogen rapidly and nondestructively by irradiation with 14-Mev neutrons.

Fast-neutron activation analysis methods for oxygen[13-16] and nitrogen[17] have been published. Since these references give detailed descriptions, no thorough discussion will be made here. The nuclear reactions used in the determination of oxygen and nitrogen are:

$$O^{16}(n,p)N^{16} \qquad \sigma_{14\ Mev} = 33\ mb$$
$$N^{14}(n,2n)N^{13} \qquad \sigma_{14\ Mev} = 6\ mb$$

Either one of the following reactions may be used to determine phosphorus:

$$P^{31}(n,2n)P^{30} \qquad \sigma_{14\ Mev} = 11\ mb$$
$$P^{31}(n,\alpha)Al^{28} \qquad \sigma_{14\ Mev} = 150\ mb$$

The values of $\sigma$ are the approximate cross sections of the reactions for 14-Mev neutrons. Nuclear characteristics of $N^{16}$, $N^{13}$, $P^{30}$, and $Al^{28}$ are:

$$N^{16}: \quad T_{1/2} = 7.36\ sec \qquad E_\gamma\ (Mev) = 6.13;\ 7.10$$
$$N^{13}: \quad T_{1/2} = 10.1\ min \qquad \text{No } \gamma \text{ rays}; \beta^+ = 1.24\ Mev$$
$$P^{30}: \quad T_{1/2} = 2.55\ min \qquad \text{No } \gamma \text{ rays}; \beta^+ = 3.31\ Mev$$
$$Al^{28}: \quad T_{1/2} = 2.30\ min \qquad E_\gamma\ (Mev) = 1.78$$

The spectra of these four nuclides that can be obtained 2.4 sec after a 20-sec irradiation of 1 g of phosphine oxide (fast-neutron flux $\cong 5 \times 10^8$ neutrons/cm$^2$ sec) are shown in Fig. 8.3. This figure is based upon a 1 min* count obtained through 4 cm of lucite, by use of a 3- by 3-in. NaI(Tl) detector (energy calibration = 10.0 kev/channel). The $\gamma$-ray photopeaks from $Al^{28}$ and $P^{30} + N^{13}$, and the low-energy portion of the $N^{16}$ spectrum that contribute to the total spectrum are shown. A complete spectrum of $N^{16}$ may be found in Ref. 13.

## 8-4.2 Procedure

A 2-g sample of phosphine oxide will be irradiated for 20 sec. A suitable standard for phosphorus, nitrogen, and oxygen is provided by 2 g of $(NH_4)_2HPO_4$ reagent. A fast-rabbit system, as described on p. 41 and Fig. 3.8, must be used because of the very short half-life of $N^{16}$. The sample and the standard can then be positioned for counting in a few seconds after irradiation. The relatively large size of the sample and the comparator (2 g), the sharp flux gradient of the generator neutrons (see p. 37 and Fig. 3.3), and the very short half-life of $N^{16}$

---

* During this time $N^{16}$ decays out; therefore its spectrum represents total counts rather than a count rate.

make it necessary to irradiate the sample and the comparator separately (unlike a reactor irradiation) but under the same conditions of geometry and irradiation time. As the neutron flux may decrease from the time of the irradiation of the sample to that of the comparator (see Fig. 3.5), it is necessary to monitor the neutron flux during both irradiations by one of the methods explained on pp.

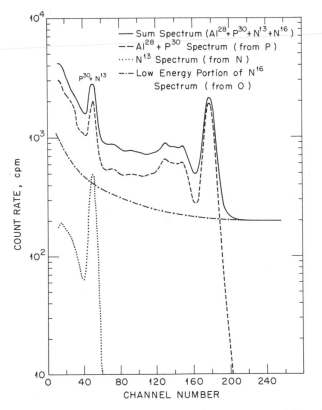

FIG. 8.3—Gamma-ray spectrum of phosphine oxide irradiated with 14-Mev neutrons.

37–38. Then, the activities obtained for a particular nuclide in both the sample and the standard must be normalized to the same flux (see Eqs. 1.10a and 1.11b) before these activities can be compared.

The rabbit with the sample (or the standard) is automatically transferred from the generator to the counting position. The radioactivities induced in it may then interfere in the measurements. Therefore the rabbit must be made of a material that does not become appreciably radioactive in these irradiation conditions. Special care must be taken, also, to keep the amount of extraneous oxygen in the rabbit negligible compared to the amount in the standard and sample.[16] Before attempting this kind of analysis, it must be ascertained (as is the case in the present example) that the amounts of silicon and fluorine[13] in the sample are not large enough to produce significant interferences through the reactions $Si^{28}(n,p)Al^{28}$ and $F^{19}(n,\alpha)N^{16}$. Since the expected concentration of nitrogen in phosphine oxide is much greater than 0.1% (Ref. 17), the interference of the reaction $C^{13}(p,n)N^{13}$ can be neglected. This reaction may be induced by bombardment of the $C^{13}$ of the organic sample with hydrogen nuclei (protons) that have been raised to a high kinetic energy by collisions with fast neutrons.

First the sample and then the standard (or vice versa) must follow the counting sequence given below:

1. Automatic transfer of the sample (or comparator) from the generator to the counting assembly (see Figs. 3.8 and 6.10). This should not take more than a few seconds (2.4 sec are assumed in this example) and the positioning for counting must be highly reproducible.

2. Measurement of $N^{16}$ for 1 min to permit calculation of the area under its 6.13 and 7.10 Mev $\gamma$-ray photopeaks (see Section 8-3, p. 131 and Refs. 13 to 16). There are no counting interferences in this measurement because of the very high-energy $\gamma$ rays of $N^{16}$ (see Fig. 8.3 and Ref. 13).

3. Measurement of $Al^{28}$. The sample is measured again, and the area under the 1.78-Mev photopeak is calculated to obtain the count rate of $Al^{28}$. The interference of $N^{16}$ shown in Fig. 8.3 has disappeared by this time because $N^{16}$ has now completely decayed.

4. Measurement of $N^{13}$. This nuclide and $P^{30}$ are positron ($\beta^+$) emitters. As explained before (see pp. 6 and 93), 0.511-Mev $\gamma$ rays are produced when positrons are annihilated, and the 0.511-Mev photopeak in Fig. 8.3 is characteristic of these two nuclides. It can be shown by Eq. 1.7a that 25 min after irradiation $P^{30}$ has decayed to less than 0.1% of its original count rate. There is still, however, enough activity of $N^{13}$ for counting (18% of the original activity). A final spectrum is then measured 25 min after the irradiation. The area under the 0.511-Mev photopeak is computed and this value taken as the count rate of $N^{13}$.

If a single-channel analyzer is used, no spectra can be obtained because of the short half-lives of the nuclides involved in this experiment. However, the measurements can still be made if conducted as explained in Section 8-3 (p. 131).

### 8-4.3 Experimental Results

Assume that a sample of phosphine oxide and an ammonium phosphate standard were irradiated successively for 20 sec with a 14-Mev neutron generator. In both irradiations the flux was monitored with a low-geometry $BF_3$ neutron counter (see p. 38). Since the neutron output of the generator can be assumed constant during short irradiations, the integrated count read on the neutron counter for each irradiation was used to normalize the activities induced in the sample and the comparator. The following data were obtained for the sample:

Type: phosphine oxide derivative
Weight: 2.0135 g
Irradiation length: 20.0 sec

End: 2 hr 30 min 00 sec (p.m.) or 14.30.00
Neutron integrated counts: 178,770 counts/20 sec

Counting: a multichannel analyzer was used. See Table 8.4.

Table 8.4—COUNTING SEQUENCE FOR THE SAMPLE

| Count start | Count length,* live min | Measurement | Peak channels† | Total counts | Count rate, counts/min |
|---|---|---|---|---|---|
| 14.30.02$\frac{4}{10}$ | 1 | N$^{16}$ | 150 to 180 | 25,778 | |
| 14.32.00 | 1 | Background | 150 to 180 | 5‡ | |
| 14.34.00 | 1 | Al$^{28}$ | 161 to 200 | 13,723 | 13,723 |
| 14.36.00 | 1 | Background | 161 to 200 | 72 | 72 |
| 14.55.00 | 4 | N$^{13}$ | 40 to 60 | 7,768 | 1,942 |
| Same measurement | 4 | Area under tangent§ | 40 to 60 | 2,148 | 537 |

* The count lengths are given in live minutes because the time was measured automatically with the live timer of the multichannel analyzer (see p. 97). For the purpose of comparison of the Al$^{28}$ and N$^{13}$ count rates of the sample and the standard by Eq. 1.11b, the start-count times can be used instead of the true count times (Fig. 5.9).

† The multichannel-analyzer gain, used in the measurements of N$^{16}$ and its background, correspond to an energy calibration of 40.0 kev/channel. The amplifier was set to a higher gain (10.0 kev/channel) before starting the Al$^{28}$ measurements.

‡ The natural background count-rate changes slowly with time. It becomes very small toward the high-energy side of any $\gamma$ spectrum.

§ Since only the 0.511-Mev annihilation $\gamma$ rays of N$^{13}$ are emitted at this time by the sample, the sum of the counts in all the channels could be used as a measure of the N$^{13}$ count rate. If radiochemical purity can be ascertained, this procedure is advisable because it results in a higher sensitivity. However, low-level spurious activities are frequently found to interfere when relatively weak low-energy $\gamma$ rays are measured in a nondestructive technique. This is assumed to happen in this example. Then, instead of subtracting the background area as is done in the other measurements, a tangent line is drawn first to the valleys at both sides of the measured photopeak (0.511 Mev of N$^{13}$), and second, the area under that tangent line is subtracted from the formerly measured gross area under said photopeak (see p. 102).

The results obtained for the comparator follow:

Type: (NH$_4$)$_2$HPO$_4$ reagent
Weight: 1.9543 g
Irradiation length: 20.0 sec

End: 15.10.00
Neutron integral counts: 153,540 counts/20 sec

Counting: a multichannel analyzer was used. See Table 8.5.

Table 8.5—COUNTING SEQUENCE FOR THE COMPARATOR

| Count start | Count length,* live min | Measurement | Peak channels† | Total counts | Count rate, counts/min |
|---|---|---|---|---|---|
| $15.10.02\frac{4}{10}$ | 1 | $N^{16}$ | 150 to 180 | 39,655 | |
| 15.12.00 | 1 | Background | 150 to 180 | 5‡ | |
| 15.17.00¶ | 1 | $Al^{28}$ | 161 to 200 | 8,692 | 8,692 |
| 15.19.00 | 1 | Background | 161 to 200 | 72 | 72 |
| 15.35.00 | 4 | $N^{13}$ | 40 to 60 | 6,864 | 1,716 |
| Same measurement | 4 | Area under tangent§ | 40 to 60 | 1,032 | 258 |

* The count lengths are given in live minutes because the time was measured automatically with the live timer of the multichannel analyzer (see p. 97). For the purpose of comparison of the $Al^{28}$ and $N^{13}$ count rates of the sample and the standard by Eq. 1.11b, the start-count times can be used instead of the true count times (Fig. 5.9).

† The multichannel-analyzer gain, used in the measurements of $N^{16}$ and its background, correspond to an energy calibration of 40.0 kev/channel. The amplifier was set to a higher gain (10.0 kev/channel) before starting the $Al^{28}$ measurements.

‡ The natural background count-rate changes slowly with time. It becomes very small toward the high-energy side of any $\gamma$ spectrum.

¶ It is assumed here that the time sequence followed for the sample could not be kept exactly for the standard because an accident caused a 3-min delay in the measurement of $Al^{28}$ in the standard.

§ Since only the 0.511-Mev annihilation $\gamma$ rays of $N^{13}$ are emitted at this time by the sample, the sum of the counts in all the channels could be used as a measure of the $N^{13}$ count rate. If radiochemical purity can be ascertained, this procedure is advisable because it results in a higher sensitivity. However, low-level spurious activities are frequently found to interfere when relatively weak low-energy $\gamma$ rays are measured in a nondestructive technique. This is assumed to happen in this example. Then, instead of subtracting the background area as is done in the other measurements, a tangent line is drawn first to the valleys at both sides of the measured photopeak (0.511 Mev of $N^{13}$), and second, the area under that tangent line is subtracted from the formerly measured gross area under said photopeak (see p. 102).

## 8-4.4 Calculations

It can be seen that the integrated neutron count, and therefore the neutron flux, during the irradiation of the comparator was lower than that observed when the sample was irradiated. Thus all the counting results obtained for the standard will be normalized to the irradiation conditions of the sample. The normalization factor $(l)$ is:

$$l = \frac{\text{sample integrated neutron count}}{\text{std. integrated neutron count}}$$

$$l = \frac{178{,}770 \text{ counts}/20 \text{ sec}}{153{,}540 \text{ counts}/20 \text{ sec}} = 1.1643$$

(a) *Oxygen concentration.* Since the decay times of $N^{16}$ in the sample and the standard, after their irradiations, are exactly the same, no decay corrections are needed. The background is negligible if compared with the recorded counts o both the sample and the standard. Hence, the only correction to be applied to the counts of the standard is the flux normalization factor $l$:

$$\text{Normalized counts of std.} = l \times (\text{counts of std.})$$
$$= 1.1643 \times 39{,}655 \text{ counts} = 46{,}170 \text{ counts}$$

The weight of oxygen in the standard ($W_s$ in Eq. 1.11b) is:

$$W_s = (\text{weight of std.}) \left( \frac{4 \times \text{at. wt. of O}}{\text{mol. wt. } (NH_4)_2HPO_4} \right)$$

$$= 1.9543 \text{ g} \left( \frac{4 \times 16.00}{132.11} \right) = 0.9467 \text{ g}$$

Before using Eq. 1.11b, it must be recalled that the measurements of $N^{16}$ in the sample and the standard are not count rates. They represent, rather, all the counts collected by the counter from the start of the count until the complete decay of $N^{16}$. By integration of Eq. 1.7c, it can be demonstrated, however, that the total counts of $N^{16}$ obtained for the sample and the standard are proportional to their respective count rates, at the start of the count. Then

$$\frac{R_x}{R_s} = \frac{C_x}{C_s} \tag{8.4}$$

where $R_x$ and $R_s$ (of Eq. 1.11b) are the count rates of $N^{16}$ in the sample and the standard, respectively, 2.4 sec after the irradiation; $C_x$ and $C_s$ are the corresponding total decay counts, which actually have been obtained in this experiment. Then, by substituting $C_x/C_s$ for $R_x/R_s$ in Eq. 1.11b:*

$$W_x = \frac{W_s R_x}{R_s} = \frac{W_s C_x}{C_s} \tag{8.5}$$

$$W_x = \frac{0.9467 \text{ g} \times 25{,}778 \text{ counts}}{46{,}170 \text{ counts}}$$

$$= 0.5287 \text{ g of oxygen in } 2.0135 \text{ g of sample}$$

Then the concentration of oxygen in the phosphine oxide sample (in weight percent) is:

$$\text{Conc. O} = \frac{0.5287 \text{ g} \times 100}{2.0135 \text{ g}} = 26.3\%$$

(b) *Phosphorus concentration.* Again the count rates of $Al^{28}$ in the sample and the comparator are several orders of magnitude larger than the background, and there is no need for background subtraction. However, the measurement of the sample started 4 min after its irradiation, whereas that of the comparator had to be delayed (see ¶ footnote in Table 8.5) and was started 7 min after its

---

* It must be pointed out that a serious error may be introduced by using the total decay counts of a short-lived nuclide, if the activity of the sample and that of the standard are very different. The multichannel analyzer dead-time losses (see p. 97) for the sample and standard also differ very much and, therefore, the measured counts are no longer comparable. The counts of the sample and comparator are assumed to be of the same order in this example (see Tables 8.4 and 8.5).

irradiation.* The $Al^{28}$ of the standard has then decayed 3 min more than the $Al^{28}$ present in the sample. By applying Eq. 1.7c, the $Al^{28}$ count rate of the standard can be corrected from the time 15.17.00 back to 15.14.00 (see * footnote in Tables 8.4 and 8.5).

$$\text{Corrected } Al^{28} \text{ count rate in std.} = \frac{8{,}692 \text{ counts/min}}{\exp\left(-\dfrac{0.693 \times 3 \text{ min}}{2.3 \text{ min}}\right)} = 21{,}462 \text{ counts/min}$$

Now the $Al^{28}$ count rates of both the sample and the standard correspond to the same delay time after their irradiations. Finally, the flux normalization factor $l$ (p. 138) must be multiplied by the corrected $Al^{28}$ count rate of the standard to obtain $R_s$ of Eq. 1.11b:

$$R_s = 1.1643 \times 21{,}462 = 24{,}988 \text{ counts/min}$$

The weight of phosphorus in the standard ($W_s$ in Eq. 1.11b) is calculated in the same manner as was done for oxygen. According to the chemical formula of ammonium phosphate:

$$W_s = 1.9543 \text{ g} \left(\frac{30.97}{132.11}\right) = 0.4581 \text{ g}$$

and $R_x$ is obviously the measured count rate of the sample (13,723 counts/min). Then, by Eq. 1.11b:

$$W_x = \frac{W_s R_x}{R_s} = \frac{0.4581 \text{ g} \times 13{,}723 \text{ counts/min}}{24{,}988 \text{ counts/min}}$$

$$= 0.2516 \text{ g of phosphorus in } 2.0135 \text{ g of sample}$$

Then, the concentration of phosphorus in the phosphine oxide (in weight percent) is:

$$\text{Conc. P} = \frac{0.2516 \text{ g} \times 100}{2.0135 \text{ g}} = 12.5\%$$

(c) *Nitrogen concentration.* It can be seen from Tables 8.4 and 8.5 that for both the sample and the standard, the same time (25 min 00 sec) has elapsed between the irradiation and the start of the measurement. Thus no decay correction is needed. However, in both measurements the area under the tangent line (see § footnote in Tables 8.4 and 8.5) is significant and must be subtracted. The count rate of the standard must also be multiplied by the flux normalization factor $l$ (p. 138). Then the count rates $R_x$ and $R_s$ of Eq. 1.11b are

$$R_x = 1{,}942 - 537 = 1{,}405 \text{ counts/min}$$

$$R_s = 1.1643 \times (1{,}716 - 258) = 1{,}697 \text{ counts/min}$$

The weight of nitrogen in the comparator ($W_s$ of Eq. 1.11b) is calculated in the

---

* This difficulty has been introduced in the present example with the sole purpose of showing how, in short-lived-nuclide activation analysis, a quick experimental procedure may be unduly lengthened by extra calculations. Considerable amounts of time (and analysis cost) can be frequently saved if a rigid schedule is planned and followed.

same manner as was done for oxygen and phosphorus; according to the chemical formula of ammonium phosphate

$$W_s = 1.9543 \left( \frac{2 \times 14.01}{132.11} \right) = 0.4145 \text{ g}$$

By Eq. 1.11b, then

$$W_x = \frac{W_s R_x}{R_s} = \frac{0.4145 \text{ g} \times 1,405 \text{ counts/min}}{1,697 \text{ counts/min}}$$

$$= 0.3432 \text{ g of N in } 2.0135 \text{ g of sample}$$

The concentration of nitrogen in the phosphine oxide (in weight percent) then is

$$\text{Conc. N} = \frac{0.3432 \text{ g} \times 100}{2.0135 \text{ g}} = 17.0\%$$

The statistical treatment of Eq. 1.11b has been discussed in Chap. 5 (pp. 75–77).

Table 8.6 compares the results obtained with the expected concentrations.

Table 8.6—COMPARISON OF THE EXPERIMENTAL RESULTS FROM THE ACTIVATION ANALYSIS OF PHOSPHINE OXIDE WITH THE THEORETICAL CONCENTRATIONS OF OXYGEN, PHOSPHORUS, AND NITROGEN

| Element | Experimental result, % | Theoretical concentration, % |
|---|---|---|
| Oxygen | 26.3 | 24.25 |
| Phosphorus | 12.5 | 11.69 |
| Nitrogen | 17.0 | 15.88 |

The results are all about 10% higher than the expected values. A second analysis may be advisable to determine if a systematic error has been introduced, e.g., in the flux monitoring. If no systematic error is found, then, the results of the analysis obviously show that the synthetic compound has a slightly different formula than expected.

This example illustrates the versatility of the neutron generator and also the rapidity with which an analysis can be carried out by using short-lived nuclides.

## REFERENCES

1. W. T. Mullins, unpublished data, 1954.
2. W. T. Mullins and G. W. Leddicotte, *The Radiochemistry of Sodium*, NAS-NS-3055, March 1962.
3. R. L. Heath, *Gamma-ray Spectrum Catalogue*, USAEC Report IDO-16408, Phillips Petroleum Company, 1957.
4. W. T. Mullins and G. W. Leddicotte, *The Radiochemistry of Phosphorus*, NAS-NS-3056, March 1962.
5. R. S. Rochlin, *Nucleonics* **17** (1): 54 (1959).
6. D. J. Hughes and R. B. Schwartz, *Neutron Cross Sections*, USAEC Report BNL-325, Brookhaven National Laboratory, 2nd ed., 1958.

7. R. W. Stoughton and J. Halperin, *Nuclear Sci. Eng.* **6**: 100 (1959).
8. D. J. Hughes, *Pile Neutron Research*, Addison-Wesley Publishing Co., Inc., 1953.
9. K. Way *et al.*, Nuclear Data Group, *Nuclear Data Sheets*, National Academy of Science, National Research Council, 1961 to date.
10. D. Strominger, J. M. Hollander, and G. T. Seaborg, *Revs. Mod. Phys.* **30**: 585 (1958).
11. V. S. Dzelepov and L. K. Peker, *Decay Schemes of Radioactive Isotopes*, Canadian Report, AECL-457, July 1957.
12. L. C. Bate, *Nucleonics* **21** (7): 72 (1963).
13. E. L. Steele and W. W. Meinke, *Anal. Chem.* **34**: 185 (1962).
14. D. J. Veal and C. F. Cook, *Anal. Chem.* **34**: 178 (1962).
15. R. F. Coleman, *Analyst* **87**: 590 (1962).
16. R. F. Coleman and J. L. Perkin, *Analyst* **85**: 154 (1960).
17. J. T. Gilmore and D. E. Hull, *Anal. Chem.* **34**: 187 (1962).

# Appendix A

Collected in this Appendix are calculated sensitivities for determination of a number of elements by activation analysis, together with some experimentally observed results. References are included for these experimental data. It should be emphasized that calculated sensitivities can be very misleading since interferences by other radioactivities present, difficulties in counting, and nuclear parameters, such as half-lives and gamma-ray branchings, may cause the actual attainable sensitivities to be much poorer than those predicted. Nevertheless, these calculated values may usefully serve as a guide line, and it is for such a purpose that they are presented here.

Table A.1—METALLURGICAL APPLICATIONS OF
NEUTRON ACTIVATION ANALYSIS

| Element | Nuclide formed | Sensitivity, $\mu g^*$ | Material analyzed | Concentration determined, $\mu g/g \cdot \dagger$ | Reference |
|---------|---------|---------|---------|---------|---------|
| Aluminum | Al$^{28}$ | 0.02 | Copper | 13–17 | F5 |
|  |  |  | Iron | 17–85 | F5 |
|  |  |  | Magnesium | 160 | L3, L4 |
|  |  |  | Silicon | <0.1–1.0 | L3, L4, T3 |
|  |  |  | Zirconium | 39 | F5 |
|  |  |  | Uranium–aluminum alloys | macro | C6 |
| Antimony | Sb$^{122}$ | 0.005 | Aluminum | 0.5–24 | A4, A5, A7, A8, A12, A19, B7, B8, B12, D4, G1, G2, I2, K11, K12, R7, Y7 |
|  | Sb$^{124}$ | 0.1 |  |  |  |
|  |  |  | Beryllium | 1–10 | N6, S4, T4 |
|  |  |  | Bismuth | 0.004–0.01 | Y6 |
|  |  |  | Copper | 0.3–10 | Y1, Y2 |
|  |  |  | Germanium | 0.6–10 | A15, A17, G6, R7, Y4–Y6 |
|  |  |  | Gold | 0.02–0.1 | Y2, Y6, Z1, Z2 |
|  |  |  | Iron | 0.002–0.23 | A8, A12, G1, G2, L3, L4, S10, T1 |
|  |  |  | Nickel | 5–100 | S10 |
|  |  |  | Phosphorus | 1 | G4 |
|  |  |  | Selenium | <0.05–10 | S5, Y3, Y6, Z4, Z5 |
|  |  |  | Silicon | 0.00015–0.23 | A18, C2, C3, C9, Z1, G11, J2, J7, K1, K5, M4, N2, R7, S10, S12, T3, Y6 |
|  |  |  | Silver | <0.02 | Y2 |
|  |  |  | Tellurium | 1–5 | S5, Z3 |
|  |  |  | Thallium | 10 | A16 |
|  |  |  | Zirconium | 0.02 | A8, A12 |
|  |  |  | Sodium–potassium alloy | 0.6–0.8 | L3, L4, S8 |
|  |  |  | Zircaloy | 0.02 | J9 |

143

## Table A.1 (continued)

| Element | Nuclide formed | Sensitivity, $\mu g$* | Material analyzed | Concentration determined, $\mu g/g$† | Reference |
|---|---|---|---|---|---|
| Arsenic | As⁷⁶ | 0.002 | Aluminum | 0.05–0.15 | A4, A5, A7, A8, A12, A13, A19, D4, G1, G2, U1 |
| | | | Antimony | <0.06–0.4 | R3, Y6 |
| | | | Beryllium | 1–10 | N6 |
| | | | Bismuth | <0.001 | Y6 |
| | | | Copper | 0.1–2.0 | L3, L4, Y1, Y2 |
| | | | Germanium | 0.001–2.0 | G14, J11, M23, S13 |
| | | | Gold | 0.04–0.3 | Y2, Y6, Z1, Z2 |
| | | | Iron | 0.002–10 | A8, A11, A12, G1, G2, S10, T1 |
| | | | Lead | 0.01–5 | H4 |
| | | | Magnesium | 0.12 | A20 |
| | | | Nickel | 5–10 | S10 |
| | | | Phosphorus | 0.3 | G4 |
| | | | Selenium | 0.2–5.0 | S5, Y3, Y6, Z4, Z5 |
| | | | Silicon | 0.00005–1.0 | C2, C3, C9, E1, G10, I1, J2, J3, J7, K5, K6, L3, L4, M21, M22, S7, S12, T3, Y6 |
| | | | Silver | <0.3 | Y2 |
| | | | Tellurium | 0.1–5.0 | S5, Y3, Z3 |
| | | | Tin | 0.046–0.36 | S10 |
| | | | Tungsten | 0.001–1.0 | C16, J5 |
| | | | Zinc | 0.035–0.045 | S10 |
| | | | Zirconium | 0.008 | A8, A12 |
| | | | Stainless steel | 117–143 | M7, R4 |
| Barium | Ba¹³¹ | 2,0 | Aluminum | 6–20 | A4, A5, A7, A8, A12, A19 |
| | Ba¹³⁹ | 0.04 | Beryllium | 1–10 | N6 |
| | | | Zirconium | <0.3 | A8, A12 |
| Bismuth | Bi²¹⁰ᵐ | 1.0 | Aluminum | <0.1 | G2 |
| | | | Iron | <0.03 | G2 |
| | | | Silicon | <0.0015–10 | C2, C3, K5, T3 |
| | | | Hastalloy | 50 | L3, L4 |
| Bromine | Br⁸⁰ | 0.002 | Aluminum | <0.01 | A8, A12, A19 |
| | Br⁸² | 0.007 | Silicon | 0.005–4.5 | N8 |
| Cadmium | Cd¹¹⁵ | 0.05 | Aluminum | 0.5–145 | A8, A12, A19, D4, G1, G2, R5, Y7 |
| | Cd¹¹⁷ | 0.1 | Beryllium | 1–10 | N6 |
| | | | Bismuth | 1–10 | K6 |
| | | | Iron | <0.01 | G2 |
| | | | Phosphorus | 0.5 | G4 |
| | | | Selenium | <0.005–4.5 | W3, Y6, Z4, Z5 |
| | | | Silicon | 0.0002–10 | C2, C3, K5, T3 |
| | | | Tellurium | 0.1 | Z3 |
| | | | Zinc | 0.005–0.55 | G7 |
| | | | Zirconium | 1,000–10,000 | L3, L4 |
| | | | Iron–nickel alloys | <0.01 | T2 |
| Calcium | Ca⁴⁵ | 7 | Aluminum | 4–5 | G2 |
| | Ca⁴⁸ | 3 | Gallium | 2–6 | L12 |
| | | | Iron | <0.5–7.5 | G2, S7 |
| | | | Magnesium | 1.3 | A20 |
| | | | Phosphorus | 30 | G4 |
| | | | Niobium | 10–50 | L3, L4 |
| | | | Silicon | 5–6 | T3 |
| | | | Tellurium | 0.1 | Z3 |
| | | | Zirconium | <1.5 | A8, A12, A19 |
| Cerium | Ce¹⁴³ | 0.2 | Aluminum | <0.01–20 | A8, A12, A19, C5, D4, G1, G2 |
| | | | Iron | <0.1 | G2 |
| Cesium | Cs¹³⁴ᵐ | 0.01 | Aluminum | <0.01 | G2 |
| | Cs¹³⁴ | 0.06 | Germanium | 1 | G6 |
| | | | Iron | <0.1 | G2 |
| | | | Sodium | 15–1,000 | L3, L4 |
| | | | Sodium–potassium alloy | 0.1–100 | C1, S7, S8 |

## Table A.1 (continued)

| Element | Nuclide formed | Sensitivity, $\mu g^*$ | Material analyzed | Concentration determined, $\mu g/g\dagger$ | Reference |
|---------|---------------|------------------------|-------------------|-------------------------------------------|-----------|
| Chlorine | Cl[38] | 0.04 | Aluminum | <0.01 | A8, A12, A19 |
| | | | Bismuth | 1–10 | K3, K4, K16 |
| | | | Silicon | 0.005–4.5 | N8 |
| | | | Titanium | 3–26 | B11, L2 |
| Chromium | Cr[51]<br>Cr[55] | 0.005<br>0.8 | Aluminum | 0.5–20 | J9, K11, K12, L3, L4, M1, M21, M22 |
| | | | Antimony | <5 | R3 |
| | | | Iron | <0.01–0.5 | A8, A12, G1, S10, T1 |
| | | | Magnesium | 0.1 | A20 |
| | | | Nickel | 1–10 | S10 |
| | | | Phosphorus | 0.3 | G4 |
| | | | Silicon | <0.1 | T3 |
| | | | Tellurium | 0.1–10 | Z3 |
| | | | Titanium | 40–50 | L3, L4 |
| | | | Tungsten | 1 | C16 |
| | | | Vanadium | 3–10 | L3, L4 |
| | | | Zirconium | 0.2–0.7 | A8, A12, K10, L2 |
| | | | Iron–nickel alloys | <0.1 | T2 |
| | | | Sodium–potassium alloys | <0.2 | S8 |
| | | | Stainless steel | 1–1000 | S3, S14 |
| | | | Zircaloy | 860 | J9 |
| Cobalt | Co[60m]<br>Co[60] | 0.0005<br>0.04 | Aluminum | <0.01–50 | B7, B8, D4, G1, G2, J8, J9, L3, L4, M1, S3, Y7 |
| | | | Antimony | <0.01 | Y6, Z1, Z2 |
| | | | Gold | <0.1 | Y6, Z1, Z2 |
| | | | Iron | <0.01–2.0 | A4–A8, A11, A12, G1, G2, S10 |
| | | | Nickel | 3–100 | L3, L4, M9 |
| | | | Phosphorus | 0.1 | G4 |
| | | | Silicon | 0.0006–5.0 | O2, T3 |
| | | | Sodium | 0.05 | G13 |
| | | | Tellurium | 0.001–0.1 | Z3 |
| | | | Zinc | 1–10 | J8 |
| | | | Ferrite | 1900–2300 | P5 |
| | | | Inconel | 10–100 | H1, L3, L4 |
| | | | Nickel alloys | 7000 | D2 |
| | | | Sodium–potassium alloys | 0.02 | S8 |
| | | | Stainless steel | 10–300 | C13, M7, M12–M14, R4, S10, S14, W2 |
| Copper | Cu[64]<br>Cu[66] | 0.003<br>0.01 | Aluminum | 0.06–3,000 | A4, A5, A7–A10, A12–A14, A19, B7, B8, B12, C4, C7, C8, D4, G1, G2, I2, J8, J9, K11, K12, L3, L4, M16, M21, M22, P1–P3, R7, U1, Y6, Y7 |
| | | | Antimony | 0.0008–0.009 | R3, Y6, Z1, Z2 |
| | | | Beryllium | 0.01–10 | L2, N6, S4, T4 |
| | | | Bismuth | <0.004–0.5 | Y6 |
| | | | Cobalt | 25–92 | L7 |
| | | | Germanium | 0.11–131 | A15, A17, G12, L6, L7, M23, R7, S15, Y4, Y5 |
| | | | Gold | 0.3–8.6 | Y2, Y6, Z1, Z2 |
| | | | Iron | 0.5–5.0 | A4, A5, A7, A8, A11, A12, G1, G2, S10, T1 |
| | | | Lithium | 20–10,000 | L3, L4 |
| | | | Magnesium | 8 | A20 |
| | | | Nickel | 0.1–10 | S10 |
| | | | Phosphorus | 0.8 | G4 |
| | | | Selenium | 0.03–0.07 | W3, Y3, Y6, Z4, Z5 |

## Table A.1 (continued)

| Element | Nuclide formed | Sensitivity, $\mu g$* | Material analyzed | Concentration determined, $\mu g/g$† | Reference |
|---|---|---|---|---|---|
| | | | Silicon | 0.0001–0.02 | A18, C9, E1, G11, J2, J7, K5, M4, N2, O2, R7, S7, S10, S12, T3, Y6 |
| | | | Silver | 0.3–8.6 | Y2 |
| | | | Tellurium | 0.1–3 | Y3, Z3 |
| | | | Thallium | 1–10 | A16 |
| | | | Titanium | 33 | B11, L2 |
| | | | Tungsten | 0.001–1.0 | C16 |
| | | | Zirconium | 3–12 | A8, L2 |
| | | | Aluminum–cobalt alloys | 6 to macro | C7, R2 |
| | | | Ferrite | 100–430 | P5 |
| | | | Stainless steel | 1 to macro | R1, R4, S10 |
| | | | Zircaloy | 11 | J9 |
| | | | Iron–nickel alloys | 0.003–0.1 | T2 |
| Dysprosium | $Dy^{165m}$ | 0.002 | Aluminum | < 0.004–0.5 | J9, M1 |
| | $Dy^{165}$ | 0.0004 | Thorium | 0.09–900 | N5 |
| Europium | $Eu^{152}$ (9.2 hr) | 0.00003 | Beryllium | 58–150 | Y4, Y5 |
| | | | Bismuth | < 0.004 | Y4–Y6 |
| | $Eu^{152}$ (13 yr) | 0.002 | Germanium | 1 | Y4, Y5 |
| | | | Lead | 0.1 | Y4, Y5 |
| | | | Manganese | 0.01–1.0 | K7 |
| | $Eu^{156}$ | 0.04 | Silicon | 0.001 | Y6 |
| | | | Thorium | 0.05–20 | N5 |
| Gadolinium | $Gd^{159}$ | 0.02 | Aluminum | < 0.01–1.0 | A8, A12, A19, C5, D4, G1 |
| | $Gd^{161}$ | 0.1 | | | |
| Gallium | $Ga^{70}$ | 0.009 | Aluminum | 0.01–530 | A4, A5, A7, A8, A12, A13, A19, B9, B10, B12, C7, C8, D4, G1, G2, J8–J10, K11, K12, L3, L4, M1, P1, U1 |
| | $Ga^{72}$ | 0.005 | | | |
| | | | Antimony | 0.003 | R3 |
| | | | Germanium | 2.9–3.7 | M23, Y6 |
| | | | Iron | 0.01–0.03 | A8, A12, G1, G2, T1 |
| | | | Selenium | 0.008–0.02 | Y6, Z4, Z5 |
| | | | Silicon | <0.0001–0.04 | A18, G11, K5, T3, Y6 |
| | | | Aluminum–gallium alloys | 100 to macro | C7 |
| Germanium | $Ge^{75}$ | 0.05 | Iron | 0.3 | S10 |
| | $Ge^{77}$ | 0.4 | Nickel | 4.9 | S10 |
| Gold | $Au^{198}$ | 0.0003 | Beryllium | 0.1–10 | N6 |
| | | | Bismuth | 0.001–1.0 | K16 |
| | | | Copper | 0.01–10 | H5, Y1, Y2 |
| | | | Iron | 0.0002–0.015 | G1 |
| | | | Lead | 0.01–1.0 | H4 |
| | | | Nickel | 0.07 | Y6 |
| | | | Palladium | 4–5 | L3, L4 |
| | | | Platinum | 0.001–1.0 | M19 |
| | | | Silicon | 0.00002–0.00001 | E1, J2, J7, K1, L3, L4, M4, N2, O2, R7, T3 |
| | | | Silver | 0.3–100 | Y2, Y6, Z1, Z2 |
| | | | Tellurium | 0.001–0.1 | Z3 |
| Hafnium | $Hf^{175}$ | 0.06 | Aluminum | <3–5 | G2, I2, J9 |
| | $Hf^{181}$ | 0.03 | Zirconium | 60–200 | A8, A12, A21, G5, J9, K10, L2–L4, L13, M3, N1, O1, W1 |
| | | | Nickel alloys | 8–220 | L3, L4 |
| | | | Zircaloy | 119 | J9, M3 |
| Holmium | $Ho^{166}$ | 0.0003 | Aluminum | <0.0001–0.3 | A8, A12, A19, C5, D4, G1, G2 |

## Table A.1 (continued)

| Element | Nuclide formed | Sensitivity, $\mu g$* | Material analyzed | Concentration determined, $\mu g/g$† | Reference |
|---------|----------------|------------------------|--------------------|----------------------------------------|-----------|
| Indium | In$^{116}$ | 0.03 | Gallium | 1–1000 | H8 |
| | | | Silicon | <0.0003–1.0 | C2, C3, K5, T3 |
| | | | Tellurium | 0.1–0.001 | Z3 |
| | | | Zinc | 1–1000 | H8, J10, K15, K20, K21 |
| | | | Zirconium | 0.05–0.3 | A8, A12 |
| | | | Zirconium–indium alloys | 100–1000 | L3, L4 |
| Iodine | I$^{128}$ | 0.003 | Silicon | 0.002–5 | I1, N7, N8 |
| Iridium | Ir$^{192}$ | 0.002 | Gold | 5–90 | K2 |
| | | | Nickel | 0.0005–0.001 | Y6 |
| | | | Palladium | 10–90 | K2, L3, L4, M18 |
| | | | Platinum | 0.1–90 | A3, J12, K2, M18 |
| | | | Rhodium | 3–175 | K2, M21 |
| | | | Silver | 0.008–0.14 | Y6, Z1, Z2 |
| | | | Osmium–iridium alloy | 10–1,000 | M6 |
| Iron | Fe$^{59}$ | 10 | Aluminum | 2–12,400 | A4, A5, A7, A8, A19, B7, B8, C4, D4, G1, G2, I2, J9, K11, K12, M1, M16, U1 |
| | | | Lead | 10–100 | B3 |
| | | | Magnesium | 10–100 | A20 |
| | | | Phosphorus | 80 | G4 |
| | | | Silicon | <0.1–3.0 | J2, J7, K5, L3, L4, M21, M22, T3, Y6 |
| | | | Sodium | 0.05 | L3, L4 |
| | | | Tin | 35–50 | L3, L4 |
| | | | Tungsten | 100 | C16 |
| | | | Zirconium | 45–450 | A8, A12, K10, L1, L2 |
| | | | Zircaloy | 1380 | J9 |
| Lanthanum | La$^{140}$ | 0.002 | Aluminum | <0.001–5.0 | A8, A12, A19, C5, D4, G1, J9, M1 |
| | | | Manganese | 0.01–1.0 | K7 |
| | | | Thorium | 60–3,000 | N5 |
| Lutetium | Lu$^{177}$ | 0.0002 | Aluminum | <0.0001–0.05 | A8, A12, A19, C5, D4, G1 |
| Magnesium | Mg$^{27}$ | 1 | Aluminum | 1.5–10 | M16, U1 |
| | | | Silicon | <0.08 | T3 |
| | | | Zirconium | <10 | F5 |
| | | | Stainless steel | 230–12,500 | H7 |
| Manganese | Mn$^{56}$ | 0.0006 | Aluminum | 0.04–6,600 | A4, A5, A7, A8, A11, A12, A13, A19, B7–B10, C7, C8, D4, G1, G2, I2, J8, J9, K11, K12, M16, P1, P3, U1, Y6 |
| | | | Antimony | 0.03 | R3 |
| | | | Beryllium | 0.001–1.0 | L2–L4, N6, S4, T4 |
| | | | Bismuth | 0.0001–1.0 | J1, K3, K4 |
| | | | Iron | 0.03–230 | A4, A5, A7, A8, A12, B6, G1, G2, O4, T1 |
| | | | Silicon | 0.0001–0.02 | E1, J2, J7, T3, Y6 |
| | | | Titanium | 0.1–10 | L2 |
| | | | Zirconium | 5–29 | A8, A12 |
| | | | Alloys | 10 | F2 |
| | | | Aluminum–manganese alloy | 1.7 to macro | C7 |
| | | | Ferrite | 850 | P5 |
| | | | Ferromanganese | Macro | D1, K17–K19 |
| | | | Molybdenum–manganese alloy | 10 to macro | M5 |

## Table A.1 (continued)

| Element | Nuclide formed | Sensitivity, $\mu g^*$ | Material analyzed | Concentration determined, $\mu g/g$† | Reference |
|---|---|---|---|---|---|
| | | | Stainless steel | 0.9–12,500 | B6, H6, M7, M15, R4, S3 |
| | | | Zircaloy | 29 | J9 |
| Mercury | $Hg^{197}$ | 0.006 | Aluminum | <0.004 | G2 |
| | | | Iron | <0.01 | G2 |
| | | | Silicon | 0.0005–0.01 | K1, T3 |
| | | | Tellurium | 0.1–0.001 | Z3 |
| | | | Sodium–potassium alloys | <0.5 | S8 |
| Molybdenum | $Mo^{99}$ | 0.1 | Aluminum | 0.1–0.2 | A8, A12, A19, G2 |
| | | | Beryllium | 1–10 | N6 |
| | | | Germanium | 1–10 | A15, A17, Y4, Y5 |
| | | | Iron | 5–38 | A8, A12, G1, G2, T1 |
| | | | Silicon | 0.001–10 | C2, C3, J2, J7, K1, T3 |
| | | | Thallium | 1–10 | A16 |
| | | | Tungsten | 0.02–2.0 | C15, C16, L3, L4 |
| | | | Zirconium | 0.1–30 | A8, A12, L2–L4 |
| | | | Inconel | 10–300 | L3, L4 |
| | | | Iron–nickel alloys | 0.04–0.1 | T2 |
| | | | Stainless steel | 1–100 | S3 |
| Neodymium | $Nd^{147}$ | 0.01 | Aluminum | <0.01–4.0 | A8, A12, A19, C5, D4, G1 |
| Nickel | $Ni^{65}$ | 0.4 | Aluminum | 0.5–4,400 | A4, A5, A7, A8, A11, A12, A19, B7, B8, D4, G1, G2, L3, L4, U1 |
| | | | Antimony | <0.01 | Y6, Z1, Z2 |
| | | | Beryllium | 10–100 | N6 |
| | | | Germanium | 0.1 | S7 |
| | | | Iron | 0.5–220 | A4, A5, A7, A8, A12, G1, G2, S10, T1 |
| | | | Phosphorus | <1 | G4 |
| | | | Selenium | <0.05 | W3 |
| | | | Silicon | 0.0001–1 | E1, O2, T3, Y6 |
| | | | Tellurium | 1–10 | Z3 |
| | | | Titanium | 5–10 | L2 |
| | | | Zirconium | 1–4 | A8, A12, K10, L1–L4 |
| | | | Sodium–potassium alloys | 1–5 | L3, L4 |
| | | | Stainless steel | 310–1,600 | S10, S14 |
| Niobium | $Nb^{94m}$ | 0.01 | Stainless steel | 10–1000 | M10 |
| Osmium | $Os^{191m}$ | 0.003 | Iron | 100–1000 | L3, L4 |
| | $Os^{191}$ | 0.02 | Palladium | 0.08–100 | L3, L4, M18 |
| | | | Platinum | 0.03–1.0 | M18 |
| Oxygen | $O^{19}$ | 60 | Aluminum | 1–1,000 | B1, L3, L4 |
| | | | Beryllium | 1–100 | B1, B4, B5, C10–C12, G9, L14, O3 |
| | | | Lithium | 0.2–10,000 | B1, L3, L4 |
| | | | Nickel | 10–100 | L11 |
| | | | Silicon | 100 | B1, L3, L4 |
| | | | Tantalum | 0.2–25 | B1, L3, L4 |
| | | | Titanium | 1–10,000 | B1, L3, L4, L14 |
| | | | Zirconium | 1–100 | B1, L3, L4 |
| Palladium | $Pd^{109}$ | 0.005 | Aluminum | <0.001 | G2 |
| | $Pd^{109m}$ | 0.3 | Gold | 10–100 | M11 |
| | | | Iron | <0.001 | G2 |
| | | | Nickel | 0.2–1.0 | L3, L4, Y6 |
| | | | Platinum | 0.1–10 | K8 |
| | | | Silver | 0.1–47 | Y2, Y6, Z1, Z2 |
| Phosphorus | $P^{32}$ | 0.04 | Aluminum | 1–3 | A8, A12, A19, F4 |
| | | | Antimony | <0.08 | R3 |
| | | | Chromium | 0.08–25 | L3, L4 |
| | | | Iodine | 1 | J6 |

## Table A.1 (continued)

| Element | Nuclide formed | Sensitivity, μg* | Material analyzed | Concentration determined, μg/g† | Reference |
|---|---|---|---|---|---|
| | | | Iron | <1–100 | A4–A6, A12, H3, O4, T1 |
| | | | Magnesium | 2.2 | A20, D6 |
| | | | Silicon | 0.002–100 | C2, C3, J2, J4, J7, K5, T3 |
| | | | Iron–nickel alloys | <0.02 | T2 |
| Platinum | Pt195 | 0.07 | Gold | 10–100 | M11 |
| | Pt197 | 0.1 | Nickel | 0.02–0.03 | Y6 |
| | Pt199 | 0.1 | Silicon | 0.0009–0.002 | T3 |
| | | | Silver | 0.3–23 | Y6, Z1, Z2 |
| Potassium | K42 | 0.07 | Aluminum | <0.01–1 | A1, A2, D4, G1, G2, L3, L4 |
| | | | Iron | <0.1 | G2 |
| | | | Magnesium | 1.4–20 | A20, D6, L5 |
| | | | Silicon | <0.002–3.0 | J2, J7, M21, M22, Y6 |
| | | | Tungsten | 1 | C16 |
| | | | Zirconium | <0.008 | A8, A12 |
| | | | Stainless steel | 1 | A1, A2 |
| Praseodymium | Pr142 | 0.002 | Aluminum | <0.001–2.5 | A8, A12, A19, C5, D4, G1, G2 |
| | | | Iron | <0.001 | G2 |
| Rhodium | Rh104 | 0.001 | Ruthenium | 26–36 | M8 |
| | | | Platinum–rhodium alloys | Macro | G3 |
| Rubidium | Rb86 | 0.03 | Aluminum | <0.001 | G2 |
| | Rb88 | 0.3 | Iron | <0.1 | G2 |
| | | | Sodium–potassium alloy | 1–100 | C1, S7, S8 |
| Ruthenium | Ru103 | 0.1 | Platinum | 0.8–2.0 | K9 |
| | Ru105 | 0.1 | | | |
| Samarium | Sm153 | 0.0005 | Aluminum | <0.0001–0.5 | A8, A12, A19, C5, D4, G1, G2, J9, K11, K12, M1 |
| | | | Cerium | 0.1–2.0 | L3, L4 |
| | | | Iron | <0.1 | G2 |
| | | | Manganese | 0.01–1.0 | K7 |
| | | | Thorium | 3–400 | N5 |
| Scandium | Sc46m | 0.0006 | Aluminum | 0.1–1.5 | A8, A12, A19, C5, D4, G1, G2, K11, K12, M1, I2, J8, J9 |
| | Sc46 | 0.003 | | | |
| | | | Beryllium | 1–10 | L3, L4 |
| | | | Iron | <0.01 | G2 |
| | | | Silicon | 0.00002–0.00003 | T3 |
| Selenium | Se75 | 0.5 | Aluminum | <0.01 | G2 |
| | Se77 | 0.02 | Arsenic | 2–20 | L3, L4 |
| | | | Germanium | 0.01–1 | G6, N3 |
| | | | Iron | <0.01 | G2 |
| | | | Phosphorus | <1.0 | G4 |
| | | | Tellurium | 1–36 | Y3, Z3 |
| | | | Stainless steel | 10–100 | F3, L3, L4 |
| Silicon | Si31 | 0.1 | Aluminum | 3–37 | A4, A12–A14, A19, B12, C4, L3, L4, M16, R6, U1 |
| | | | Bismuth | 2.8–7 | N4 |
| | | | Lead | 1–22 | N4 |
| | | | Titanium | 12–15 | B11, L2 |
| | | | Zirconium | 4–100 | K10, L2–L4 |
| Silver | Ag108 | 0.0001 | Aluminum | <0.1 | G2 |
| | Ag110 | 0.3 | Bismuth | 1–10 | K16 |
| | | | Copper | <80 | Y2 |
| | | | Iron | <0.02 | G2 |
| | | | Nickel | 0.8–5.0 | L3, L4 |
| | | | Palladium | 0.1–1.0 | L3, L4 |

## Table A.1 (continued)

| Element | Nuclide formed | Sensitivity, $\mu g$* | Material analyzed | Concentration determined, $\mu g/g$† | Reference |
|---|---|---|---|---|---|
| | | | Platinum | 1–10 | M17 |
| | | | Silicon | 0.001–0.37 | G10, K5, T3 |
| | | | Tellurium | 0.1–1 | Z3 |
| | | | Zirconium | 1–11 | A8, A12 |
| | | | Sodium–potassium alloys | <0.02–5 | S7, S8 |
| Sodium | Na²⁴ | 0.006 | Aluminum | 0.2–10 | A1, A2, A4, A5, A7, A10, A12, A14, A19, C4, D3, D4, F1, G1, G2, I2, K11, K12, L3–L5, M16, P1, P3, P4, R6, S1, U1, Y6 |
| | | | Germanium | 9–60 | M23 |
| | | | Iron | <0.01–1.5 | A8, A12, G1, G2, T1 |
| | | | Lead | 1–10 | F1, F2 |
| | | | Lithium | 10–30 | L3, L4, S7, S11 |
| | | | Magnesium | 1–10 | A20, D6, L3, L4 |
| | | | Phosphorus | 10 | G4 |
| | | | Silicon | <0.00004–5.0 | J2, J7, M21, M22, T3, Y6 |
| | | | Tungsten | 1 | C16 |
| | | | Zirconium | <0.004 | A8, A12 |
| | | | Ferrite | 780–3,300 | P5 |
| | | | Stainless steel | 1.0 | A1, A2, R4 |
| Strontium | Sr⁸⁵ | 10 | Aluminum | <0.5 | G2 |
| | Sr⁸⁷ | 0.1 | Iron | <0.5 | G2 |
| | | | Magnesium | 2 | A20 |
| | | | Zirconium | <2 | A8, A12 |
| | | | Sodium–potassium alloys | <0.5 | S9 |
| Sulfur | S³⁵ | 50 | Aluminum | 1–15 | A8, A12, A19 |
| | S³⁷ | 1 | Lithium | 87–89 | L3, L4 |
| | | | Nickel | 70–88 | L3, L4 |
| Tantalum | Ta¹⁸² | 0.1 | Aluminum | <2 | G2 |
| | | | Niobium | 10–100 | H2, L3, L4, L15 |
| | | | Silicon | <0.0004–1.0 | J2, J7, M21, M22, O22, T3, Y6 |
| | | | Sodium | 0.001–0.1 | G13 |
| | | | Zirconium | <0.2–2.0 | A8, A12, L3, L4 |
| | | | Ferroniobium | 1–1,000 | K13, K14 |
| | | | Iron–nickel alloys | <0.01 | T2 |
| | | | Tantalum–ferro alloys | Macro | G8 |
| Tellurium | Te¹³¹ | 0.2 | Aluminum | <1 | G2 |
| | | | Antimony | 0.01–0.02 | Y6, Z1, Z2 |
| | | | Arsenic | 10–350 | L3, L4 |
| | | | Gold | 0.6–5.0 | Y6, Z1, Z2 |
| | | | Iron | <0.5 | G2 |
| | | | Phosphorus | <1 | G4 |
| | | | Selenium | 0.024–1.0 | W3, Y3, Y6, Z4, Z5 |
| Terbium | Tb¹⁶⁰ | 0.003 | Aluminum | <0.001–0.2 | A8, A12, A19, C5, D4, G1 |
| | | | Yttrium | 200–20,000 | M24 |
| Thallium | Tl²⁰⁶ | 0.3 | Lithium | 1–5 | L3, L4 |
| | | | Silicon | <0.008 | K5 |
| | | | Zinc | 1–10 | J8 |
| Thorium | Th²³² | 0.004 | Aluminum | 0.002–0.12 | A8, A12, A19, D4, G1 |
| | | | Beryllium | 0.1–10 | M25 |
| | | | Zirconium | <0.05–0.3 | A8, A12 |
| Thulium | Tm¹⁷⁰ | 0.002 | Germanium | 1 | G6 |
| Tin | Sn¹¹² | 10 | Beryllium | 10–100 | N6 |
| | | | Phosphorus | 3 | G4 |
| | | | Silicon | <0.006–100 | C2, C3, E1, K1, T3 |
| | | | Tungsten | 100 | C16 |
| | | | Iron–nickel alloys | <0.2 | T2 |

## Table A.1 (continued)

| Element | Nuclide formed | Sensitivity, $\mu g^*$ | Material analyzed | Concentration determined, $\mu g/g$† | Reference |
|---------|----------------|------------------------|-------------------|--------------------------------------|-----------|
| Titanium | $Ti^{50}$ | 0.1 | Aluminum | 160–1,600 | B7, B8 |
|  |  |  | Beryllium | 10–15 | L2–L4 |
| Tungsten | $W^{187}$ | 0.002 | Aluminum | 0.002–0.1 | A8, A12, A19, G2, J9 |
|  |  |  | Iron | 0.02–1.3 | A8, A12, G1, T1 |
|  |  |  | Silicon | 0.0005 | K1, M21, M22 |
|  |  |  | Titanium | 6–160 | B11 |
|  |  |  | Zirconium | 0.004–10,000 | A8, A12, L3, L4 |
|  |  |  | Iron–nickel alloys | 0.02–0.6 | T2 |
|  |  |  | Stainless steel | 1,700 to macro | L8, L10, R4, S3 |
|  |  |  | Zircaloy | 98 | J9 |
| Uranium | $U^{239}$ | 0.01 | Aluminum | <0.002–2.2 | A8, A12, A19, G2, J9, L3, L4, M2 |
|  |  |  | Beryllium | 0.01–5.0 | L2, M25, S4, S9, T4 |
|  |  |  | Lead | 0.01–1.0 | B3, D4, G1 |
|  |  |  | Zirconium | 0.1–1.7 | A8, A12, L3, L4 |
|  |  |  | Zircaloy | 0.2–1.6 | J9 |
| Vanadium | $V^{52}$ | 0.002 | Aluminum | 0.1–0.4 | A8, A12, A19, D5 |
|  |  |  | Copper | <0.2 | F5 |
|  |  |  | Iron | 1.5–3.5 | F5 |
|  |  |  | Silicon | <5 | T3 |
|  |  |  | Titanium | 0.01–10 | S6 |
|  |  |  | Zirconium | 0.6 | F5 |
|  |  |  | Stainless steel | 10–10,000 | H6, L8, L9, R4 |
| Yttrium | $Y^{90}$ | 1 | Aluminum | 0.0001–1.0 | A8, A12, A19, C5, D4, G1, G2 |
|  | $Y^{89}(n,n')Y^{89m}$ | 0.1 | Iron | <0.01 | G2 |
| Zinc | $Zn^{65}$ | 1 | Aluminum | 0.5–15,000 | A8, A12, A19, B7, B8, D4, G1, G2, J8, J9, M16, R7, U1, Y7 |
|  |  |  | Antimony | <0.007 | R3 |
|  |  |  | Beryllium | 0.4–25 | L2–L4 |
|  |  |  | Bismuth | 0.01–1.0 | J1 |
|  |  |  | Gallium | 0.01–0.05 | L12 |
|  |  |  | Germanium | 1–39 | A15, A17, M23, R7, Y4, Y5 |
|  |  |  | Iron | <0.1–1.4 | A8, A12, G1, G2, T1 |
|  |  |  | Phosphorus | 20 | G4 |
|  |  |  | Selenium | 0.018–0.05 | W3 |
|  |  |  | Silicon | <0.007–0.6 | J2, J7, K5, M21, R7, T3, Y6 |
|  |  |  | Thallium | 1–10 | A16 |
|  |  |  | Tin | 100 | A14 |
|  |  |  | Tungsten | 1 | C16 |
|  |  |  | Zirconium | 0.03 | A8, A12 |
|  |  |  | Iron–nickel alloys | <0.3–5.0 | T2 |
| Zirconium | $Zr^{95}$ | 5 | Aluminum | 0.5–3.0 | A8, A12, A19, G2 |
|  | $Zr^{97}$ | 5 | Hafnium | 10–100 | L3, L4 |
|  |  |  | Iron | <0.5–1.2 | A8, A12, G1, T1 |
|  |  |  | Silicon | <0.003 | T3 |
|  |  |  | Zirconium–hafnium alloys | 0.2 to macro | H9 |

* Calculated sensitivities for $\mu g$ of element detectable by use of the product nuclide indicated. Calculations based on:
    1. Thermal flux of $1 \times 10^{12}$ neutrons/cm²/sec.
    2. Lower limit of 40 dis/sec detectable.
    3. Saturation factor of 0.5 or 1-wk irradiation whichever is shorter.
    4. $\sigma$ values from Sullivan Trilinear Chart of Nuclides.
  † Experimentally determined. Range of concentration shown established on the basis of the number of determinations.

## REFERENCES

A1   L. Adamski, J. Bouzhyk, and K. Jozefowicz, *Nukleonika* **5**: 13 (1960).
A2   L. Adamski, J. Bouzhyk, and K. Josefowicz, *Nukleonika* **5**: 317 (1960).
A3   G. Airoldi and E. Germagnoli, *Energia Nucl.* (Milan) **4**: 301 (1957).
A4   P. Albert, *Chim. Ind.* (Paris) **75**: 275–286 (1956).
A5   P. Albert, *Ann. Chim.* (Paris) **1**: 827–896 (1956).
A7   P. Albert, *Pure Appl. Chem.* **1**: 111 (1960).
A8   P. Albert, in *Proceedings, 1961 International Conference, Modern Trends in Activation Analysis*, December 15–16, 1961, A & M College of Texas, 1961.
A9   P. Albert, M. Caron, and G. Chaudron, *Compt. Rend.* **233**: 1108–10 (1951).
A10  P. Albert, M. Caron, and G. Chaudron, in *Proceedings of the Isotopes Techniques Conference (Oxford 1951)* Vol. 2, pp. 171–177, His Majesty's Stationery Office, London, 1952.
A11  P. Albert, M. Caron, and G. Chaudron, *Compt. Rend.* **236**: 1030–1 (1953).
A12  P. Albert and J. Gaittet, *Proc. of a Conf. on Radioisotopes in the Physical Sciences and Industry, Copenhagen*, September 6–17, 1960. Vol. 2, p. 243, International Atomic Energy Agency, Vienna, 1961.
A13  P. Albert, F. Montariol, and M. Caron, *International Congress of Aluminum, Paris, June 14–19, 1954*, Vol. I, Blanchard, Paris, 1955; see also, *Congr. Intrn. Aluminum, Paris* **1**: 187 (1954).
A14  P. Albert, F. Montariol, R. Reich, and G. Chaudron, *Proc. Radioisotopes Conf.*, 1954, Vol. II, pp. 75–83, Butterworth's, London, 1954.
A15  I. P. Alimarin and Y. V. Yakovlev, AEC-tr-4497.
A16  I. P. Alimarin, Y. V. Yakovlev, M. N. Shchulephikov, D. A. Valasov, G. M. Chernov, and Y. A. Surkov, *Zh. Analit. Khim.* **16**: 213–216 (1961).
A17  I. P. Alimarin, Y. V. Yakovlev, and A. I. Zhabin, *Primeneonie Mechenykh At. v Analit. Khim. Akad. Nauk SSSR, Inst. Geokhim. Analit. Khim.* p. 58 (1955).
A18  H. Amano, *Tohoku Univ. Sci. Report Res. Inst.* [A] **12** (1): 16–23 (1960).
A19  Anon., Centre d'Étude de l'Énergie Nucléaire, Brussels Report NP-7121, 1958.
A20  G. J. Atchison and W. H. Beamer, *Anal. Chem.* **24**: 1812 (1952).
A21  A. H. W. Aten, Jr., *Ned. Tijdschr. Natuurk.* **10**: 257 (1943).

B1   L. C. Bate and G. W. Leddicotte, Paper presented at the Conf. on Analytical Chemistry and Applied Spectroscopy, Pittsburg (1958).
B3   P. Benson, W. Holland, and R. Smith, *Anal. Chem.* **34**: 1113 (1962).
B4   H. J. Born and P. Wilkwiss, *Intern. J. Appl. Radiation Isotopes* **10**: No. 2–3 133–136 (1961).
B5   H. J. Born and P. Wilkniss, *Z. Elektrochem.* **64**: 1083 (1960).
B6   P. Bouten and J. Hoste, *Talanta* **8**: 322–9 (1961).
B7   W. A. Brooksbank, Jr., USAEC Report ORNL-2226, Oak Ridge National Laboratory, 1956.
B8   W. A. Brooksbank, Jr., G. W. Leddicotte, and J. A. Dean, *Anal. Chem.* **30**: 1785 (1958).
B9   W. A. Brooksbank, Jr., G. W. Leddicotte, and H. A. Mahlman, USAEC Report CF-53-10-52, Oak Ridge National Laboratory, 1953.
B10  W. A. Brooksbank, Jr., G. W. Leddicotte, and H. A. Mahlman, *J. Phys. Chem.* **57**: 815–819, (1953).
B11  W. A. Brooksbank, G. W. Leddicotte, and S. A. Reynolds, *Anal. Chem.* **28**: 1033–1035 (1956).
B12  D. Brune, Swedish Report AE-51, January 1961.

# REFERENCES

C1   M. J. Cabell and A. Thomas, British Report AERE-C/R-1725, p. 1, September 1955.

C2   J. P. Cali, L. F. Lowe, E. M. Reilly, and H. D. Thompson, Report ERD-CRRC-TM-57-103, Air Force Cambridge Research Center, 1957.

C3   J. P. Cali and J. R. Weiner, (rev.), *J. Electro. Chem. Soc.* **107**: 1015–19 (1960).

C4   G. Chaudron, *Bull. Soc. Chim. France* **21** (Series 5): 419 (1954).

C5   G. Chaudron, *Rec. Trav. Chim.* **79** (6): 502–509 (1960).

C6   G. Chaudron and P. Leveque, *Intern. J. Appl. Radiation Isotopes* **1**: 115–122 (1956).

C7   B. Chinaglia and R. Malvano, *Automazione Strumentozione* **9** (2): 92–96 (1961).

C8   B. Chinaglia and R. Malvano, *Energia Nucl.* **8** (9): 571–578 (1961).

C9   V. Cojocaru, M. Cristu, D. Dorcioman, and M. Badanoiu, *Inst. fiz. Atomica si Inst. fiz. Studie Cercetari fiz.* **11**: 447 (1960), *Nuclear Sci. Abstr.* **15**: 145 (1961).

C10  R. F. Coleman, British Report PG-171, p. 73, 1960.

C11  R. F. Coleman and J. L. Perkin, *Analyst* **84**: 233–236 (1959).

C12  R. F. Coleman and J. L. Perkin, *Analyst* **85**: 154–155 (1960).

C13  P. Cornand and J. Gillis, *Ind. Chim. Belge* **20**: 269 (1955).

C14  R. Corth, *Anal. Chem.* **24**: 517 (1962).

C15  J. F. Cosgrove, *ASTM Special Technical Bulletin No. 261, ASTM*, Philadelphia, 1960.

C16  J. F. Cosgrove and G. H. Morrison, *Anal. Chem.* **29**: 1017–1019 (1957).


D1   A. K. De and W. W. Meinke, *Anal. Chem.* **30**: 1474–1482 (1958).

D2   J. Debiesse, J. Challansonnet, and G. Neyret, *Compt. Rend.* **232**: 602–604 (1951).

D3   Nguyen-Long-Den, M. Borot, and P. Albert, *Compt. Rend.* **253**: 2067–2068 (1961).

D4   N. Deschamps, A. Loeillet, and P. Albert, *Compt. Rend.* **254**: 682–684 (1962).

D5   M. Deyris and P. Albert, (rev.) *Metallurg.* **59**: 14–20 (1962).

D6   USAEC Report COO-85, Dow Chemical Company, 1951.


E1   K. I. Erokhina, I. K. Lemberg, I. E. Makasheva, I. A. Moslov, and A. P. Obukhov *Zabodskaya Lab.* **26**: 821 (1960).


F1   C. Fisher, *Ind. Chim. Belge* **19** (8): 785–788 (1954).

F2   C. Fisher and J. Beydon, *Bull. Soc. Chim. France* **20** (5): 102–103 (1953).

F3   I. Fineman, K. Ljunggren, H. G. Forsberg, and L. G. Erwall, *Intern. J. Appl. Radiation Isotopes* **5**: 280 (1959).

F4   E. M. Foster and C. D. Gaitanis, *Anal. Chem.* **27**: 1342 (1955).

F5   L. Fournet, N. Deschamps, and P. Albert, *Compt. Rend.* **254**: 1640–1642 (1962).


G1   J. Gaittet, *Ann. Chim.* (Paris) **5**: 1219 (1960).

G2   J. Gaittet and P. Albert, *Compt. Rend.* **247**: 1861–1863 (1958).

G3   P. Gauthier, *Ind. Chem. Belge* **20**: (II) 281 (1954).

G4   W. Gebauhr and J. Martin, *Intern. J. Appl. Radiation Isotopes* **4**: 173–178 (1959).

G5   N. Getoff, *Atompraxis* **5**: 472 (1959).

G6   M. M. Golutvina and E. A. Tikhomirova, *Radiokhimiya* **2**: 112–119 (1960).

G7   D. Gibbons, in *Proceedings of the International Symposium on Microchemistry*, Birmingham University, Aug. 20–27, 1958, pp. 332–335, 1960.

G8   D. Gibbons and H. Simpson, *Pure Appl. Chem.* **1**: 135 (1960).

G9   A. R. Gilman and S. Isserow, USAEC Report NMI-1234, Nuclear Metals, Inc., May 3, 1960.

G10  II. Goto, II. Amano, and Y. Inoue, *J. Japan Inst. Metals* **24**: 85 (1960).

G11    H. Goto, S. Ikeda, and H. Amano, *Abstracts of the 3rd Japan Conference on Radio-isotopes*, Sept. 14–16, 1959, 59/P-101, Japan Atomic Industrial Forum, Tokyo, 1959.
G12    J. Gottfried and Y. V. Yakolev, *Chem. Prumysl* **9**: 179–182 (1959).
G13    J. A. Grand *et al.*, *J. Phys. Chem.* **63**: 1192 (1959).
G14    M. Green and J. A. Kaplan, *J. Chem. Soc.* **1955** (Part 2): 1604.

H1    W. Haerdi, J. Vogel, and D. Monnier, *Helv. Chim. Acta* **43**: 1585–95 (1960).
H2    G. Halverson and A. Shtasel, *Anal. Chem.* **33**: 1627–8 (1961).
H3    W. Herr, *Arch. Eisenhuettenw.* **26**: 523 (1955).
H4    S. Hirano, A. Mizuike, and S. Takagi, *Japan Analyst* **10**: 951 (1961).
H5    S. Hirano, A. Mizuike, and K. Yamada, Tokyo, Japan, Sept. 14–16, 1959.
H6    J. Hoste, *Pure Appl. Chem.* **1**: 99 (1960).
H7    J. Hoste, F. Bouten, and F. Adams, *Nucleonics* **19** (3): 118 (1961).
H8    J. Hoste and H. Van der Berghe, *Mikrochim. Acta* 797, (1956).
H9    J. E. Hudgens and H. J. Dabagian, *Nucleonics* **10** (5): 25 (1952).

I1    T. Ichimiya, H. Baba, and K. Nozaki, *Radioisotopes in the Physical Sciences and Industry*, Vol. I, pp. 533–42, International Atomic Energy Agency, Vienna, 1962.
I2    P. Iredale, British Report AERE EL/M-96, October 1957.

J1    J. W. Jakowlaw and Z. Allina, First National Symposium on Technical Use of Radioisotopes, Rogow, June 8–12 1960, Report No. 10.
J2    J. A. James, *Proc. Intern. Symp. Microchem.*, Birmingham Univ., August 1958, pp. 319–24, Pergamon Press, London, 1960.
J3    J. A. James and D. H. Richards, *Nature* **175**: 769 (1955).
J4    J. A. James and D. H. Richards, *Nature* **176**: 1026 (1955).
J5    J. A. James and D. H. Richards, *Anal. Chim. Acta* **15**: 118 (1956).
J6    J. A. James and D. H. Richards, *Nature* **177**: 1230 (1956).
J7    J. A. James and D. H. Richards, *J. Electron. Control* **3**: 500–506 (1957).
J8    R. E. Jervis, *Chem. Can.* **8** (3): 27–31 (1956).
J9    R. E. Jervis and W. D. Mackintosh, *Progress in Nuclear Energy*, Series IX, Vol. 1, Pergamon Press, New York, 1959.
J10    H. Jaskolska and J. Minczewski, *Chem. Anal.* (Warsaw) **6**: 149–159 (1961).
J11    H. Jaskolska and L. Wodiewicz, *Chem. Anal.* (Warsaw) **6**: 161–5 (1961).
J12    L. S. Jowanovitz *et al.*, *Anal. Chem.* **32**: 1270 (1960).

K1    A. I. Kalinin, R. A. Kuznetsov, V. V. Moiseev, and A. N. Murin, *Dokl. Akad. Nauk SSSR* **141**: 98 (1961).
K2    Y. Kamemoto, K. Shiba, and Y. Onoda, *J. Chem. Soc. Japan, Pure Chem. Sect.* **83**: 57 (1962).
K3    Y. Kamemoto and S. Yamagiski, *J. Chem. Soc. Japan, Pure Chem. Sect.* **82**: 1653 (1961).
K4    Y. Kamemoto and S. Yamagishi, *J. Chem. Soc. Japan, Pure Chem. Sect.* **83**, 463 (1962).
K5    A. Kant, J. P. Cali, and H. D. Thompson, *Anal. Chem.* **28**: 1867 (1956).
K6    T. Kawaskima, *Denki Tsushin Kenkyusho Kenkyu Jitsuyoka Hokoku* **9** (7): (1960).
K7    T. Kawaskima, M. Osawa, Y. Mochizuki, and H. Hamaguchi, *Bull. Chem. Soc. Japan* **34**: 701 (1961).
K8    R. A. Killick and D. F. C. Morris, *Talanta* **8**: 601 (1961).
K9    R. A. Killick and D. F. C. Morris, *Talanta* **9**: 349 (1962).
K10    G. D. Kneip and J. O. Betterton, *J. Electrochem. Soc.* **103**: 684 (1956).

K11  M. Kobayashi and H. Natsume, Abstracts of the 3rd Japan Conference of Radio-isotopes, Sept. 14–16, 1959, Paper 59/P-28, Japan Atomic Industrial Forum, Tokyo, 1959.

K12  M. Kobayashi and T. Mihara, in Proceedings of the 4th Japan Conference on Radioisotopes, Oct. 10–12, 1961, pp. 554–557, Japan Atomic Industrial Forum, Inc., Tokyo, 1961.

K13  A. Kohn, *Compt. Rend.* **236**: 1419–1421 (1953).

K14  A. Kohn, *Chim. Ind.* **71**: 69 (1954).

K15  N. Kosaric and G. Leliaret, *Nature* **191**: 703–704 (1961).

K16  R. Kurosawa, *Waseda Univ. Bull. Sci. and Eng. Res. Lab.* **18**: 15 (1961).

K17  Y. Kusaka, *Radioisotopes* **6**: 1 (1957).

K18  Y. Kusaka, *Radioisotopes* **6**: 73–84 (1957).

K19  Y. Kusaka, *Bull. Chem. Soc. Japan* **31**: 216 (1958).

K20  Y. Kusaka, *J. Chem. Soc. Japan, Pure Chem. Sect.* **80**: 1419 (1959).

K21  Y. Kusaka and H. Tsuji, *Nippon Kagaku Zasshi* **81**: 1087 (1960).

L1  G. W. Leddicotte, *Nucleonics* **14** (5): 47 (1956).

L2  G. W. Leddicotte et al., USAEC Report TID-7555, pp. 192–215, 1958.

L3  G. W. Leddicotte et al., in *Proceedings of the Second International Conference on the Peaceful Uses of Atomic Energy*, Geneva, 1958, Vol. 28, pp. 478–485, United Nations, New York, 1958.

L4  G. W. Leddicotte et al., *Progress in Nuclear Energy*, Series IX, Vol. 1, pp. 123–126, Pergamon Press, New York, 1959.

L5  G. W. Leddicotte and S. A. Reynolds, USAEC Report ORNL-1623, Oak Ridge National Laboratory, 1953.

L6  G. Leliaert, *Pure Appl. Chem.* **1**: 121 (1960).

L7  G. Leliaert and D. Decat, *Intern. J. Appl. Radiation Isotopes* **12**: 63–4 (1961).

L8  G. Leliaert, J. Hoste, and Z. Eeckhaut, *Nature* **182**: 600 (1958).

L9  G. Leliaert, J. Hoste, and Z. Eeckhaut, *Anal. Chim. Acta* **19**: 100 (1958).

L10  G. Leliaert, J. Hoste, and Z. Eeckhaut, *Talanta* **2**: 115 (1959).

L11  W. Leonhardt, *Kernenergie* **5**: 166 (1962).

L12  P. Lerch and L. Kreienbuehl, *Chimia* (Switz.) **15**: 519 (1961).

L13  P. Leveque and H. Goenvec, *Bull. Soc. Chim. France* **5**: 1213 (1955).

L14  P. Leveque, M. Kobayaski, and S. May, Abstract of the Japan Conference on Radioisotopes, Sept. 14–15, 1959, 59/P-27, Japan Atomic Industrial Forum, Tokyo, 1959.

L15  P. Leveque, P. Martinelli, and S. May, *Intern. J. Appl. Rad. Isotopes* **4**: 41 (1958).

M1  W. D. Mackintosh, *Anal. Chem.* **32**: 1272 (1960).

M2  W. D. Mackintosh and R. E. Jervis, Canadian Report CRDC-904, 1957.

M3  W. D. Mackintosh and R. E. Jervis, *Anal. Chem.* **30**: 1180 (1958).

M4  I. E. Makasheva, I. A. Maslov, and A. P. Obukhov, *J. Anal. Chem., USSR* **15**: 375 (1960).

M5  V. Maxia, *Ric. Sci.* **29**: 1476 (1959).

M6  V. Maxia et al., *Ric. Sci.* **1** (2): 17 (1961).

M7  S. May and G. Pinte, *Bull. Soc. Chim. France* **2**: 287 (1962).

M8  W. W. Meinke, Progress Report 7, November 1957–October 1958, Department of Chemistry, University of Michigan, Ann Arbor, Mich., Nov. 1, 1958.

M9  C. E. Millen, USAEC Report ORNL-2715, Oak Ridge National Laboratory, May 1959.

M10  G. W. C. Milner and A. A. Smales, *Analyst* **79**: 425 (1954).

M11  M. Miyamoto, *Bunseki Kagaku* **9**: 925 (1960).

M12 D. Monnier, W. Haerdi, and J. Vogel, *Helv. Chim. Acta* **43:** 675 (1960).
M13 D. Monnier, W. Haerdi, and J. Vogel, *Helv. Chim. Acta* **44:** 1565 (1961).
M14 D. Monnier *et al.*, *Chimia* (Switz.) **14:** 128 (1960).
M15 H. Mori and H. Umezawa, *J. Japan Inst. Metals* **24:** 641 (1960).
M16 F. Montariol and G. Chaudron, Publications Scientifiques et Techniques du Minis-tère de l'Air, Report No. 344, Paris, 1958.
M17 D. F. C. Morris and R. A. Killick, *Talanta* **1:** 34 (1959).
M18 D. F. C. Morris and R. A. Killick, *Talanta* **8:** 129 (1961).
M19 D. F. C. Morris and R. A. Killick, *Talanta* **8:** 793 (1961).
M21 G. H. Morrison, *Appl. Spectr.* **10:** 71 (1956).
M22 G. H. Morrison and J. F. Cosgrove, *Anal. Chem.* **27:** 810 (1955).
M23 G. H. Morrison and J. F. Cosgrove, *Anal. Chem.* **28:** 320 (1956).
M24 K. Mo Wong and A. F. Voigt, USAEC Report IS-376, Iowa State University, August 1961.
M25 W. T. Mullins and G. W. Leddicotte, USAEC Report ORNL-3060, Oak Ridge National Laboratory, Feb. 15, 1961.

N1 T. Naki, S. Yajima, I. Fujii, and M. Okada, *J. Chem. Soc. Japan* **80:** 49 (1959).
N2 T. Nakai *et al.*, *Japan Analyst* **8:** 367 (1959).
N3 T. Nakai *et al.*, *Nippon Kagaku Zasshi* **81:** 107 (1960).
N4 T. Nakai *et al.*, *Nippon Kagaku Zasshi* **81:** 1422 (1960).
N5 T. Nakai *et al.*, *J. Chem. Soc. Japan, Pure Chem. Sect.* **82:** 197 (1961).
N6 V. P. Negina and V. N. Zamyatmina, *Zh. Anal. Khim.* **16:** 209 (1961).
N7 T. Nozaki, H. Baba, and H. Araki, *Bull. Chem. Soc. Japan* **33:** 320 (1960).
N8 T. Nozaki *et al.*, *Bull. Chem. Soc. Japan* **33:** 1329 (1960).

O1 T. Okada, T. Nishi, and C. Matsumoto, AEC-tr-4482, 1960.
O2 M. Ordogh and V. Upor-Juvancz, *Acta Chim. Acad. Sci. Hung.* **26** (1-4): 253 (1961).
O3 R. G. Osmond and A. A. Smales, *Anal. Chim. Acta* **10:** 117 (1954).
O4 R. T. Overman and J. A. Swartout, USAEC Report AECD-2245, 1948.

P1 D. H. Peirson, *Atomica* **7:** 316 (1956).
P2 D. H. Pierson and P. Iredale, *1st International Conference on Radioisotopes in Scientific Research*, Vol. II, p. 197, 1957, Pergamon Press, New York, 1958.
P3 R. C. Plumb, *Nucleonics* **14** (5): 48 (1956).
P4 R. C. Plumb and R. H. Silverman, *Nucleonics* **12** (12): 29 (1954).
P5 J. L. Putnam, in *Proceedings of the Second International Conference on the Peaceful Uses of Atomic Energy, Geneva*, 1958, Vol. 19, p. 22, United Nations, 1958.

R1 E. Rabinowicz, *Proc. Phys. Soc. Sci. A* **64:** 939 (1951).
R2 M. Radman and J. Zmiga, Report No. R-49 in *First National Symposium on Technical Uses of Radioisotopes*, Rogow, Poland, June 8–12, 1960, Osrpdek, Informacji, Warsaw, 1961.
R3 E. E. Rakovskii *et al.*, *Zavodskaya Lab.* **26:** 1199 (1960). *Nuclear Sci. Abstr.* **15:** 8761 (1961).
R4 W. Reiser and H. Schneider, *Arch. Eisenhuettenw.* **32:** 31 (1961).
R5 E. Ricci and W. D. Mackintosh, *Anal. Chem.* **33:** 230 (1961).
R6 W. Riezler, *Z. Naturforsch.* **4a:** 545 (1949).
R7 R. S. Rychkov and N. A. Glukhareva, *Zavodsk. Lab.* **27:** 1246 (1961).

S1 L. Salmon, British Report AERE-C/R-1324, 1954.
S3 K. Samshl, *Acta Chem. Scand.* **12:** 1292 (1958).

S4   A. P. Seyfang and R. Todd, British Report PG-172, 1961.
S5   V. I. Shamaev, *Radiokhim.* **2**: 624 (1960).
S6   M. B. Shustova and Y. A. Nazarenko, *Zavodsk. Lab.* **26**: 1339 (1960).
S7   A. A. Smales, in *Proceedings of the First International Conference on the Peaceful Uses of Atomic Energy, Geneva, 1955*, Vol. 9, p. 9, United Nations, 1956.
S8   A. A. Smales, in *Proceedings of the First International Conference on the Peaceful Uses of Atomic Energy, Geneva, 1955*, Vol. 9, p. 273, United Nations, 1956.
S9   A. A. Smales, British Report AERE R-3313, 1960.
S10  A. A. Smales and D. J. Ferrett, *Proc. of the Congr. Mod. Anal. Chem. Ind.*, Univ. St. Andrews, June 24–28, 1957, pp. 177–191, W. Heffer & Sons, Cambridge, 1958.
S11  A. A. Smales and B. A. Loveridge, *Anal. Chim. Acta* **13**: 566 (1955).
S12  A. A. Smales *et al.*, British Report AERE-C/R-2254, 1957.
S13  A. A. Smales and B. D. Pate, *Anal. Chem.* **24**: 717 (1952).
S14  R. R. Smith, T. O. Passell, and S. D. Reeder, USAEC Report AECD-3889, 1955.
S15  G. Szekely, *Anal. Chem.* **26**: 1500 (1954).

T1   J. Talbot *et al.*, *Rev. Met.* **50**: 817 (1953).
T2   B. A. Thompson, *Anal. Chem.* **31**: 1492 (1959).
T3   B. A. Thompson, B. M. Strause, and M. B. Leboeuf, *Anal. Chem.* **30**: 1023 (1958).
T4   R. Todd, British Report BG-171, 1960.

U1   P. Urech, *Mitt. Lebensmitt. Hyg. Bern.* **49** (6): 442 (1958).

W1   F. W. Walker, USAEC Report KAPL-MFW-4, Knolls Atomic Power Laboratory, December 21, 1961.
W2   T. Westermark and I. Fineman, in *Proceedings of the Second International Conference on the Peaceful Uses of Atomic Energy, Geneva, 1958*, Vol. 28, p. 506, United Nations, New York, 1958.
W3   A. I. Williams, *Analyst* **86**: 172 (1961).

Y1   S. Yajima *et al.*, *J. Chem. Soc. Japan, Pure Chem. Sect.* **82**: 38 (1961).
Y2   S. Yajima *et al.*, *J. Chem. Soc. Japan, Pure Chem. Sect.* **82**: 194 (1961).
Y3   S. Yajima *et al.*, *J. Chem. Soc. Japan, Pure Chem. Sect.* **82**: 343 (1961).
Y4   J. V. Yakovlev, *Issledov Obl. Geolog. Khim. Metallurg. M. Izdar Akad. Nauk SSSR*, 90-104 (1955).
Y5   J. V. Yakovlev, in *Proceedings of the First International Conference on the Peaceful Uses of Atomic Energy, Geneva, 1955*, Vol. 15, p. 54, United Nations, New York, 1956.
Y6   J. V. Yakovlev, in *Proceedings of the Second International Conference on the Peaceful Uses of Atomic Energy, Geneva, 1958*, Vol. 28, p. 496, United Nations, New York, 1958.
Y7   H. Yamaki, *J. At. Energy Soc. Japan*, **3**: 323 (1961).

Z1   O. E. Zvyaginstev and A. I. Kulak, AEC-tr-4057, 1960.
Z2   O. E. Zvyaginstev and A. I. Kulak, AEC-tr-4497, 1961.
Z3   O. E. Zvyaginstev and V. I. Shamaev, *Radiokhimiya* **1**: 717 (1959).
Z4   O. E. Zvyaginstev and V. I. Shamaev, *Zh. Analit. Khim.* **14**: 603 (1959).
Z5   O. E. Zvyaginstev and V. I. Shamaev, *Zhur. Analit. Khim.* **15**: 325 (1960).

## Table A.2—BIOCHEMISTRY AND MEDICAL RESEARCH APPLICATIONS OF NEUTRON ACTIVATION ANALYSIS

| Element | Nuclide formed | Sensitivity, $\mu g^*$ | Material analyzed | Concentration determined, $\mu g/g$ † | Reference |
|---|---|---|---|---|---|
| Antimony | Sb$^{122}$ | 0.005 | Blood (human) | 0.1–1.0 | B19 |
|  | Sb$^{124}$ | 0.1 |  |  |  |
| Arsenic | As$^{76}$ | 0.002 | Plants and soils | 0.006 | Y1 |
|  |  |  | Beans | 0.17–0.35 | S9 |
|  |  |  | Blood | 0.09–3.1 | G2, O2, S9 |
|  |  |  | Milk (dried) | 0.038–0.048 | G2 |
|  |  |  | Hair | 0.12–24 | F1, L2–L5, M1, S9, S10 |
|  |  |  | Nail | 0.11–7 | F1, L5, S9 |
|  |  |  | Skin (human) | 0.4–7.2 | B6, D6, F1, L5, S8 |
|  |  |  | Tissues (mouse, rat) | 0.003–0.038 | D1, S9 |
|  |  |  | Tissue (carcinoma) | 0.005–1.0 | F1, L1, D4 |
|  |  |  | Tobacco powder | 3.3–3.7 | G2, L2, L5 |
|  |  |  | Teeth | 0.13–0.145 | G3, L2, N2 |
|  |  |  | Bone | 0.1–0.5 | K8, M3 |
|  |  |  | Vomitus | 0.15 | L5 |
|  |  |  | Lungs (mouse) | 0.18–1.01 | L5 |
|  |  |  | Urine | 0.0003–0.57 | O2, S9 |
|  |  |  | Tissue (eye) | <10 | S12 |
| Barium | Ba$^{131}$ | 2.0 | Tissues (nonskeletal) | <10 | S11 |
|  | Ba$^{139}$ | 0.04 | Feces | 320–1,190 | H2 |
|  |  |  | Urine | 10–48 | H2 |
|  |  |  | Tomato seeds | 0.1–10.0 | B16 |
|  |  |  | Bone | 10–100 | S13 |
|  |  |  | Plants and soils | 0.1–10 | B18 |
| Bromine | Br$^{80}$ | 0.002 | Teeth | <1 | S1 |
|  | Br$^{82}$ | 0.007 | Fluid | 1 | H1 |
|  |  |  | Corn‡ | 2–4 | G5 |
|  |  |  | Lemon peel | 3–5 | G5 |
|  |  |  | Peaches | <1 | G5 |
|  |  |  | Banana peel‡ | 3–9 | G5 |
|  |  |  | Pineapple‡ | 7–11 | G5 |
|  |  |  | Carrots‡ | 8–16 | G5 |
|  |  |  | Asparagus | 7–11 | G5 |
|  |  |  | Beans (bush)‡ | <10–448 | G5 |
|  |  |  | Beans (lima)‡ | <10–80 | G5 |
|  |  |  | Blood (human) | 1.5–3.9 | B14, S14–S16 |
|  |  |  | Tomato seeds | 0.005–0.5 | B14, B16 |
|  |  |  | Orange juice‡ | <0.03–5.2 | C1 |
|  |  |  | Orange peel‡ | <0.03–5.5 | C1 |
|  |  |  | Tobacco (cigarette) | 129–241 | G2, W5 |
|  |  |  | Tobacco (pipe) | 47–234 | G2 |
|  |  |  | Potatoes (Irish)‡ | <10–94 | G5 |
|  |  |  | Potatoes (sweet)‡ | <10–205 | G5 |
|  |  |  | Tissue | 1–10 | L1 |
| Cadmium | Cd$^{115}$ | 0.05 | Blood (human) | 0.1–1.0 | B19 |
|  | Cd$^{117}$ | 0.1 | Bone | 1–5 | L1, W2 |
| Calcium | Ca$^{45}$ | 7 | Blood (human) | 10–100 | B19, H6, O2 |
|  | Ca$^{48}$ | 3 | Fluid | 10–100 | H1 |
|  |  |  | Chicken ash | Macro | K9 |
|  |  |  | Urine | 10–100 | O2 |
|  |  |  | Teeth | Macro | S1 |
| Cesium | Cs$^{134m}$ | 0.01 | Blood (human) | 0.1–10 | B19 |
|  | Cs$^{134}$ | 0.06 | Fluid | 0.1–10 | H1 |
|  |  |  | Tissues (human) | 1–10 | L1 |
| Chlorine | Cl$^{38}$ | 0.04 | Blood (human) | 10–3,050 | B14, H6, S14–S16 |
|  |  |  | Chicken ash | Macro | K9 |
|  |  |  | Teeth | <10 | S1 |
|  |  |  | Butter fat§ | 1.8–7.1 | S4 |
|  |  |  | Muscle | 0.1–1.0 | B5 |
|  |  |  | Tomato seeds | 0.01–66.7 | B14, B16 |
|  |  |  | Orange juice‡ | 30–31 | C1 |
|  |  |  | Orange peel‡ | 24–31 | C1 |
| Chromium | Cr$^{51}$ | 0.005 | Blood serum | 0.1–1.0 | P4 |
|  | Cr$^{55}$ | 0.8 |  |  |  |

## Table A.2 (continued)

| Element | Nuclide formed | Sensitivity, $\mu g$* | Material analyzed | Concentration determined, $\mu g/g$† | Reference |
|---|---|---|---|---|---|
| Cobalt | $Co^{60m}$ | 0.0005 | Blood | 0.1 | K7, P4, W6 |
| | $Co^{60}$ | 0.04 | Fluid | 1 | H1 |
| | | | Kidney (rat) | 1–3 | K1 |
| | | | Plant ash | 0.3 | B3 |
| | | | Tissue | 0.1 | D1 |
| | | | Tissue (human) | 0.1–1.0 | H3, T2, W6 |
| | | | Spleen | 0.1 | K7 |
| | | | Plants and soils | 1 | Y1 |
| Copper | $Cu^{64}$ | 0.003 | Blood (human) | 0.05–1.0 | B19, H6, O2, P4, S14–S16, W6 |
| | $Cu^{66}$ | 0.01 | Biol. materials | 0.05–1.0 | C2 |
| | | | Cellulose | 1–10 | F2 |
| | | | Chicken ash | 18–24 | K9 |
| | | | Rubber latex ash | 0.01–1.0 | D2 |
| | | | Tomato seeds | 0.05–0.5 | B12, B16 |
| | | | Blood serum | 2 | J1 |
| | | | Tissues (human) | 0.1–700 | L1, W6 |
| | | | Urine | <1 | O2 |
| | | | Teeth | <1 | S1 |
| | | | Plants and soils | 0.02 | Y1 |
| Dysprosium | $Dy^{165m}$ | 0.002 | Bone (cuttlefish) | 0.4 | K2 |
| | $Dy^{165}$ | 0.0004 | Gill (angles) | 0.4 | K2 |
| | | | Skin (shark) | 1.0 | K2 |
| Gallium | $Ga^{70}$ | 0.009 | Blood (rat) | 0.00055 | B13 |
| | $Ga^{72}$ | 0.005 | Tomato seeds | 0.002–0.014 | B13, B16 |
| Gold | $Au^{198}$ | 0.0003 | Blood (human) | 0.001–0.05 | B19, D5, H6, T1 |
| | | | Biol. materials | 0.001–0.05 | V1 |
| | | | Liver | 0.01–24 | G1 |
| | | | Pleural fluid | 0.75–0.85 | G1 |
| | | | Tissue (mouse, rat) | 0.01–0.05 | D1, M5 |
| | | | Hair (male) | 0.04–0.13 | G2 |
| | | | Hair (female) | 0.06–0.19 | G2 |
| | | | Teeth | 0.01–10 | S1 |
| Iodine | $I^{128}$ | 0.003 | Blood (human) | 0.03–0.05 | B14, H6, K3 |
| | | | Thyroglobulin | 0.03–1.0 | B20 |
| | | | Urine | 1–5 | W1 |
| | | | Tomato seeds | 0.005–0.5 | B14, B16 |
| | | | Biol. materials | <1 | C2 |
| Iron | $Fe^{59}$ | 10 | Blood | Macro | W6 |
| | | | Fluid | | H1 |
| | | | Tissue | 10–500 | H3, W6 |
| | | | Chicken ash | 620–640 | K9 |
| Magnesium | $Mg^{27}$ | 1 | Blood | | O2 |
| | | | Urine | | O2 |
| Manganese | $Mn^{56}$ | 0.0006 | Teeth | <1 | S1 |
| | | | Chicken ash | 26–30 | K9 |
| | | | Blood serum | 1 | J1 |
| | | | Bone meal | 35 | G2 |
| | | | Blood (human) | 2.4–6.5 | B11, B19, H6, O2, P1 |
| | | | Blood cells | 0.5–1.5 | B11 |
| | | | Hair | 1.4–1.6 | B11 |
| | | | Biol. materials | | C2 |
| | | | Cellulose | 1–10 | F2, P2 |
| | | | Mouse brain and other tissues | 0.01 | B8–B10 |
| | | | Tomato seeds | 0.002–0.2 | B16 |
| | | | Orange juice‡ | 1.7–2.1 | C1 |
| | | | Orange peel‡ | 9–9.5 | C1 |
| | | | Tobacco | 100 | G2 |
| | | | Urine | <1 | O2 |
| Mercury | $Hg^{197}$ | 0.006 | Biol. materials | <1 | C2 |
| | | | Fluid | <1 | H1 |
| | | | Brain (rabbit) | 0.03–3.0 | L6, W3 |
| | | | Liver (rabbit) | 0.03–3.0 | L6, W3 |
| | | | Feces (human) | 0.03–3.0 | L6, W3 |
| | | | Blood | <1 | O2 |
| | | | Urine | <1 | O2 |

## Table A.2 (continued)

| Element | Nuclide formed | Sensitivity, $\mu$g* | Material analyzed | Concentration determined, $\mu$g/g † | Reference |
|---|---|---|---|---|---|
| Molybdenum | Mo⁹⁹ | 0.1 | Clover | 0.1–1.0 | V2 |
| | | | Tomato seeds | 0.09–2.5 | B13, B16 |
| | | | Blood (rat) | 0.014 | B13 |
| | | | Plants and soils | 1 | Y1 |
| Nickel | Ni⁶⁵ | 0.4 | Fluid | 1–3 | H1 |
| | | | Tissues (human) | 0.5–2.0 | L1 |
| | | | Plants and soils | 3 | Y1 |
| Oxygen | O¹⁹ | 60 | Algae¶ | 1–40 | F3 |
| Phosphorus | P³² | 0.04 | Bone | <1 | S2 |
| | | | Teeth | 10–100 | S1 |
| | | | Beetle wings | 0.1 | B2 |
| | | | Blood serum** | 1.0 | B3, B4, S17 |
| | | | Algae** | †† | B3, B4, S17 |
| | | | Spermatozoon | †† | B3, B4, S17 |
| | | | Cerebrospinal fluid** | †† | B7 |
| | | | Blood (human) | 0.5–400 | B19 |
| | | | Chicken ash | Macro | K9 |
| | | | Biol. materials | <1 | B17 |
| | | | Tissue (mouse) | <1 | C3 |
| | | | Tissue (human) | 0.5–300 | H3 |
| | | | Liver | 0.1–1.0 | · N1 |
| | | | Bile | 0.1–1.0 | N1 |
| | | | Cervical mucus | 0.1–1.0 | O1 |
| | | | Muscle | 1 | R1, W4 |
| Potassium | K⁴² | 0.07 | Chicken ash | Macro | K9 |
| | | | Fluids | 1–10 | H1, P3 |
| | | | Blood | <100 | O2, S14–S16 |
| | | | Urine | 1–10 | O2 |
| | | | Biol. materials | 1–10 | B17 |
| | | | Orange juice‡ | 2,900–3,300 | C1 |
| | | | Orange peel‡ | 1,900–2,300 | C1 |
| | | | Tissue (mouse) | 1–10 | C3 |
| | | | Nerve fibers | 3 | K4, K5 |
| | | | Tissues (human) | 100–1,000 | L1 |
| | | | Muscle | 1–10 | R1, W4 |
| Rubidium | Rb⁸⁶ | 0.03 | Blood | 0.1–1.0 | B19 |
| | Rb⁸⁸ | 0.3 | Tissues (human) | 10–100 | L1 |
| Selenium | Se⁷⁵ | 0.5 | Kidney (pig) | 0.5–2.5 | G4 |
| | Se⁷⁷ | 0.02 | Skeletal muscle (pig) | <0.3–1.0 | G4 |
| | | | Liver (pig) | <0.3–0.9 | G4 |
| | | | Hay | 0.05–0.10 | H4 |
| | | | Corn | 0.02–0.06 | H4 |
| | | | Oats | 0.026 | H4 |
| | | | Wheat bran | 0.64 | H4 |
| | | | Linseed oil meal | 1.10–1.18 | H4 |
| | | | Beans (kidney) | 0.01–0.09 | H4 |
| | | | Soybean meal | 0.3 | H5 |
| | | | Tissues (human) | 0.001–10 | L1 |
| | | | Cystine | 0.96–1.87 | S7 |
| | | | Torula yeast | 0.02–1.6 | S5 |
| | | | Organo selenium compounds | 0.02–3.0 | S4 |
| Silver | Ag¹⁰⁸ | 0.0001 | Tissues (human) | 0.1–1.0 | L1 |
| | Ag¹¹⁰ | 0.3 | | | |
| Sodium | Na²⁴ | 0.006 | Teeth | 10–100 | S1 |
| | | | Blood (human) | 0.05–32,000 | B19, H6, S14–S16 |
| | | | Bone (human) | 10–100 | D7, S2, V3 |
| | | | Fluids | <1 | P3 |
| | | | Biol. materials | <1 | B17 |
| | | | Orange juice‡ | 1.4–2.2 | C1 |
| | | | Orange peel‡ | 5.8–7.9 | C1 |
| | | | Cervical mucus | 0.1–1.0 | O1 |
| | | | Tissue (mouse) | 1–10 | C3 |
| | | | Nerve fibers | 0.3 | K4, K5 |
| | | | Chicken ash | Macro | K9 |
| | | | Tissue (human) | 10–10,000 | L1 |
| | | | Muscle | 1–10 | R1, W4 |

## Table A.2 (continued)

| Element | Nuclide formed | Sensitivity, $\mu g^*$ | Material analyzed | Concentration determined, $\mu g/g$ † | Reference |
|---|---|---|---|---|---|
| Strontium | Sr[85] | 10 | Blood (human) | 0.5–1 | B19 |
| | Sr[87] | 0.1 | Feces (human) | 1,450–3,760 | H2 |
| | | | Bone (rat) | 120–2550 | M2, S3 |
| | | | Tomato seeds | 0.5–50 | B16 |
| | | | Urine | 300–1,440 | H2 |
| | | | Tissues (human) | 6.5–30 | L1, S11, S12 |
| | | | Milk | 0.1–10 | M4 |
| | | | Chicken ash | Macro | K9 |
| | | | Teeth | 1–10 | S1 |
| | | | Eye tissues | 1–10 | S13 |
| | | | Plants and soils | 1–10 | B18 |
| Tellurium | Te[131] | 0.2 | Tissues (human) | 10–100 | L1 |
| Tungsten | W[187] | 0.002 | Biol. materials | <1 | B15 |
| Vanadium | V[52] | 0.002 | Tomato seeds | 0.1–1.0 | B16 |
| Zinc | Zn[65] | 1 | Blood (human) | 0.3–10 | B1, B19, H6, O2, P4 |
| | | | Biol. materials | 1–10 | C2 |
| | | | Blood (erythrocytes, leucocytes) | 0.2–0.6 | D3 |
| | | | Chicken ash | 810–970 | K9 |
| | | | Liver | 0.3–0.8 | B1 |
| | | | Tissue | 0.3–10 | H3, W6 |
| | | | Tomato seeds | 0.5–50 | B12, B16 |
| | | | Fluid | 1–10 | H1 |
| | | | Thyroid (human) | 700–1,920 | K6 |
| | | | Tissues (human) | 1–1,000 | L1 |
| | | | Urine | <1 | O2 |
| | | | Teeth | <10 | S1 |
| Zirconium | Zr[95] | 5 | Tissues (human) | 1–10 | L1 |
| | Zr[97] | 5 | Plants and soils | 0.1 | Y1 |

\* Calculated sensitivities for $\mu g$ of element detectable by use of the product nuclide indicated.  Calculations based on:
    1. Thermal flux of $1 \times 10^{12}$ neutrons/cm²/sec.
    2. Lower limit of 40 dis/sec detectable.
    3. Saturation factor of 0.5 or 1-wk irradiation whichever is shorter.
    4. $\sigma$ values from Sullivan Trilinear Chart of Nuclides.
† Experimentally determined.  Range of concentration shown established on basis of a number of determinations.
‡ Nematocide residue studies.
§ Pesticide residue studies.
¶ Photosynthesis study by proton bombardment.
\*\* Phosphatide determinations using electrophoresis separation before activation.
†† Chemical form determined.

## *REFERENCES*

B1    J. E. Banks *et al.*, *Intern. J. Appl. Radiation Isotopes* **4**: 221 (1959).

B2    J. Beck and T. Manney, *Science* **37**: 320 (1962).

B3    A. A. Benson, *Methods in Enzymology*, Vol. 1, p. 1, Jan. 10, 1959.

B4    A. A. Benson *et al.*, in *Proceedings of the Second International Conference on the Peaceful Uses of Atomic Energy, Geneva, 1958*, Vol. 24, pp. 289–293, United Nations, New York, 1959.

B5    J. Bergstrom, *Nature* **184**: 1504 (1959).

B6    G. Blom, *XI e Intern. Congr. of Dermatology*, Stockholm, 1957 (printed in *Acta Derm.*).

B7    R. Blomstrand and F. Makayoma, *T. Neurochem.* **8**: No. 3/4, 230 (1961).

B8    D. C. Borg, in *Proceedings of the Second International Conference on the Peaceful Uses of Atomic Energy, Geneva, 1958*, Vol. 24, pp. 283–288, United Nations, New York, 1958.

B9    D. C. Borg, L. E. Grodzins, and G. C. Cotzias, USAEC Report BNL-419, Brookhaven National Laboratory, 1956.

B10  D. C. Borg *et al.*, *Intern. J. Appl. Radiation Isotopes* **11**: 10 (1961).
B11  H. J. M. Bowen, *J. Nucl. Energy* **3**: 18 (1956).
B12  H. J. M. Bowen, *Intern. J. Appl. Radiation Isotopes* **4**: 214 (1959).
B13  H. J. M. Bowen, *Intern. J. Appl. Radiation Isotopes* **5**: 227 (1959).
B14  H. J. M. Bowen, *Biochem. J.* **73**: 381 (1959).
B15  H. J. M. Bowen, *Biochem. J.* **77**: 79 (1960).
B16  H. J. M. Bowen and P. A. Cawse, British Report AERE-R/2925, 1959.
B17  H. J. M. Bowen and P. A. Cawse, *Analyst* **86**: 506 (1961).
B18  H. J. M. Bowen and J. A. Dymond, *Proc. Roy. Soc.* **B 144**: 355 (1958).
B19  D. Brune, Swedish Report AE-60, November 1961.
B20  A. M. Brues and O. H. Robertson, *J. Lab. Clin. Med.* **36**: 804 (1950).

C1  C. E. Castro and R. A. Schmitt, *Agricultural and Food Chemistry* **10**: 236 (1962).
C2  D. Comar *et al.*, *Bull. Soc. Chim. France* (1): 56 (1962).
C3  H. J. Curtis and J. D. Teresi, USAEC Report AECD-2872, 1946.

D1  R. McS. Dale, *Dissert. Abstr.* **20** (2): 472 (1959).
D2  J. A. W. Dalziel and R. C. H. Hsia, *J. Sci. Food Agr.* **12**: 127 (1961).
D3  E. Dennes, R. Tupper, and A. Wormall, *Nature* **187**: 302 (1960).
D4  W. A. Dewar and J. M. A. Lenihan, *Scot. Med. J.* **1**: 236 (1956).
D5  R. N. Diekel and A. B. Garrett, USAEC Report HW-SA-2206, 1961.
D6  A. N. Domonkos, *A.M.A. Arch. Dermatol.* **80**: 672 (1959).
D7  R. Druyan, T. G. Mitchell, and E. R. King, *J. Lab. Clin. Med.* **52**: 304 (1958).

F1  A. G. Ferguesson, W. A. Dewar, and H. Smith, *British Assoc. of Dermatology*, July 9, 1959.
F2  I. Fineman *et al.*, *Svensk Papperstid.* **60**: 132 (1957).
F3  I. Fogelstrom *et al.*, *Intern. J. Appl. Radiation Isotopes* **2**: 280 (1957).

G1  D. Gibbons, *Intern. J. Appl. Radiation Isotopes* **4**: 45 (1958).
G2  T. T. Gorsuch, *Analyst* **84**: 135 (1959).
G3  H. Gotte and J. A. Hattemer, *Z. Naturforsch.* **10b**: 343 (1955).
G4  C. A. Grant, B. Thafivelin, and R. Christell, *Acta Pharmacol. Toxicol.* **18**: 285 (1961).
G5  V. P. Guinn and J. C. Potter, *T. Agr. Food Chem.* **10** (3): 232 (1962).

H1  T. A. Hall, *Nucleonics* **12** (3): 34 (1954).
H2  G. E. Harrison and W. H. A. Raymond, *J. Nucl. Energy* **1**: 290 (1955).
H3  H. L. Helwig, J. K. Ashikawa, and E. R. Smith, USAEC Report UCRL-2655, University of California Radiation Laboratory, 1954.
H4  D. E. Hogue *et al.*, *J. Animal Sci.* **21**: 25 (1962).
H5  E. L. Hove, G. S. Fry, and K. Schwarz, *Proc. Soc. Exp. Biol. Med.* **98**: 27 (1958).
H6  W. P. Hutchinson, British Report AERE-MED/R-2317, 1960.

J1  A. Jacobson *et al.*, *J. Nucl. Med.* **2**: 289 (1961).

K1  D. G. Kaiser and W. W. Meinke, *Talanta* **3**: 255 (1960).
K2  K. Kameda, Abstract of the *3rd Japan Conference on Radioisotopes*, Tokyo, Sept. 14–16, 1959, 59/P-105, Japan Atomic Industrial Forum, Tokyo, 1959.
K3  C. Kellershohn, D. Comar, and C. LePoec, *Intern. J. Appl. Radiation Isotopes* **12**: 87 (1961).
K4  R. D. Keynes and P. R. Lewis, *Nature* **165**: 809 (1950).

REFERENCES

K5    R. D. Keynes and P. R. Lewis, *J. Physiol.* (London) **114:** 151 (1951).
K6    H. J. Koch and E. R. Smith, *J. Clin. Endocrinol. Metab.* **16:** 123 (1956).
K7    H. J. Koch *et al.*, *Cancer* **9:** 499 (1956).
K8    M. E. Kohn-Abrest, *Ann. Fals. Fraudes* **49:** 407 (1956).
K9    P. Kruger and I. J. Gruverman, *Intern. J. Appl. Radiation Isotopes* **13:** 106 (1962).

L1    G. W. Leddicotte *et al.*, in *Proceedings of the Second International Conference on the Peaceful Uses of Atomic Energy, Geneva, 1958*, Vol. 24, pp. 478–485, United Nations, New York, 1959.
L2    J. M. A. Lenihan, *Nature* **184:** 951 (1959).
L3    J. M. A. Lenihan, *Pure Appl. Chem.* **1:** 81 (1960).
L4    J. M. A. Lenihan, H. Smith, and J. G. Chalmers, *Nature* **181:** 1463 (1958).
L5    J. M. A. Lenihan and H. Smith, in *Proceedings of the Second International Conference on the Peaceful Uses of Atomic Energy, Geneva, 1958*, Vol. 26, p. 238, United Nations, New York, 1959.
L6    K. Ljunggren and T. Westermark, *Pure Applied Chem.* **1:** 127 (1960).

M1    W. D. Mackintosh and R. E. Jervis, USAEC Report CRDC-958, August 1960.
M2    Y. Matsumura and R. Fujino, *J. Biochem.* (Tokyo) **49:** 561 (1961).
M3    R. Michon, *Ann. Fals. Fraudes* **49:** 284 (1956).
M4    D. W. Moeller and G. W. Leddicotte, USAEC Report ORNL-2866, Oak Ridge National Laboratory, Feb. 18, 1960.
M5    J. H. Muller, in *Proceedings of the International Conference on Radioisotopes in Scientific Research, Paris, 1957*, Vol. 3, p. 667, Pergamon Press, New York, 1958.

N1    F. Nakyama and R. Blomstrand, *Acta Chem. Scand.* **15:** 595 (1961).
N2    G. S. Nixon, *Ph.D. Thesis*, Glasgow University, Scotland, 1959.

O1    E. Odeblad, B. Westin, and K. G. Malmford, *Acta Radiol.* **49:** 137 (1958).
O2    R. E. Ogborn *et al.*, *Am. J. Roentgenol., Radium Therapy Nucl. Med.* **85:** 976 (1961).

P1    P. S. Papavasiliou and G. C. Cotzias, *J. Biol. Chem.* **236:** 2365 (1961).
P2    D. H. Peirson and P. Iredale, in *Proceedings of the International Conference on Radioisotopes in Scientific Research*, Vol. 2, p. 197, Pergamon Press, New York, 1958.
P3    J. Pijck and J. Hoste, *Clin. Chim. Acta* **7:** 5 (1962).
P4    J. Pijck, J. Gillis, and J. Hoste, *Intern. J. Appl. Radiation Isotopes* **10:** 149 (1961).

R1    L. Reiffel and C. A. Stowe, *J. Lab. Clin. Med.* **49:** 286 (1957).

S1    K. Samsahl and R. Soeremark, Swedish Report AE-61, December 1961.
S2    R. Sato and W. P. Norris, USAEC Report ANL-4531, Argonne National Laboratory, p. 153, Oct. 1950.
S3    W. B. Savachuck, *J. Dental Research* **38** (1): 49 (1959).
S4    R. A. Schmitt and G. Zweig, *J. Agri. Food Chem.* **10:** 481 (1962).
S5    K. Schwarz and C. M. Foltz, *Federation Proc.* **17:** No. 1, March 1958.
S6    K. Schwarz and C. M. Foltz, *J. Biol. Chem.* **233** (1): 245 (1958).
S7    K. Schwarz *et al.*, *Metabolism* **8** (1): 88 (1959).
S8    A. Scott, *Brit. J. Dermatology* **70:** 196 (1958).
S9    A. A. Smales and B. D. Pate, *Analyst* **77:** 196 (1952).
S10   H. Smith, *Anal. Chem.* **31:** 1361 (1959).
S11   E. M. Sowden, *Biochem. J.* **70:** 712 (1958).
S12   E. M. Sowden and A. Pirie, *Biochem. J.* **70:** 716 (1958).

S13   E. M. Sowden and S. R. Stitch, *Biochem. J.* **67**: 104 (1957).
S14   R. P. Spencer, T. G. Mitchell, and E. R. King, *J. Lab. Clin. Med.* **50**: 646 (1957).
S15   R. P. Spencer, T. G. Mitchell, and E. R. King, *Intern. J. Appl. Radiation Isotopes* **3**: 104 (1958).
S16   R. P. Spencer, T. G. Mitchell, and E. R. King, *Am. J. Roentgenol. Therapy Nucl. Med.* **79**: 1053 (1958).
S17   E. H. Strickland and A. A. Benson, *Arch. Biochem. Biophys.* **88**: 344 (1960).

T1    C. A. Tobias and R. W. Dunn, *Science* **109**: 109 (1949).
T2    C. A. Tobias *et al.*, *Acta, Unio Intern. Contra Cancrum* **7**: 874 (1952).

V1    J. P. Vacick and J. E. Christian, *J. Pharm. Sci.* **50**: 225 (1961).
V2    B. Van Zanten, D. Decat, and G. Leliaenet, *Talanta* **9**: 213 (1962).
V3    J. Vincent, *Nature* **184** (7): 1332 (1959).

W1    H. N. Wagner, W. B. Nelp, and J. H. Dowling, *J. Clin. Invest.* **40**: 1984 (1961).
W2    T. Westermark and B. Sjostrand, *Intern. J. Appl. Radiation Isotopes* **9**: 78 (1960).
W3    T. Westermark and B. Sjostrand, *Intern. J. Appl. Radiation Isotopes* **9**: 1 (1960).
W4    J. D. Williams *et al.*, *Lancet* **1**: 464 (1957).
W5    F. P. W. Winteringham, *Analyst* **75**: 627 (1950).
W6    R. Wolfe, R. W. Dunn, and C. A. Tobias, *Extract from Radiation Laboratory,* USAEC Report UCRL-480, University of California, 1949.

Y1    Y. Yamada and M. Miyaguchi, *Japan Atomic Industrial Forum, Inc., and Japan Radioisotope Association*, Tokyo, Sept. 14–16, 1959.

## Table A.3—GEOSCIENCE APPLICATIONS OF NEUTRON ACTIVATION ANALYSIS

| Element | Nuclide formed | Sensitivity, $\mu g^*$ | Material analyzed | Concentration determined, $\mu g/g\dagger$ | Reference |
|---|---|---|---|---|---|
| Aluminum | $Al^{28}$ | 0.02 | Rocks | 10–1,000 | B15, R6 |
| | | | Ores | 0.5 to macro | L3, L4 |
| | | | Minerals | 10 to macro | R6 |
| Antimony | $Sb^{122}$ | 0.005 | Meteorites | 0.01–0.78 | S6, S7 |
| | | | Rocks | 0.2–1.1 | A3, H5 |
| | $Sb^{124}$ | 0.1 | Fresh waters | 0.01–0.06 | B7–B9 |
| Argon | $Ar^{41}$ | 0.01 | Potassium minerals | 1–100 | F1, M3 |
| | | | Sylvite | <10 | C5, C6 |
| | | | Meteorites | 1–100 | S16, W2 |
| Arsenic | $As^{76}$ | 0.002 | Pyrites | 0.18–0.33 | G1 |
| | | | Marine organisms | 0.3–5.4 | H2, F4, F5 |
| | | | Meteorites | 0.6–33 | S6, S7 |
| | | | Sea water | 0.018–0.051 | S10, D1 |
| | | | Rocks | 0.64–2.2 | H5 |
| | | | Fresh waters | <0.00002 | B7–B9 |
| Barium | $Ba^{131}$ | 2.0 | Sea water | <1.0 | B10, D1 |
| | $Ba^{139}$ | 0.04 | Stone meteorites | 0.39–310 | H6 |
| | | | Fresh waters | <0.005–0.02 | B7–B9 |
| Bismuth | $Bi^{210m}$ | 1.0 | Stone meteorites | 0.0001–0.006 | E3, R3, R4 |
| Bromine | $Br^{80}$ | 0.002 | Fresh waters | 0.05–0.3 | B7–B9 |
| | $Br^{82}$ | 0.007 | | | |
| Cadmium | $Cd^{115}$ | 0.05 | Rocks | 0.1–1.0 | B6, V1 |
| | $Cd^{117}$ | 0.1 | | | |
| Calcium | $Ca^{45}$ | | Fresh waters | 8.5–63 | B7–B9 |
| | $Ca^{48}$ | 3 | Feldspars | 5–100 | B12 |

## Table A.3 (continued)

| Element | Nuclide formed | Sensitivity, μg* | Material analyzed | Concentration determined, μg/g† | Reference |
|---|---|---|---|---|---|
| Cerium | Ce¹⁴³ | 0.2 | Monazite | 947 | F2 |
| | | | Allanite | 947 | F2 |
| | | | Rare earth minerals | 1–1000 | F3 |
| Cesium | Cs¹³⁴ᵐ | 0.01 | Basic rocks | 0.1–1.5 | A6, C1, C2, W4 |
| | Cs¹³⁴ | 0.06 | | | |
| | | | Minerals | 82 to macro | C1, C2 |
| | | | Meteorites | 0.005–0.1 | C1, C2, G8 |
| | | | Sea waters | 0.021–0.026 | D1, S8, S9, S11 |
| | | | Marine organisms | 0.04–0.15 | H8, S11 |
| | | | Marine sediments | 0.34–1.5 | B1, S11 |
| Chlorine | Cl³⁸ | 0.04 | Fresh waters | 3–21 | B7–B9 |
| Chromium | Cr⁵¹ | 0.005 | Meteorites | 5–185 | B5, S6, S7 |
| | Cr⁵⁵ | 0.8 | Granite rocks | <10 | C4, T1 |
| Cobalt | Co⁶⁰ᵐ | 0.0005 | Rocks | 2–54 | C3, S7, S8 |
| | Co⁶⁰ | 0.04 | | | T1 |
| | | | Meteorites | 3–1135 | G5, S8 |
| | | | Marine sediments | 3–12 | S8 |
| | | | Magnetic spherules | 0.01–0.3 | S9 |
| Copper | Cu⁶⁴ | 0.003 | Minerals | 1–100 | A2, H3 |
| | Cu⁶⁶ | 0.01 | Marine organisms | 1–10 | H2 |
| | | | Ores | 300–9,000 | L5 |
| | | | Rocks | 9–120 | A3, H5, S7, S8 |
| | | | Meteorites | 8–390 | S6–S8 |
| | | | Marine sediments | 25–79 | B1, H8, S8 |
| | | | Magnetic spherules | 0.0006–0.53 | S9 |
| | | | Fresh waters | 0.003–0.017 | B7–B9 |
| Dysprosium | Dy¹⁶⁵ᵐ | 0.002 | Monazite | 339 | F2 |
| | Dy¹⁶⁵ | 0.0004 | Allanite | 339 | F2 |
| | | | Rare earth minerals | 1–100 | F3 |
| Erbium | Er¹⁶⁹ | 0.03 | Monazite | 70 | F2 |
| | Er¹⁷¹ | 0.02 | Allanite | 70 | F2 |
| | | | Rare earth minerals | 1–100 | F3 |
| Europium | Eu¹⁵² (9.2 hr) | 0.00003 | Meteorites | <1 | B5 |
| | | | Monazite | 93 | F2 |
| | Eu¹⁵² (13 yr) | 0.002 | Allanite | 93 | F2 |
| | | | Rare earth minerals | 1–1,000 | F4 |
| | Eu¹⁵⁶ | 0.04 | Rocks | <0.8 | H5 |
| Gadolinium | Gd¹⁵⁹ | 0.02 | Monazite | 80 | F2 |
| | Gd¹⁶¹ | 0.1 | Allanite | 80 | F2 |
| | | | Rare earth minerals | Macro | F4 |
| Gallium | Ga⁷⁰ | 0.009 | Iron meteorites | 20–90 | B14, G5 |
| | Ga⁷² | 0.005 | Sphalerites | <10 | M4, M5 |
| Germanium | Ge⁷⁵ | 0.05 | Meteorites | 0.3–359 | S6, S7 |
| | Ge⁷⁷ | 0.4 | | | |
| Gold | Au¹⁹⁸ | 0.0003 | Ores | 1–100 | A1 |
| | | | Smaltine | 5.2–45.8 | G2, G3 |
| | | | Iron meteorites | 2.2–3.5 | G4, G5 |
| | | | Marine organisms | 0.002–0.09 | F5, F6 |
| | | | Rocks | 0.01–0.02 | H5, S5, V2–V4 |
| Hafnium | Hf¹⁷⁵ | 0.06 | Minerals | 1–100 | M2, R1 |
| | Hf¹⁸¹ | 0.03 | Meteorites | 1–100 | M1 |
| Holmium | Ho¹⁶⁶ | 0.0003 | Monazite | 290 | F2 |
| | | | Allanite | 290 | F2 |
| | | | Rare earth minerals | 1–100 | F3 |
| Indium | In¹¹⁶ | 0.03 | Meteorites | <0.001 | S3 |
| | | | Rocks | 0.02–0.18 | I1, I2, S12, W1 |
| | | | Minerals | 0.02–0.5 | W1 |
| Iodine | I¹²⁸ | 0.003 | Meteorites | <10 | G6, G7 |
| Iridium | Ir¹⁹² | 0.002 | Sphalerites | <1.0 | A4 |
| | | | Meteorites | <1.0 | R8 |

## Table A.3 (continued)

| Element | Nuclide formed | Sensitivity, $\mu g$* | Material analyzed | Concentration determined, $\mu g/g$† | Reference |
|---|---|---|---|---|---|
| Iron | Fe$^{59}$ | 0.10 | Magnetic spherules | 10–60 | S9 |
| | | | Ores | 10–100 | L3 |
| Lanthanum | La$^{140}$ | 0.002 | Monazite | 273 | F2 |
| | | | Allanite | 273 | F2 |
| | | | Rare earth minerals | 1–1,000 | F5 |
| | | | Rocks | 27–150 | H5 |
| Lutetium | Lu$^{177}$ | 0.0002 | Monazite | 65–130 | F2 |
| | | | Allanite | 65–130 | F2 |
| | | | Rare earth minerals | 1–100 | F3 |
| | | | Minerals | 0.0001–0.1 | H11 |
| | | | Meteorites | 0.0001–0.1 | H11 |
| Magnesium | Mg$^{27}$ | 1 | Fresh waters | 1–21 | B7–B9 |
| Manganese | Mn$^{56}$ | 0.0006 | Ores | 300–3,000 | L3, L5 |
| | | | Fresh waters | 0.0004–0.001 | B7–B9 |
| Mercury | Hg$^{197}$ | 0.006 | Stone meteorites | 0.016–0.052 | E3 |
| | | | Marine organisms | <0.01 | H2 |
| Molybdenum | Mo$^{99}$ | 0.1 | Silicate minerals | <10 | H4 |
| | | | Marine organisms | 17 | F4, F5 |
| Neodymium | Nd$^{147}$ | 0.01 | Monazite | 390 | F2 |
| | | | Allanite | 390 | F2 |
| | | | Rare earth minerals | 1–1,000 | F3 |
| Nickel | Ni$^{65}$ | 0.4 | Tektites | 1–15 | E2 |
| | | | Meteorites | 68–20,000 | G5, S8 |
| | | | Rocks | 1–78 | S5 |
| | | | Marine sediments | 9–68 | H8, S8, S13 |
| | | | Magnetic spherules | 0.03–3.9 | S9 |
| Osmium | Os$^{191m}$ | 0.003 | Iron meteorites | 0.01–1.0 | H12, H13 |
| | Os$^{191}$ | 0.02 | Molybdenites | 0.006–8 | M2, R1 |
| | | | Gadolinite | 0.0003 | M2, R1 |
| Palladium | Pd$^{109}$ | 0.005 | Iron meteorites | 2–6 | B14, G5 |
| | Pd$^{109m}$ | 0.3 | Rocks | 0.01–0.02 | S5, V4 |
| Phosphorus | P$^{32}$ | 0.04 | Fresh waters | 0.0017–0.029 | B7–B9 |
| Potassium | K$^{42}$ | 0.07 | Rocks | 1–10,000 | A6, W6 |
| | | | Dunite | 1–1,000 | S1 |
| | | | Silicates | Macro | W6, W7 |
| | | | Minerals | Macro | W7, W8 |
| | | | Fresh waters | 9.5–3.6 | B7–B9 |
| | | | Feldspars | Macro | B12 |
| Rhenium | Re$^{186}$ | 0.0007 | Iron meteorites | 0.1 to 100 | B13, G4, H11–H13 |
| | Re$^{188}$ | 0.0006 | | | |
| | | | Marine organisms | 0.005–0.07 | F4, F5 |
| | | | Molybdenites | 100–3,300 | M2, R1 |
| | | | Gadolinites | 0.52 | M2, R1 |
| | | | Rocks | 0.010–0.012 | M6, M7 |
| Rhodium | Rh$^{104}$ | 0.001 | Meteorites | 0.186 | S3 |
| Rubidium | Rb$^{86}$ | 0.03 | Rocks | 1–219 | C1, C2, S7 |
| | Rb$^{88}$ | 0.3 | Minerals | 66 to macro | C1, C2 |
| | | | Meteorites | 0.04–3.2 | C1, C2, S6, S7 |
| | | | Sea water | 1–1.4 | D1, S11 |
| | | | Marine organisms | 5.4–19 | S11 |
| | | | Marine sediments | 9.6–24.2 | S11 |
| | | | Fresh waters | <0.2 | B7–B9 |
| Ruthenium | Ru$^{103}$ | 0.1 | Minerals | 0.000001 | M2 |
| | Ru$^{105}$ | 0.1 | Iron meteorite | 0.000001 | M2 |
| Samarium | Sm$^{153}$ | 0.0005 | Monazite | 187 | F2 |
| | | | Allanite | 187 | F2 |
| | | | Rare earth minerals | 1–1,000 | F3 |
| | | | Rocks | 5–12 | H5 |
| Scandium | Sc$^{46m}$ | 0.0006 | Stone meteorites | 3.0 | B5, K3 |
| | Sc$^{46}$ | 0.003 | Rocks | 2.8–34 | H5, K1, K3 |

## Table A.3 (continued)

| Element | Nuclide formed | Sensitivity, $\mu g$* | Material analyzed | Concentration determined, $\mu g/g$† | Reference |
|---------|---------------|----------------------|-------------------|-------------------------------------|-----------|
| Selenium | Se$^{75}$ | 0.5 | Stone meteorites | 0.01–10 | S2 |
|  | Se$^{77}$ | 0.02 |  |  |  |
| Silicon | Si$^{31}$ | 0.1 | Rocks | 10–1,000 | B15 |
|  |  |  | Fresh waters | 1.7–6.6 | B7–B9 |
|  |  |  | Ores | Macro | L3 |
| Silver | Ag$^{108}$ | 0.0001 | Galena | 0.03–0.5 | M8 |
|  | Ag$^{110}$ | 0.3 | Blende | 0.03–0.5 | M8 |
|  |  |  | Rocks | 0.03–0.17 | M9, M10 |
|  |  |  | Meteorites | 0.094 | S3 |
| Sodium | Na$^{24}$ | 0.006 | Rocks | 10–1,000 | B15 |
|  |  |  | Dunite | 0.1–10,000 | S1 |
|  |  |  | Biotite | Macro | W7 |
|  |  |  | Fresh waters | 0.1–21.2 | B7–B9 |
|  |  |  | Feldspars | Macro | B12 |
| Strontium | Sr$^{85}$ | 10 | Sea water | <1.0 | D1, B10 |
|  | Sr$^{87}$ | 0.1 | Rocks | <10 | L6, T1 |
|  |  |  | Fresh waters | 0.10–1.2 | B7–B9 |
| Tantalum | Ta$^{182}$ | 0.1 | Rocks | 0.4–317 | A7, A9, B11, H10, M11 |
|  |  |  | Meteorites | 0.0009–0.030 | A8, A13 |
|  |  |  | Ores | 0.01–10,000 | E4, K5 |
|  |  |  | Silicate minerals | 0.1–10 | H4 |
| Tellurium | Te$^{131}$ | 0.2 | Meteorites | 0.1–2.3 | G7, S2 |
| Thallium | Tl$^{206}$ | 0.3 | Meteorites | 0.0001–0.0014 | E3, K4, R3, R4 |
|  |  |  | Rocks | 0.001–1.0 | K4, M9, M10 |
|  |  |  | Minerals | 0.001–0.01 | K4 |
| Thorium | Th$^{232}$ | 0.004 | Stone meteorites | 0.006–0.54 | B2, E3, J1 |
|  |  |  | Iron meteorites | 0.00005–0.0001 | B3, B4, J1 |
|  |  |  | Ores | 10–100 | L1 |
|  |  |  | Minerals | 0.1–10 | R7 |
|  |  |  | Fresh waters | <0.001–0.2 | B7–B9 |
| Thulium | Tm$^{170}$ | 0.002 | Monazite | 40 | F2 |
|  |  |  | Allanite | 40 | F2 |
|  |  |  | Rare earth minerals | 1–100 | F3 |
| Tin | Sn$^{112}$ | 10 | Silicate minerals | <100 | H4 |
| Tungsten | W$^{187}$ | 0.002 | Rocks | 0.08–1.2 | A8, A9 |
|  |  |  | Meteorites | 0.07–2.7 | A8, A9 |
|  |  |  | Silicate minerals | 0.1–10 | H4, P2 |
|  |  |  | Marine organisms | 0.005–0.46 | F4, F5 |
|  |  |  | Ores | 1–200 | L1 |
|  |  |  | Minerals | 0.001–0.10 | M2 |
| Uranium | U$^{239}$ | 0.01 | Sea water | 0.0001–0.5 | D1, S17, W5 |
|  |  |  | Ores | 0.1–10,000 | A1, H1, L1, W3 |
|  |  |  | Minerals | 0.1–10 | A2, F3, S6 |
|  |  |  | Rocks | 0.2–3.2 | A5, E5, H5, S4 |
|  |  |  | Stone meteorites | 0.001–0.13 | B2, E1, H6, H9, P1, S14 |
|  |  |  | Iron meteorites | 0.0002–0.001 | G7, R2, R5, S14 |
|  |  |  | Limestone | 0.1–10 | H7 |
| Vanadium | V$^{52}$ | 0.002 | Marine organisms | 1–262 | F4, F5 |
|  |  |  | Rocks | 13–246 | K1, K2 |
|  |  |  | Meteorites | 13 | K2 |
|  |  |  | Ores | 1–1,000 | L3 |
| Zinc | Zn$^{65}$ | 1 | Fresh waters | <0.01–0.47 | B7–B9 |
| Zinconium | Zr$^{95}$ | 5 | Meteorites | 0.1–5 | M1 |
|  | Zr$^{97}$ | 5 |  |  |  |

* Calculated sensitivities for $\mu g$ of element detectable by use of the product nuclide indicated. Calculations based on:

    1. Thermal flux of $1 \times 10^{12}$ neutrons/cm$^2$/sec.

    2. Lower limit of 40 dis/sec detectable.

    3. Saturation factor of 0.5 or 1-wk irradiation whichever is shorter.

    4. $\sigma$ values from Sullivan Trilinear Chart of Nuclides.

† Experimentally determined. Range of concentration shown established on basis of a number of determinations.

*REFERENCES*

A1  A. Abrao, Brazilian Report IEA-7, Sao Paulo Universidade, Instituto de Energia Atomica, 1959.
A2  A. Abrao, Brazilian Report IEA/RQ-8, Sao Paulo Universidade, Instituto de Energia Atomica, April 1959.
A3  A. A. Abdullaev *et al.*, *Izv. Akad. Nauk. Turkm.*, *SSR. Ser. Fiz-5 Tekhn. Khim. i Geol. Nauk* **5**: 126–130 (1960).
A4  A. A. Abdullaev *et al.*, *Zh. Analit. Khim.* **15**: 701 (1960).
A5  J. A. S. Adams, J. E. Richardson, and C. C. Templeton, *Geochim. Cosmochim. Acta* **13**: 270 (1958).
A6  L. H. Ahrens and R. A. Edge, *Geochim. Cosmochim. Acta* **25**: 91 (1961).
A7  E. Anders, R. N. Sen Sarma, and P. H. Hato, *J. Chem. Phys.* **24**: 622 (1956).
A8  D. H. F. Atkins and A. A. Smales, British Report AERE-R-3099, September 1957.
A9  D. H. F. Atkins and A. A. Smales, *Anal. Chim. Acta* **22** (5): 462 (1960).

B1  V. I. Baranov and L. A. Kuzmina, in *Proceedings of the International Conference on Radioisotopes in Scientific Research, Paris, 1957*, Vol. 2, p. 601, Pergamon Press, New York, 1958.
B2  G. L. Bate, J. R. Huizenga, and H. A. Potratz, *Science* **126**: 612 (1957).
B3  G. L. Bate, H. A. Potratz, and J. R. Huizenga, *Geochim. Cosmochim. Acta* **14** (1–2): 118 (1958).
B4  G. L. Bate, J. R. Huizenga, and H. A. Potratz, *Geochim. Cosmochim. Acta* **16**: 88 (1959).
B5  G. L. Bate, H. A. Potratz, and J. R. Huizenga, *Geochim. Cosmochim. Acta* **18**: 101 (1960).
B6  L. I. Bilefield and E. A. Vincent, *Analyst* **86**: 386 (1961).
B7  R. L. Blanchard and G. W. Leddicotte, USAEC Report ORNL-2620, Oak Ridge National Laboratory, 1959.
B8  R. L. Blanchard, G. W. Leddicotte, and D. W. Moeller, in *Proceedings of the Second International Conference on the Peaceful Uses of Atomic Energy, Geneva, 1958*, Vol. 28, p. 511, United Nations, New York, 1959.
B9  R. L. Blanchard, G. W. Leddicotte, and D. W. Moeller, *J. Am. Water Works Assoc.* **51** (8): 967 (1959).
B10  H. J. M. Bowen, *J. Marine Biol. Assoc. U. K.* **35**: 451 (1956).
B11  G. E. Boyd and Q. V. Larson, *J. Phys. Chem.* **60**: 707 (1956).
B12  J. E. S. Bradley and O. Bradley, *Mineral. Mag.* **31**: 164 (1956).
B13  H. Brown and E. D. Goldberg, *Phys. Rev.* **76**: 1260 (1949).
B14  H. Brown and E. D. Goldberg, *Science* **109**: 347 (1949).
B15  G. M. Brownell *et al.*, *Trans. Roy. Soc. Canada*, [IV] **51**: 19 (1957).

C1  M. J. Cabell and A. A. Smales, *Analyst* **82**: 390 (1957).
C2  M. J. Cabell and A. Thomas, British Report AERE-C/R-1725, 1955.
C3  M. H. Carr and K. K. Turekian, *Geochim. Cosmochim. Acta* **23**: 9 (1961).
C4  M. H. Carr and K. K. Turekian, *Geochim. Cosmochim. Acta* **26**: 411 (1962).
C5  S. C. Curran, *Atomics* **3**: 5 (1952).
C6  S. C. Curran, *Quart. Rev.*, London **7**: 1 (1953).

D1  D. Dyrssen and P. O. Nyman, *Acta Radiol.* **43**: 421 (1955).

E1  K. H. Ebert, H. Koenig, and H. Waenke, *Z. Naturforsch.* **12a**: 763 (1957).
E2  W. D. Ehmann, *Geochim. Cosmochim. Acta* **19**: 149 (1960).

E3     W. D. Ehmann and J. R. Huizenga, *Geochim. Cosmochim. Acta* **17**: 125 (1959).

E4     G. J. Eicholz, *Nucleonics* **10** (12): 58 (1952).

E5     G. J. Eicholz, *Nucleonics* **15** (7): 114 (1957).

F1     H. Fechtig, W. Gentner, and J. Zahringer, *Geochim. Cosmochim. Acta* **19**: 70 (1960).

F2     I. Fujii, *J. At. Energy Soc. Japan* **3**: 9 (1961).

F3     I. Fujii, *J. At. Energy Soc. Japan* **3**: 186 (1961); *Nucl. Sci. Abstr.* **15**: 18018 (1961).

F4     R. Fukai and W. W. Meinke, *Nature* **184**: 815 (1959).

F5     R. Fukai and W. W. Meinke, *Limnol. Oceanog.* **4**: 398 (1959).

G1     P. Gauthier, *International Congress of Pure and Applied Chemistry. 15th, Lisbon, 1956.* Actas do Congresso, pp. 627–33, Lisbon, 1957.

G2     P. Gauthier, *Acta Electronica* **3** (3-4): 295 (1959).

G3     P. Gauthier, *Ind. Chim. Belge* **20** (II): 281 (1954).

G4     E. D. Goldberg and H. Brown, *Anal. Chem.* **22**: 308 (1950).

G5     E. Goldberg, A. Uchiyama, and H. Brown, *Geochim. Cosmochim. Acta* **2**: 1 (1951).

G6     G. C. Goles and E. Anders, *J. Geophys. Research* **66**: 3075 (1961).

G7     G. C. Goles and E. Anders, *Geochim. Cosmochim. Acta* **26**: 723 (1962).

G8     B. M. Gordon, L. Friedman, and G. Edwards, *Geochim. Cosmochim. Acta* **12**: 470 (1957).

H1     W. W. Happ and J. L. Horwood, *Science* **115**: 622 (1952).

H2     H. Hamaguchi, R. Kuroda, and K. Hosohara, *J. At. Energy Soc. Japan* **2**: 317 (1960).

H3     H. Hamaguchi, R. Kuroda, N. Onuma, and T. Yasunaga, *Nippon Kagaku Zasshi* **82**: 7190 (1961).

H4     H. Hamaguchi *et al.*, *J. At. Energy Soc. of Japan* **3**: 800 (1961).

H5     H. Hamaguchi *et al.*, *Geochim. Cosmochim. Acta* **23**: 296 (1961).

H6     H. Hamaguchi, G. W. Reed, and A. Turkevich, *Geochim. Cosmochim. Acta* **12**: 337 (1957).

H7     L. A. Haskin, H. W. Fearing, and F. S. Rowland, *Anal. Chem.* **33**: 1298 (1961).

H8     L. Haskin and M. A. Gehl, *J. Geophys. Research* **67**: 2537 (1962).

H9     F. Hernegger and H. Waenke, *Z. Naturforsch.* **12a**: 759 (1957).

H10    W. Herr, *Z. Naturforsch.* **9a**: 907 (1954).

H11    W. Herr, *Pure Appl. Chem.* **1**: 35 (1960).

H12    W. Herr and W. Hoffmeister, Report RICC-155, Sept. 6–17, 1960.

H13    W. Herr, *Z. Naturforsch.* **15a**: 99 (1960).

I1     H. Irving, *Anal. Khim.* **9**: 249 (1958); *Anal. Abstr.* **7**: 414 (1960).

I2     H. Irving, R. Van, J. Smith, and L. Salmon, *Analyst* **82**: 549 (1957).

J1     E. N. Jenkins, *Analyst* **80**: 301 (1955).

K1     D. M. Kemp and A. A. Smales, *Geochim. Cosmochim. Acta* **18**: 149 (1960).

K2     D. M. Kemp and A. A. Smales, *Anal. Chim. Acta* **23**: 397 (1960).

K3     D. M. Kemp and A. A. Smales, *Anal. Chim. Acta* **23**: 410 (1960).

K4     C. Kim, *J. Korean Chem. Soc.* **1**: 26 (1961).

K5     A. Kohn, *Compt. Rend.* **236**: 1419 (1953).

L1     G. W. Leddicotte, J. F. Emery, and A. P. Grimanis, USAEC Report ORNL-2866, Oak Ridge National Laboratory, Feb. 18, 1960.

L2    G. W. Leddicotte and D. W. Moeller, ORNL CF-61-6-118 (May 1961).
L3    D. I. Leipunskaya, Z. E. Gauer, and G. N. Flerov, *Atomnaya Energiya* **6**: 315 (1959).
L4    J. E. Lewis, *Symposium on Radioisotopes in Metals Analysis and Testing, 62nd Annual Meeting, Atlantic City, 1959 Special Training Publication No. 261*, ASTM, Philadelphia, 1960.
L5    E. M. Lobanov et al., *Zhur. Anal. Khim.* **16**: 25 (1961).
L6    B. A. Loveridge et al., *Anal. Chim. Acta* **23**: 154 (1960).

M1    E. Merz, *Geochim. Cosmochim. Acta* **26**: 347 (1962).
M2    E. Merz and W. Herr, in *Proceedings of the Second International Conference on the Peaceful Uses of Atomic Energy, Geneva, 1958*, Vol. 28, p. 491, United Nations, New York, 1958.
M3    A. Moljk, R. W. P. Drever, and S. C. Curran, *Nucleonics* **13** (2): 44 (1955).
M4    D. F. C. Morris and F. M. Brewer, *Geochim. Cosmochim. Acta* **5**: 134 (1954).
M5    D. F. C. Morris and M. E. Chambers, *Talanta* **5**: 147 (1960).
M6    D. F. C. Morris and F. W. Fifield, *Talanta* **8**: 612 (1961).
M7    D. F. C. Morris and F. W. Fifield, *Geochim. Cosmochim. Acta* **25**: 232 (1961).
M8    D. F. C. Morris and R. A. Killick, *Anal. Chim. Acta* **20**: 587 (1959).
M9    D. F. C. Morris and R. A. Killick, *Talanta* **4**: 51 (1960).
M10   D. F. C. Morris and R. A. Killick, *Geochim. Cosmochim. Acta* **19**: 139 (1960).
M11   D. F. C. Morris and A. Olya, *Talanta* **4**: 194 (1960).

P1    K. A. Petrzhak, I. N. Semenyushkin, and M. A. Bak, *Geochemistry* **2**: 149 (1958).
P2    I. N. Plaksin, I. F. Slepchenko, and L. P. Starik, *Doklady Akad. Nauk. SSSR* **137**: 880 (1961).

R1    A. Rassoul, J. Langhoff, and W. Herr, *Z. Electrochem.* **64**: 1036 (1960).
R2    G. W. Reed, H. Hamaguchi, and A. Turkevich, *Geochim. Cosmochim. Acta* **13**: 248 (1958).
R3    G. W. Reed, K. Kigoshi, and A. Turkevich, in *Proceedings of the Second International Conference on the Peaceful Uses of Atomic Energy, Geneva, 1958*, Vol. 28, p. 486, United Nations, New York, 1958.
R4    G. W. Reed, K. Kigoshi, and A. Turkevich, *Geochim. Cosmochim. Acta* **20**: 794 (1955).
R5    G. W. Reed and A. Turkevich, *Nature* **176**: 794 (1955).
R6    D. Rhodes and W. Motts, *Anal. Chem.* **34**: 1507 (1962).
R7    G. Rona, *Trans. Am. Geophys. Union* **38** (5): 754 (1957).
R8    P. R. Rushbrook and W. D. Ehmann, *Geochim. Cosmochim. Acta* **26**: 649 (1962).

S1    L. Salmon, British Report AERE-C/M-323, 1957.
S2    U. Schindewolf, *Geochim. Cosmochim. Acta* **19**: 134 (1960).
S3    U. Schindewolf and M. Wahlgren, *Geochim. Cosmochim. Acta* **18**: 36 (1960).
S4    A. A. Smales, *Analyst* **77**: 778 (1952).
S5    A. A. Smales, *Geochim. Cosmochim. Acta* **8**: 300 (1955).
S6    A. A. Smales, in *Proceedings of the First International Conference on the Peaceful Uses of Atomic Energy, Geneva, 1955*, Vol. 9, p. 273, United Nations, New York, 1956.
S7    A. A. Smales et al., in *Proceedings of the Second International Conference on the Peaceful Uses of Atomic Energy, Geneva, 1958*, Vol. 2, p. 242, United Nations, New York, 1958.
S8    A. A. Smales, D. Mapper, and A. J. Wood, *Analyst* **82**: 75 (1957).

S9    A. A. Smales, D. Mapper, and A. J. Wood, *Geochim. Cosmochim. Acta* **13:** 123 (1958).

S10   A. A. Smales and B. D. Pate, *Analyst* **77:** 188 (1952).

S11   A. A. Smales and L. Salmon, *Analyst* **80:** 37 (1955).

S12   A. A. Smales, R. J. Van Smit, and H. Irving, *Analyst* **82:** 539 (1957).

S13   A. A. Smales and J. D. H. Wiseman, *Nature* **175:** 464 (1955).

S14   I. E. Starik and M. M. Shats, *Geochemistry* **2:** 140 (1956).

S15   D. C. Stewart and W. C. Bentley, *Science* **120:** 50 (1954).

S16   R. S. Stoenner and J. Zahringer, *Geochim. Cosmochim. Acta* **15:** 40 (1958).

T1    K K. Turckian and M. H. Carr, *Geochim. Cosmochim. Acta* **24:** 1 (1961).

V1    E. A. Vincent and L. I. Bilfield, *Geochim. Cosmochim. Acta* **19:** 63 (1960).

V2    E. A. Vincent and J. H. Crocket, *Geochim. Cosmochim. Acta* **18:** 130 (1960).

V3    E. A. Vincent and J. H. Crocket, *Geochim. Cosmochim. Acta* **18:** 143 (1960).

V4    E. A. Vincent and A. A. Smales, *Geochim. Cosmochim. Acta* **9:** 154 (1956).

W1    L. R. Wager, R. J. Van Smit, and H. Irving, *Geochim. Cosmochim. Acta* **13:** 81 (1958).

W2    H. Wanke and H. Koenig, *Z. Naturforsch.* **14a:** 860 (1959).

W3    H. Wanke and E. U. Monse, *Z. Naturforsch* **10a:** 667 (1955).

W4    R. K. Webster, J. W. Morgan, and A. A. Smales, *Geochim. Cosmochim. Acta* **15:** 150 (1958).

W5    J. D. Wilson *et al.*, *Anal. Chim. Acta* **23:** 505 (1960).

W6    J. W. Winchester, *Anal. Chem.* **33:** 1007 (1961).

W7    J. W. Winchester, *Trans. Am. Geophys. Union* **39:** 536 (1958).

W8    J. W. Winchester and M. I. Goldstein, USAEC Report AECU-3772, 1958.

# *Appendix B*

This presents general information on safe-handling techniques for radio-isotopes and on licensing requirements. In activation analysis these requirements usually can be met without undue difficulty. Those interested in more in-depth information should consult the vast radiation-safety literature available in technical libraries. Several suggested references are listed at the end of this Appendix.

## B-1 RADIATION SAFETY

Oscar M. Bizzell

U. S. Atomic Energy Commission

In radiochemical analysis, the radioisotope is perhaps the safest item in the procedure. The total amount of radioactivity will usually be in the low micro-curie range. The potential hazard from this quantity is quite small when compared to strong acids, organic solvents, flame, electricity, etc., that may be used in carrying out the analysis.

In some activation procedures, however, appreciable unwanted short-lived radioactivity may be generated along with radioisotopes of the element being analyzed. For some types of samples (e.g., those containing appreciable sodium) this unwanted additional radioactivity might reach a millicurie or more. Therefore it is advisable to determine the total radioactivity of the sample before starting the analysis and to design the handling procedures accordingly.

In case remote handling and processing of the sample is indicated, many pieces of standard laboratory equipment can be adapted for this purpose. The complexity of the equipment and the degree of remoteness necessary depend on the type and level of activity and on the nature of the procedure involved. For operations involving microcurie quantities of radioisotopes, it is possible to use standard equipment and techniques with very few modifications. External radiations present no particular problem at this level if operations are performed quickly and carefully by hand. If handling operations are prolonged, however, tongs and test tube holders probably should be used. When millicurie quantities of beta- and gamma-ray emitters with a total radiation energy of greater than approximately 0.3 Mev are involved, all operations should be carried out at

172

extended distances and with some added shielding. Much of this equipment can be fabricated from general laboratory supplies or constructed in a small laboratory shop.

No specific type of equipment or set of laboratory handling techniques will be applicable to all situations. Thus a few rules of common sense should be applied in every instance. It is usually advisable that no radioisotope work be carried out until dummy runs are made with nonradioactive materials. Such runs should be repeated until the worker has acquired the manual dexterity necessary for efficient operation and the procedure is routinized.

A great deal of time and expense may be saved if the importance of distance as a protection from radiation is fully realized and applied. An example will serve to illustrate how effective remote handling may be. Two inches of lead will lower the roentgen dosage rate from 1 mc of an isotope emitting 1.0-Mev gamma rays from approximately 210 mr/hr to 5 mr/hr. This is based on the assumption that the active material is resting on the lead surface, that it is a point source, and that measurements are taken at the opposite face of the shield. To achieve the same roentgen dosage rate per millicurie for the same sample by the use of distance alone, it is only necessary to have 14 in. between the radioactive source and the point at which it is desired to have a dosage of only 5 mr/hr.

Three simple laboratory operations, Figs. B.1 to B.3, illustrate the degree of remoteness and the amount of shielding necessary with increasing levels of radioactivity.

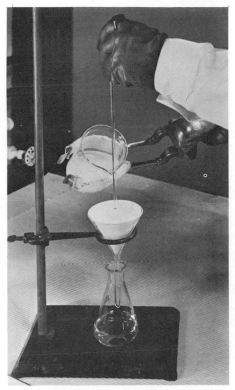

FIG. B1—Filtering $P^{32}$ labeled ammonium phosphomolybdate at 10-$\mu$c level.

The radiation from pure beta-ray-emitting radioisotopes has a comparatively low penetrating power; therefore massive shielding usually is not necessary. Figure B.1 illustrates precautions that should be observed when filtering a solution containing a hard beta emitter (e.g., $P^{32}$) at the 10-$\mu$c level. The suggested auxiliary equipment for work at the 10-$\mu$c level includes rubber gloves, a simple pair of tongs for holding the beaker containing the radioactive solution, and perhaps a beta-ray-sensitive personnel monitoring device.

The hands and other parts of the worker's body should be kept out of the area immediately over the open radioisotope container. It should be remembered that there is a sharp increase in radiation intensity as solutions containing beta-ray-emitting isotopes are evaporated.

Owing to its absorption characteristics, gamma radiation requires the use of

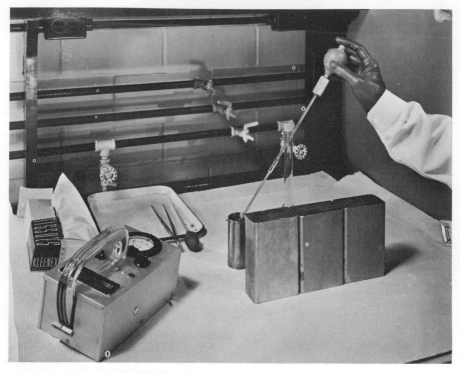

Fig. B2—Preparing a 10-$\mu$c dilution of $I^{131}$.

more dense shielding or of greater distance from the source for personnel protection. Indeed, a combination of both is generally used to achieve a maximum degree of economy consistent with safe-handling techniques. Figs. B.2 and B.3 illustrate precautions that should be observed when preparing dilutions of radioiodine, $I^{131}$, containing 10 $\mu$c and 10 mc, respectively. The suggested auxiliary equipment for performing this operation at the 10-$\mu$c level includes a few lead or steel bricks for shielding, a bulb type pipet, rubber gloves, and perhaps a suitable survey instrument for checking radiation field intensities. When gamma emitters are used, whole-body irradiation is of primary importance.

Figure B.3 illustrates additional protective measures that should be observed when performing this operation at the 10-mc level. At this level, a suitable personnel monitoring device probably should be worn by the worker. The same type of handling procedures will suffice for beta emitters, such as $P^{32}$. Also, it is usually advisable that the work be performed inside a radioisotope fume hood with an open-face linear air velocity of 50 to 100 ft/min. A more elaborate shield is provided for the protection of the worker; a mirror which permits the equipment to be viewed indirectly is mounted in the back of the hood, and a pipetting unit is used which affords the worker a greater degree of protection.

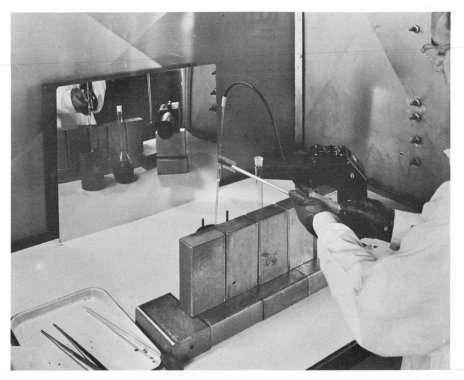

FIG. B3—Preparing a 10-mc dilution of $I^{131}$.

### B-1.1 Assorted Tongs

Practically all work up to the 1-mc level is based on the *tongs-and-tweezers* technique. This means that regular laboratory procedures with few modifications are used if adequate distance between the source and the worker is maintained by the appropriate use of tongs. Figure B.4 shows an assortment of commercially available tongs, tweezers, and modifications thereof that has found wide use in radioisotope laboratories. Whenever possible, the tips or jaws of the tongs should be covered with a removable material such as asbestos or rubber as illustrated on two of the tongs. This often permits a better grip on the object being handled and also helps prevent the tongs from becoming contaminated.

### B-1.2 Trays and Disposable Surfaces

It is often more expedient to use disposable trays and surfaces in the immediate work areas where the probability of contamination is extremely high rather than

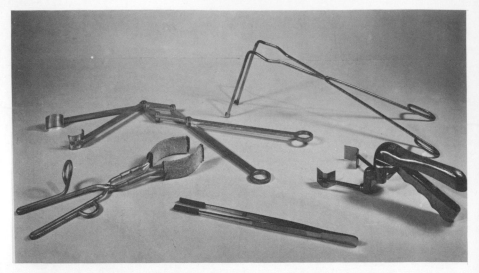

Fig. B4—Assorted tongs for use in a radioisotope laboratory.

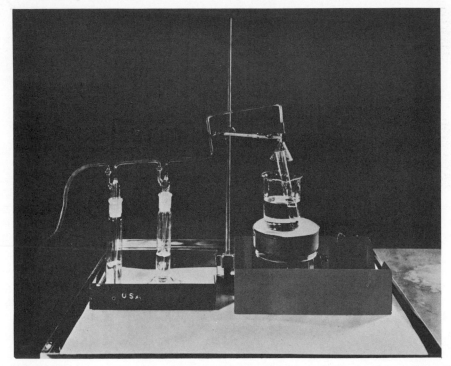

Fig. B5—Apparatus for concentrating radioactive solutions and for dissolving radioactive solids.

to rely completely on decontamination of the permanent surfaces. The expendable surfaces should have a high susceptibility to contamination, e.g., absorbent paper with a plastic backing, and should be readily interchangeable so that contaminated sections can be replaced. Disposable trays may be made of wood or plastic and coated with a strippable paint to make them watertight. The strippable coat also lengthens the average usable life of the tray since small amounts of contamination may be removed by stripping away the protective coating and the tray may be repainted for future use. Nonexpendable trays, e.g., stainless steel, are often used as auxiliary equipment and are sometimes incorporated as a part of the table top.

### B-1.3 Dissolution and Evaporation Apparatus

It is often necessary to use heat in concentrating radioisotope solutions or in dissolving radioactive solids. When the activity exceeds the tracer (microcurie) level, the heating should be done under a closed system to prevent the spread of contamination. Figure B.5 shows a system that might be used for accomplishing this operation. The radioactive material is contained in a test tube that is heated by a water or oil bath. An inverted funnel is mounted so that vapors or particulate matter evolved from the radioactive solution will be carried to the scrubbing flasks and trapped. The scrubbing solutions, which are determined by the radioisotope being used, remove radioactive droplets that are entrained and, hence, prevent the spread of contamination. As an added precaution, a sheet of asbestos is used to cover the hot plate, and the entire unit is placed in disposable trays.

### B-1.4 Addition of Reagents

The simple addition of reagents to radioactive solutions may be accomplished as illustrated in Fig. B.6. The use of long droppers permits reagents to be added in a conventional manner without excessive radiation exposure to the hands. Stirring may be performed with a regular stirring rod held in the manner shown. More elaborate equipment, of course, can be readily assembled from stock items.

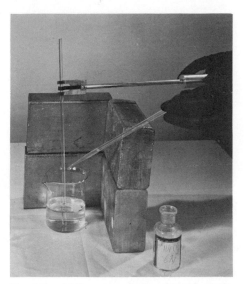

Fig. B6—Adding reagents to radioactive solution.

### B-1.5 Radioisotope-waste Containers

A variety of containers for both solid and liquid waste is advisable for the efficient operation of a radioisotope laboratory. Small quantities of radioactivity in solution may be disposed of directly down the drain under carefully controlled conditions. One should be careful to avoid radioactive contamination around the sink, however, since it can easily lead to cross contamination of other glassware. This is a technical problem well known to radioisotope workers and a factor that has ruined many otherwise good experiments.

Large-mouthed polyethylene bottles are excellent for radioactive liquid waste too concentrated for disposal down the drain. The container should be appropriately labelled.

Radioactive-waste receptacles (usually small containers) are located in the immediate work area, and possibly larger containers for intermediate storage are kept at a safe distance from the worker. A waxed paper bag or polyethylene liner inside a secondary container, such as a metal can, makes a good receptacle for *solid* radioactive waste. Cardboard ice cream containers have also been used for this purpose; the container and contents are disposed of as a sealed unit. A garbage can, painted red and appropriately labelled, can be used for low-level dry-waste storage. The dry waste may be held for decay of the radioactivity to a level safe for disposal or incinerated under proper conditions.

## B-2 OTHER SOURCES OF INFORMATION

Although the above treatment of radiation safety is briefly discussed, it should provide the activation analyst with most of the information he needs to know in getting started.

Thousands of books and papers have been written on radiation safety, and many cover situations involving very high levels of radiation and very intricate operations. If one desires to make a more exhaustive study of the subject, technical libraries should provide ample published material.

## B-3 LICENSING REQUIREMENTS

James W. Hitch
U. S. Atomic Energy Commission

In the USA, until 1962, the Atomic Energy Commission had licensing jurisdiction over radioisotopes produced in nuclear reactors. Accelerator-produced radioisotopes and most of the naturally occurring radioactive materials, such as radium, were not included under this authority. Now, several states have assumed this regulatory responsibility for both reactor-produced and other radioisotopes. Thus one should direct licensing questions to the appropriate state agency or to the Licensing Branch, Division of Licensing and Regulation, U. S. Atomic Energy Commission, Washington 25, D. C.

For those radioisotope materials regulated by the USAEC, licensing requirements may be found in *Code of Federal Regulations*, Title 10, Parts 20 and 30. Individual copies may be obtained upon request to the USAEC.

For most activation analysis, however, the small quantities of radioisotopes produced will require no specific license (levels not greater than 1 to 250 $\mu c$ are generally licensed, depending on the particular isotope(s)). Their use is covered by a general license as provided in Section 30.21, or the appropriate section in state regulations, and is effective without the filing of an application with the appropriate regulatory agency.

Radioisotopes produced by neutrons from certain radioisotope–beryllium irradiators, such as plutonium–beryllium and americium–beryllium, are also subject to *Code of Federal Regulations*, Title 10, Part 70. However, the amount of radioactivity that can be produced by such irradiators seldom exceeds the quantities permitted under the general license described above.

In some cases a neutron generator may require a license, e.g., if it contains a tritium target. However, radioisotopes produced in these generators usually do not require a license. Information on this may be obtained from the responsible state agency; no AEC license is required for the radioisotopes generated in the machine.

## SUPPLEMENTARY REFERENCES

Oscar M. Bizzell, *Equipment for Radioisotope Laboratories*, USAEC Report AECU-2875, July 1954.

J. E. Dummer, Jr. (ed.), *General Handbook for Radiation Monitoring*, USAEC Report LA-1835 (3rd ed.), Los Alamos Scientific Laboratory, November 1958.

J. Kohl, R. D. Bentner, and H. R. Lukens, *Radioisotope Applications Engineering*, Chaps. 7, 8, and 9, D. Van Nostrand Co., Inc., Princeton, N. J., 1961.

K. Z. Morgan, Techniques of Personnel Monitoring and Radiation Surveying in (A. H. Snell, ed.), *Nuclear Instruments and Their Uses*, John Wiley & Sons, Inc., New York, 1962.

J. R. Novak (ed.), *Radiation Safety Guide*, USAEC Report ANL-5574, Argonne National Laboratory, 1956.

R. T. Overman and H. M. Clark, *Radioisotope Techniques*, Chap. 4, McGraw-Hill Book Co., Inc., New York, 1960.

Donald R. Ward, *Design of Laboratories for Safe Use of Radioisotopes*, USAEC Report AECU-2226, 1952.

Control and Removal of Radioactive Contamination in Laboratories, *Natl. Bur. Standards (U. S.) Handbook No. 48*, 1951.

Maximum Permissible Amounts of Radioisotopes in the Human Body and Maximum Permissible Concentrations in Air and Water, *Natl. Bur. Standards (U. S.) Handbook No. 69*, 1959.

Photographic Dosimetry of X- and Gamma Rays, *Natl. Bur. Standards (U. S.) Handbook No. 57*, 1954.

Radiological Monitoring Methods and Instruments, *Natl. Bur. Standards (U. S.) Handbook No. 51*, 1952.

*Radiation Safety and Control Manual*, USAEC Report TID-7027, Oak Ridge National Laboratory, 1962.

Rules and Regulations, *Code of Federal Regulations, Title 10*, Chap. 1, available from Superintendent of Documents, U. S. Government Printing Office, Washington 25, D. C.

Safe Handling of Radioactive Isotopes, *Natl. Bur. of Standards (U. S.) Handbook No. 42*, 1949.

Safe Handling of Radioisotopes, *International Atomic Energy Agency, Safety Series No. 1*, 1958.

# INDEX